THE MAMMOTH BOOK OF
WORD GAMES

Also available

The Mammoth Book of
WORD GAMES

Peter Newby

Robinson
LONDON

Robinson Publishing
7 Kensington Church Court
London W8 4SP

First published in the UK by Robinson Publishing 1995

A copy of the British Library Cataloguing in Publication
data is available from the British Library

ISBN 1–85487–320–2

Printed and bound in the EC

10 9 8 7 6 5 4 3 2 1

Contents

CONTENTS

CONTENTS

Dedicated to
Mad Eric Ovid
and all who
Rail with **Lady Ann Beeswax**
also to the memory of
the **tope** of **Ensport**
Ben Pewtery
(1745–1827)

Preface

Although, as its name suggests, *The Mammoth Book of Word Games* contains many and varied amusements using words as playthings, I have resisted the temptation merely to cram in as many games as possible, preferring, instead, to provide a selection of entertainments which have either proved themselves 'worthy' or else appear promising, and to utilize the remainder of the available pages in providing useful information for both beginner and adept. Thus, this work consist of both the tried and tested games which featured in my original book, *Pears Word Games*, and the best of those subsequently brought to my attention, together with many new games of my own.

First, let me set the record straight as to what I mean by the term 'word game'. To me, it is a competition between two or more people using words as the basic material. This I contrast with 'word play': solitaire dabbling with a word or words to achieve an effect (ideally, witty), and which can also be termed 'recreational linguistics' (though some of the best practitioners of these arts tend to adopt the grandiloquent term of 'logology' for this wordsmithery and to call themselves 'logologists').

Whilst, mainly for the benefit of those without suitable company, I have included a measure of recreational linguistics, the essence of the book is directed to the needs of the competitively minded and, for them, a number of important considerations – however obvious – need to be stressed from the outset.

1   Wherever possible play word games with a competitor or competitors of a similar ability to your own, as many of the problems which arise in play stem from a person of low attainment who attempts to bend the rules as a form of compensation.

2   Decide in advance not only how but who arbitrates in the event of a legitimate dispute over such matters as word validity (a guideline follows below).

3   Don't restrict yourself purely to those games at which you have a proven expertise – choose according to the needs of the intended participants. For this purpose I'll categorize five types of player:

  (a) **Competitive Wordsmith**   One who has not only a mastery of the language but is a skilled player of any mentally taxing game.
  (b) **Wordsmith**   One who has highly developed lexical skills such as an expert solver of crosswords but has never developed the competitive skills.
  (c) **Gamesman**   One who excels at any parlour game and has a natural desire to be a winner.
  (d) **The Pi-Man**   One who merely makes up the number but has neither word power nor a competitive spirit.
  (e) **Simple Simon**   One included purely for the sake of social politeness.

Few of us will admit to being Simple Simon(e), the bane of any parlour game, and most of us can assign ourselves to one of the other four categories. However, many of the games can be scaled up or down to meet the requirements of the players. To give a basic example, the children's game of I Spy could be played by wordsmiths using esoteric synonyms whereas Simon and Simone might have difficulties even at nursery level – a standard which would also appeal greatly to a slightly inebriated assembly of gamesmen! Lovers – drunk or sober – could devise a version of I Spy best left within the pages of a sex manual; whilst prisoners sharing a cell and possessing a vivid imagination could devise a unique cerebral version.

Arbitration guideline

Having chosen a game best suited to the needs of the willing competitors and having tailored its demand to the talents of the assembly, one now faces the problems of arbitration over the 'legal niceties'. The ideal solution is to engage an intelligent, literate, pi-man, give him the dictionary, and accept his opinions – however bizarre. This is rarely possible, so the next best move is to agree which reference work will be consulted and decide a rotation of the role of arbitrator. The choice of reference work is vital as, despite popular belief, there is no such thing as 'the dictionary'; each publisher's dictionary is unique and even the same word can be spelt differently in different works. I don't mean such things as the obvious differences between American and British English, but some works, especially older ones, will have been edited by a lexicographer with a penchant for hyphenating a simple two-syllable word like, say, 'peacetime', which others prefer as a single unbroken word – yet a third editor will record it as a two-word phrase. Should it be GIPSY or GYPSY? Is there a 'correct' way to spell, for instance, the title of the former emperors of Russia? Taken from CAESAR, should it be CZAR, TSAR, TZAR or CSAR? Check your own dictionary but agree on *categories* of words which will prove acceptable. Bearing in mind that you can amend any rules to suit the circumstances, I'll summarize the general guidelines. For convenience, I will name these rules after the unofficial patron saint of wordsmiths, recreational linguists and 'logologists', Saint Aldhelm.

The Aldhelm Word-Validity Rules

1   Unless special conditions prevail (such as, when the game is confined to specific proper names of people or geographic locations) the only words acceptable for play are those found in an agreed dictionary, occurring as bold-face headwords, printed in lower case, and all logically inferred derivations such as plurals of nouns, inflections of verbs, and the comparative and superlative forms of adjectives. No other words may be played. Note that hyphenated words, those requiring an apostrophe or those deemed foreign are normally considered invalid. No other exclusions pertain (see rule 3, below).

2   It follows that one must observe the rules of grammar when making inferences noted above and that modern

grammar applies solely to modern words; archaic grammar is only tolerable where the dictionary specifically notes the word as archaic, and Middle English should be treated with similar respect. (In other words, the verb MAKE shown in the dictionary as in current usage may be held to validate such words in play as MAKE, MAKES or MAKING but not the archaic MAKETH nor the Middle English MAKYN.) Where the dictionary notes older forms of the language such as the delightful YCLEPT (meaning 'named") it is safer, unless one is a grammarian, to accept *only* the dictionary headword and avoid making inferences.

3 All dictionary headwords are valid including the English of a part of the world different to one's own. Thus American slang is perfectly acceptable in Buckingham Palace; the Scottish English of such as Rabbie Burns in the White House, and no one can object to Yorkshire dialect terms at a contest held at the South Pole and hosted by a scientist from Trinidad. But *foreign* words in an English dictionary must be looked at with great care. If the lexicographer deems these to have been 'assimilated' into our language – such as AARDVARK from South African Dutch – then these are perfectly valid, but if they are still labelled or printed as foreign then they cannot be used. Foreign words usually appear in English dictionaries if they are commonly used in English literature or general prose and each dictionary has its own method of distinguishing them from native words.

Caution needs to be exercised when using a dictionary with which you may be unfamiliar as they may follow different conventions as well as favour different spellings. The *Shorter Oxford*, for example, capitalizes all of its headwords, even words normally written in lower case, whilst the 3rd edition of the magnificent *Webster's International* often has normally capitalized words in lower case! Consult other players if in doubt and take the majority opinion.

4   Be consistent in your judgements, even if you subsequently realize that you were in error in allowing a particular word at the beginning. Taking as an absurd example the duty arbitrator having accepted one person's playing the nonsensical 'yclepted', everyone else must be permitted to make the same mistake. Once control of the dictionary has passed to another arbitrator then he or she can rule on the acceptability or otherwise of such absurdities in *future* play but cannot penalize a previous misjudgement.

5   Use common sense. If no dictionary is available, or ambiguity of status applies to a dictionary word, get general agreement to a possibly contentious arbitration.

Do these same rules apply to non-competitive word-based entertainment, word play? Yes and no. Essentially, it depends upon the task and who sets it. If one is rising to a challenge set by a publication then the editor will normally set his or her own rules but, generally speaking, an adherence to the first three Aldhelm Rules should stand you in good stead.

Which dictionary should you choose? The simple answer

is the one with which you are most familiar. If you find that I quote words which are not in your own reference work do not be surprised, as for the purpose of this book I shall range freely over most of the better dictionaries. Elsewhere I mention crossword-solving books. These arrange words in lists according to the number of letters in an individual word, which is helpful for certain games, but you should be aware of the fact that these have rarely been compiled with the same attention to accurate detail as the better dictionaries.

Finally, a few words of gratitude to two highly intelligent and charming ladies without whom this book would never have been realized: Joan Smith, who not only typed the whole thing but made some valuable contributions, such as her wise selection of proverbs and the wickedly witty 'Cold Cockles"; and my fellow contributor to the magazine *Word Ways*, Susan Thorpe, who provided some very useful terms of her own coinage to describe various word play activities. Both Joan and Susan are brilliant wordsmiths, and indeed, the high proportion of female winners in these games is a reflection on my own experience competing against Joan and Susan, and two other ladies whom I admire in this respect: Maggie Warburton and Alexandra Lisa Newby.

Have fun.

Peter Newby
Chesterfield, England

The Shape of Things to Come

Far more important than an impressive vocabulary is a feeling for the 'shape' of words if you wish to achieve success with word games, and by shape I mean the vowel-consonant distribution of an individual word. Let me illustrate this with two words, IOUEA and CRWTH, both of which should strike you as being 'peculiar'. IOUEA is a scientific term for a particular fossil sponge, whilst a CRWTH is an old Welsh musical instrument. The former term is found only in specialized works but the latter occurs in at least two English dictionaries. As the proof of most puddings is in the eating then I recommend that you try out these words in a session of the good old-fashioned game of Hangman, against an opponent who prides himself or herself on having a good vocabulary! Hangman, with a small series of related games, commences the book as an introduction to the deductive reasoning that lies behind many of the word games. This feeling for shape is one of the most significant factors in the greatest of all challenges based on words, codebreaking (an international codebreaking society centred in the USA has flourished for over half a century). Thus, whatever your level, if you wish to compete against the best then I urge you to acquire this feeling for shape even if it means taking on a child at the simplest form of Hangman.

In the Preface I have divided likely participants into five types, with the 'competitive wordsmith' as the top of the heap, but I would back a good 'gamesman' against a mere wordsmith any day of the week. Word power alone is insufficient to win most of the better games – tactics and strategy also come into the reckoning.

Playing with words is one of the most ancient of the magic arts, and shape is significant even in that respect. Consider the *palindrome*, a statement which reads the same backwards as well as forwards. Though modern formists construct these purely for fun, nevertheless they have to pay attention to shape, using the natural distribution of vowels and consonants:

Madam, I'm Adam.
Mary bred a Derby ram.
Fresh silo polish, serf!
Able was I, ere I saw Elba.

This is even true of 'Cheater's Palindromes' (ones featuring nonce words):

Samorael bats at times emit tastable aromas.
'Gniebne! ilaeht demaercsiii!' screamed the alien being.

('Samorael bats' have, subsequent to their invention by the New Zealand writer, Jeff Grant, found their niche in spurious zoology; having been defined in *Word Ways* magazine as being 'unlike other bats which rely on their ears for echo location, the samoraels use their noses to detect reflections from their constant breaking of wind which, fuelled by a perpetual diet of figs, has an especially sweet aroma.' The poor alien being had the misfortune to 'wander into a Samora cave at the time of day when the sleeping bats establish colonial identity by mutual breaking of wind.')

But, moving away from the fun of word play to the more serious stuff of word games, let me begin by discussing the value of the first series of games, the Hangman Series. Most people familiar with Hangman will associate it with childhood, completely overlooking the fact that by using 'grown-up' words one can play a demanding, adult, challenge, and one in which the shape of words plays a highly significant role in deduction. This applies not only to the original game, but to the others as well, including Pardon Me, a new game especially created for this book.

Not that shape is the only factor which a player should consider if he or she is new to word games, but it is as good a starting point as any and, once mastered, will stand that player in very good stead. I am not suggesting that you attempt *every* game in that series but, if you are a tiro and wish to become an expert word gamesman, do try at least one of the Hangman games. If you are already a good games player in other disciplines then I would recommend that you try some of the Deck of Card series. All are brand-new but, as they are patterned on existing known card games, you might well have an understanding of the skills required to win and, by using words instead of cards, gradually acquire that feeling for the language which will stand you in excellent stead in some of the other challenges which this book offers.

One of the 'reference sections' in this book is the Miniglossary which, by providing and defining some very valuable 'little words'', will be of considerable value in quite a number of the games. The two-letter words, incidentally, whilst including all those which are used by the international Scrabble movement also goes beyond those which they accept as, unlike them, no attempt has been made to confine selections to a single reference source. Thus, if you are already, say, a competitor in the North American Scrabble Championship and complain that not only are some of the words not in the *OSPD* (the American *Official Scrabble Players' Dictionary*) but some of the meanings are different, do not despair as an English player will doubtless make similar objections, for I have not slavishly adhered to the language of my native country. Having said that, all of the lower-case two-letter words are well and truly valid in the spirit in which the late Alfred Butts conceived the greatest of all the commercially marketed word games. Readers who 'graduate' from the games in this book to the deadly serious world of competitive Scrabble might well feel that I have done them a disservice in querying some of the accepted 'words' in that highly specialized field of lexical sport, be they Britons using the *OSW* (*Official Scrabble Words*) or Americans or Australians who prefer the *OSPD*, as, in both cases, I query various of their cherished notions; the British use of a 'non-word'', or the American pluralization of certain words whose prime sources confirm as having identical singular and plural forms.

Already I have plunged you into one of the drawbacks in playing with words: when is a word 'valid' and when is it not?

This is why I drew up the Aldhelm Rules (page xvi), based upon established practice of wordsmith games players throughout the English-speaking world. We – I consider myself a 'competitive wordsmith' – maintain contact with each other via various privately produced publications (detailed in Useful Addresses, page 461) and tend to follow certain approaches to validity even if, individually, we favour different dictionaries. Who *is* Saint Aldhelm? He was a Bishop who lived about 640–709 and, to quote the *Penguin Dictionary of Saints*, "in his lighter moments he composed Latin verse and metrical riddles" and was "the first English scholar of distinction". His feast day is 25 May, which if you wish to throw a word-game party is as good a date as any. You might even request that all who attend wear an 'old hat' as a form of tribute to this ancient wordsmith. *Word Ways* magazine, in its 'adoption' of him as the patron of recreational linguistics quoted the following riddle:

Q. 'Whose word play is old hat?'
A. 'Aldhelm's.' (*Ald* = old; *helm* = hat.)

So, come next 'Old Hat Day' or whenever you play the games of this book . . . enjoy yourselves.

Jargon

In order to minimize ambiguity I include here a short list of the technical terms I use, where necessary contrasting my use of certain terms with those of the international 'logology' movement espoused by *Word Ways*, the brilliant journal of recreational linguistics published in Morristown, New Jersey, and also, as I understand, by the American National Puzzler's League.

ALPHOME (SET) Susan Thorpe's ingenious term for the alphabetically-ordered set of letters which transpose into one or more genuine words. Thus, AABELRT is the alphome, or alphome set, of the anagrams, ALBERTA/ RATABLE. The alphomes of some words sometimes form words in their own right and therefore anagrams. CAT having ACT as its alphome, for example. (The name is from *alpha* and *omega*.)

ANAGRAM A word which can be made into another by the action of rearranging its constituent letters – for example, BROTH/THROB. The same term is also used for a rearrangement of a complete phrase such as my friend Susan Thorpe's conversion of *The Mammoth Book of Word Games* into 'Mom's got a fab homework method'.

'Logologists' would, by contrast, call these simply **transposals** as neither is especially apt. What to me is an apt anagram such as STAR PINE and PINASTER (both terms for the same tree) and Lewis Carroll's perception of Florence Nightingale as 'Flit on, cheering angel' they would describe as **anagrams**, pure and simple. Personally, I use 'transposal' to mean something different again (*see* **transposal**).

ANDAGRAM The combination of the constituent letters of a word with an additional letter – as EMPIRICAL + D produces LAMPRICIDE. The equivalent logological term is **transaddition.**

CIPHERTEXT A **plaintext** (q.v.) message rendered into a simple substitution of other symbols for the standard letters. Contrast with **codetext**.

CODETEXT A message transmitted in a form which is intended to deceive a third party. Sometimes it can be as simple as a **ciphertext** but, more usually, it is far more complex.

DOUBLE (WORD) SQUARE A **word square** (q.v.) in which the words in both the horizontal and vertical planes are identical. For example:

```
C A T
A R E
T E N
```

HETEROGRAM A word – like SCHWARZKOPF – which is composed of entirely different letters, i.e. no letter is repeated. (I am indebted to Susan Thorpe for this term, constructed from the Greek *hetero-* (different) and *gram* (something written or drawn).

KEYWORD   In the esoteric world of codes and ciphers a keyword is a (standard) word which has the effect of both concealing and revealing the truth of either the **ciphertext** (q.v.) or the **codetext** (q.v.).

LOGOLOGIST   A **wordsmith** who takes himself seriously.

LOGOLOGY   The science of words.

NONCE WORD   A word coined for a specific occasion and which may, unless taken up by others, become simultaneously obsolete. Any nonce word recorded in your dictionary is valid for play but such as SAMORAEL (mentioned on page xxii) is hardly likely to follow in the wake of Darwin's LUMPER ('It is good to have hair-splitters and lumpers') and become an established word as it has such a limited application!

OED   The complete *Oxford English Dictionary*, not to be confused with any of the smaller *Oxford* dictionaries such as the *Shorter* or the *Concise*.

PALINDROME   A word such as MUM or a phrase such as the classic 'A man, a plan, a canal: Panama' which reads the same backwards as forwards.

PLAINTEXT   The intended data written in plain language of a message either enciphered or encoded.

POLYGRAM   A set of letters of any length thus including both **trigram** (q.v.) and **bigram** (a two-letter combination) as well as any other miscellaneous combination.

STANDARD (WORD) SQUARE A **word square** in which the vertically perceived words differ from those on the horizontal. For example:

```
C A T
O R E
B E D
```

TRANSADDITION An **andagram** (q.v.)

TRANSPOSAL The rearrangement of a mere collection of letters such as AACEIMNR into either of the mutual anagrams AMERICAN or CINERAMA, either anagram being viewed as a transposal of that collection of letters; also, that collection of letters being viewed as an alphabetical-order transposal of either word. (*See* **Anagram**.)

TRIGRAM A set of three letters written in a fixed sequence – such as the PAL of *PAL*INDROME or of O*PAL*. (A standard wordsmith's term.)

WORDSMITH An expert in word play.

WORD SQUARE See **Standard (Word) Square** and **Double (Word) Square**. Technically, a word square is an acrostic having perceived words in all vertical columns. (Simple acrostics usually have only one, sometimes two, vertical perceptions.)

THE
HANGMAN
SERIES

The Hangman Series

Ten games of which only the first is suitable for children.

1 Hangman

A popular pencil and paper game for two people, children using simple words, or adults using the more horrendous words distilled from a good dictionary.

A word is chosen (but not divulged) by the first player. All the second player knows at the start is the number of letters, which is usually indicated by dots or dashes drawn on the paper by the first player. He or she has to find out what this word is, guessing at it letter by letter within a limit of eleven errors, each error represented by a single line making up a progressive drawing of a man being hanged.

In the example below of failure to discover the word CATHEDRAL, nine dots were drawn to represent each individual letter.

As the letters were nominated, so the correct ones were placed over their corresponding dots (both As going down simultaneously) or else part of the drawing was made, either a straight line or a circle/oval.

Hangman is the perfect game to hone one's skills in word recognition which will be of subsequent value in the aristocrat of word play, Codebreaking.

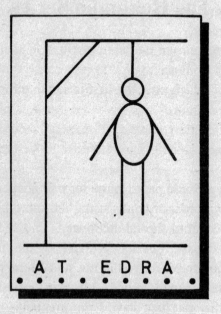

2 Double Execution

Hangman for three people, two of whom attempt to discover the same word, neither knowing the other's situation.

To play it simply and effectively, have the two contestants seated at opposite ends of a table with the taskmaster seated in the middle. Each person's playing area is *carefully concealed*, all have paper and pencil, and the taskmaster has a pack of playing cards. A full round of play will comprise six games with each person being the taskmaster for two consecutive games, so that all will attempt four words and the winner will emerge at the end of. an agreed number of full rounds. In the following example, Tom, Dick and Harriet are the players with Tom as the taskmaster.

Tom, having chosen the word CATHEDRAL, sets out two rows of cards from ace to nine to represent the nine letters of his word. He chooses clubs for Dick and hearts for Harriet. He announces that his word contains nine letters so Dick and Harriet place nine dots on their respective pieces of paper. He tells Dick to have the first choice of a letter.

Dick, very sensible, goes for the vowels, beginning with E, the most widely used letter in the English language. As E is the fifth letter of the chosen word Tom hands him the five of clubs.

Harriet, equally sensibly, chooses A. Tom now picks up both the two and the eight of hearts taking care to conceal from Dick the fact that two cards are being passed to Harriet. (A simple method of concealment, if you are not especially adept at handling cards, is always to pass on two or sometimes three cards, the contestant ignoring the irrelevant one(s) – kings, queens, etc.)

Dick now selects the letter I, so Tom hands him the first spade or diamond from the top of the pack of 'dead' cards. Dick now has to begin the drawing of his own execution. Harriet chooses E and so she receives the five of hearts.

In lieu of a letter, a player may guess at the word. Failure results in immediate execution. But the player still 'at liberty' can now continue without the need for secrecy; the game can still be tied if he or she is subsequently hanged. Award a point to the winner. The outright winner emerges at the end of an agreed session. As the player going second is at a nominal disadvantage so two games are played before the taskmaster is changed, one player having the first choice of letter in game one, the other having the first choice in game two.

It is not the responsibility of the taskmaster to remember who has previously mentioned a particular letter. If a player foolishly mentions the same letter twice that is his misfortune.

3 Mass Execution

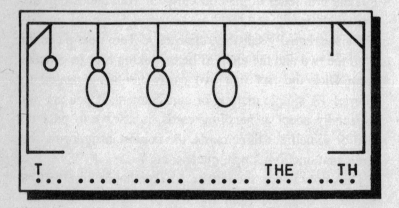

A proverb is selected. For each word, a man might be hanged. In the example shown it was TOO MANY COOKS SPOIL THE BROTH.

Play began with the ground and the gallows already

drawn so, unlike Hangman, the maximum number of errors per word possible is only seven.

The person guessing has started with the letters E, T and H. So THE is complete. However, for the words where these letters are not present we have started drawing the hanged men – for the words MANY COOKS SPOIL, the rope, the head and the body have been drawn as they don't contain any of the three letters. The object of the game is to discover the proverb before any one man is hanged.

(For a list of proverbs see page 441.)

4 Reprisals

Mass execution in which both players take turns to hang as many of their opponent's men as they can. This time each hanged man is a victory and scores a point. However, as each man is hanged no additional letters may be placed on the dots which he represented.

No points are gained for partial executions.

5 Selective Reprisals

In this version of Mass Execution, the person guessing chooses the word he or she wishes to attempt – the art lies in clever selection. Thus, keeping to the example TOO MANY COOKS SPOIL THE BROTH, the first word might be ALL, THE or YOU, but AND is highly unlikely – however, the fifth word could easily be AND.

If the player decides to attempt one of the longer words,

he or she might consider that as the letter E is the most widely used of all letters it may well feature in one of these – this ploy of course would not work in our chosen example.

Winning is either on the basis of Mass Execution (as soon as any one man is hanged, the game is over) or else on the basis of Reprisals (scoring points for hanged men).

6 Confess

The name derives from the proverb 'Confess and be hanged'. It is a form of Hangman, played with proverbs, in which confession brings about your own execution.

Two players select proverbs containing the same number of words. (See page 441 for a wide selection, all of a similar half a dozen words length. See the next game, Acid Drop, for a note on how to treat punctuation.)

Jack chooses TOO MANY COOKS SPOIL THE BROTH.

Jill chooses A STITCH IN TIME SAVE NINE.

On the same playing sheet, they represent their proverbs with dots spacing them in word formation thus:

    Jack: . . .   .
    Jill: .   . . .

Jack is to go first and it is fairly obvious to him that Jill's first word is A. If he is wrong, he will then have to reveal one of the letters in *his* first word, either the T or else both of the Os. (If he has a guess at a letter in her third word and gets it wrong, he'll have to reveal a letter of his third word, and so on.) As he cannot think of any possible proverb which begins with either of the words I or O (the only two other possibilities) so he is fairly safe. His guess of A is correct.

Jill considers Jack's proverb. The first word could well be THE. She has nothing to lose anyway, Jack has already robbed himself of the chance of forcing her to reveal the A. She can attack his first word with abandon. Does she wish to do that? What about his fifth word, is it THE or could it be AND? If she attacks it, which of the letters in SAVES is the best one to reveal if she is wrong? She decides to expose the E if she is wrong; so she now has to choose a letter from either THE or AND to make her play.

A wrong guess at the complete proverb and a player hangs himself or herself. It must be correct in every particular.

A player who makes an error in numbers of dots must, on revealing that error, put himself at the mercy of his opponent.

7 Acid Drop

'Sharp acids corrode their own containers' is an Albanian proverb and, as the basis of a Hangman game, its significance lies not only in the fact that few will ever have heard of it but that it is an entertaining statement capable of deduction from partial evidence.

The game can be played by teams or by individuals and, at its most pleasing, uses such delights of wit and wisdom as: English proverbs (e.g. 'When an ass climbs a ladder, you may find wisdom in women'); quotations (Kipling's

'The silliest woman can manage a clever man'); classic graffiti ('Snoopy has fleas'); famous last words (such as Lord Palmerston's 'Die, my dear Doctor, that's the last thing I shall do'); devilish definitions ('Acorn, an oak in a nutshell'); acidic observations (Jules Feiffer's 'I know she's alive. I saw her lips curl'); or picturesque phrasings (like Woody Allen's 'Her figure described a set of parabolas that would cause cardiac arrest in a yak').

In Acid Drop, each word is guessed at individually but, no matter which word is being attempted, the hanging is a collective result of those guesses. The object of the game, therefore, is to hang as many men as possible.

Consider the example of a team told to discover a Turkish proverb containing six words. The first word has three letters, the second has six letters, the third has six, the fourth has four, the fifth has three and the sixth has eleven.

The team may now apportion words amongst its members or they may, if they prefer, work collectively using a single sheet of paper. The team decides how it will tackle the problem. The 'executioners' merely record the hangings.

At some point, the guessing team will face a partial revelation something like this: ONE AR . . IT CANNOT . OLD T . O . ATER . ELONS and the executioners will have scored, say, one complete hanging and a partial hanging.

The guessing team now has the option of 'reprieving' the partially hanged man. If the team members can now state what the Turkish proverb is, only the first hanging scores a success for the executioners. However, if they are wrong in any one particular, then a full execution of the second man is made and they must now face the prospect of beginning a third hanging. The rule is that a wrong guess at a letter builds a hanging and a wrong guess at the full statement produces a full execution.

The winning team is the one with the greater number of hangings over the session of play.

That proverb? 'One armpit cannot hold two watermelons.'

Punctuation Only full stops and commas are given as part of the basic information. Apostrophes give away too much information and are not revealed. Thus, a word such as SHE'S is merely described as a 4-letter word. However, when answering, the guessing team is told that the first letter is s and the fourth letter is apostrophe s – but only if both teams agree in advance to this particular kindness. One type of punctuation can be delightfully confusing and I am grateful to New Zealander Jeff Grant for pointing this out to me: hyphens.

The *English Dialect Dictionary* contains the names of the following two flowers:

'Kitty-come-down-the-lane-jump-up-and-kiss-me' and
'Meet-her-in-the-entry-kiss-her-in-the-buttery'.

The first is a Kentish term for the cuckoo-pint or wild arum; the second is a Lincolnshire expression for the pansy, and both share the unusual distinction of having nine hyphens.

8 Acid Prod

A variation of Acid Drop which brings a touch of bedevilment when playing with 'easy' statements such as the proverb 'Too many cooks spoil the broth'.

This time you write the words as anagrams (or as near to true anagrams as you can devise) – thus:

OOT MYAN SOCKO ISLOP HET THROB – and reply to guesses with your anagrammed sequence.

The rules are otherwise the same as for Acid Drop.

9 Pardon Me

The visual image is that of an inmate of Death Row in the States awaiting a pardon whilst the electric chair is being repaired in the execution chamber. He or she has only a short time in which to achieve a stay of execution by supplying the missing initial letters which complete a word in the vertical plane; each wrong guess adds another piece of 'Old Sparky' to the chair being reassembled by the 'executioner' (person who set the puzzle). Guessing is attempted one-letter-per-word in any sequence of the 'convict's' choice.

The 'executioner' chooses any word of any length and then devises a new word for each letter of the word to be determined. Suppose, for the sake of argument, the 'executioner' selected DEATH and decided to hint at this with simple plant names such as DAFFODIL for the D of death; EGGPLANT for the E; ASH for the A; TULIP for the T; and HYACINTH for the H. He or she would then write down the words minus the initial letters one at a time in their correct sequence thus:

.   AFFODIL

.   GGPLANT

.   SH

.   ULIP

.   YACINTH

But, it would have to be a very Simple Simon who could not see immediately what the missing word was; far better to be subtle and, for the D, choose a word like DEAR which with a different initial could be BEAR, FEAR or, indeed, start with any of the following: G, H, N, P, R, S, T, W or Y.

Contrast the easy-to-guess 'horticultural' DEATH with an 'execution' based on DOG shown below, adjacent a fully restored electric chair:

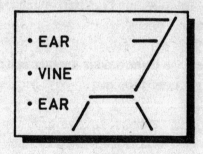

10 Pentery Web

The game of Pentery Web, a form of Hangman played with a pair of words, anagrams of each other, was first described in *Pears Advanced Word-Puzzler's Dictionary*, which is the ideal reference work for this game as it contains words with their anagrams. However, you may enjoy constructing perfect anagrams.

In the following example, Jack had set Jill the task.

Jack has chosen the pair PINITE and TIEPIN, fully aware that Jill will know TIEPIN but is unlikely to know PINITE, the name of a chemical substance. Not that this will matter as Jill is such a good wordsmith she will still be able to cope. Jack displays the two words with dots for the letters, and with one letter (the same) revealed in both. There are ten dots left, so she can score 10 points if she can guess the pair at once.

. . . I . .
. . . . I .

She cannot guess, so he now adds another matched pair to his display. Eight dots, 8 points.

. I . I . .
. I . . I .

Jill remains baffled, and he adds another pair. Six dots, 6 points. At this stage Jill might well come up with TIEPIN even though she is at a loss for the other word. She must be correct with *both* words.

. I N I . .
. I . . I N

She fails. He adds another matched pair of letters.

. I N I . E
. I E . I N

Once again she fails, but she knew the answer before Jack placed the matching T's in the display. They were given for fun, however, and she scored 2 points.

. I N I T E
T I E . I N

Jill soon got her revenge with STOITS and TSOTSI! ('Stoit' being a Scottish verb meaning to stumble, while 'tsotsi' is a young South African hooligan.)

(The reason for the peculiar name of this game should be fairly obvious to those who enjoy this particular type of word play.)

THE
MOBILE
SERIES

The Mobile Series

The games which follow are intended for playing in the car using the letters and complete words found on fixed road signs. The first four games, all appearing in print for the first time, are visualized as being played by me in the company of my and MHW's granddaughters and how I anticipate they would progress in such circumstances. Only the last game is intended for adults.

1 Sally Forth

Sally Barton is my youngest granddaughter and I would love to challenge her to see which of the two of us is the first to spell his or her name from letters we observe through the car's windows. Will we restrict ourselves to just one letter per sign? And, must we find the letters of SALLY and GRANDPA in sequence? *That* I would have to discover as I rather suspect that Grandpa will be outvoted by the ladies in the car – especially if the lexically deadly MHW is present.

2 Maggie Pie

This time I challenge MHW's first grandchild to see which of the two of us is the first to create certain words chosen for us by MHW. With rules approved by the female democracy then I would probably have to construct such as, say, ZANZIBAR whilst my opponent has to garner the letters of, say, MOUSE.

3 Grum Pie

MHW's schoolgirl grandchild who, for reasons totally beyond my comprehension calls me 'Grumpy', then suggests that I compete against the ladies in a contest of true wordsmithery whereby they have the first 'long' word in any sign spotted on the right-hand side of the road – it might be CORPORATION, whereas I have, perhaps, STREET, the 'longest' (e.g., in a sign reading *High Street*) on the left-hand side. The letters of these words are then eliminated one by one, turn by turn till all I have is ET to my credit whereas the female team has C . . P . RATIO . so making them the winners with RATIO as the longest perceivable word remaining. This is young Miss W's 'mobile' version of a pencil-and-paper game she plays at home with her grandma, when each chooses a 'secret' word and they then take it in turns to suggest random elimination by such references to letter-position as 'first letter/vowel/consonant', or 'last letter/vowel/consonant', or 'the first pair of double letters', or whatever else takes their fancy.

4 Melemzo

The name is a portmanteau of Melissa (Caulfield), Emmaline and Zoe (Barton) and it has the three of them joining forces with the Warburtons in confronting Grumpy Grandpa with an anagram challenge. We see a road sign – reading BEDFORD, for example, and both teams try to make the longest possible word from its constituent letters. Smirking, I offer FORDED, but democracy rules in favour of a soprano-voiced FRED BOD!

5 The Pangrammic Highway

The discovery, whilst travelling by car or coach, of a complete alphabet, letter-by-letter irrespective of order of appearance, in as short a distance as possible. The only competitive element is in making a new record; be it personal or against the established 'records'. The rules stipulate that only *fixed* signs may be logged from any starting point of the players' choice. For example, Faith and her husband Ross Eckler achieved some remarkable findings. To quote Faith, 'We waited until we neared an area where we knew, or suspected, there would be a Q or J and started writing down signs there. On a trip south on the 1–95 in Maryland, we suspected that the region of the Susquehanna River would prove fruitful, and, *voilà*! a pangrammic distance of only 2.4 miles: JFK HIGHWAY MONITOR CHANNEL, AUTHORIZED VEHICLES ONLY, BRIDGE SUBJECT TO CROSS WINDS, EXIT, SUSQUEHANNA STATE PARK.

'We thought that distance might be hard to reduce until

we realized how easy it was going to be to find a J in our home state of New Jersey. When it also occurred to us that there is a Squirrelwood Road exit in Paterson on 1–80, we took to the road to check it out. Travelling eastbound, we achieved the remarkable (so we thought) pangrammic distance of 1.7 miles: INTERSTATE NEW JERSEY 80, SQUIRRELWOOD RD, WEST PATERSON EXIT 1 MILE, PASSAIC RIVER, BRIDGE FREEZES BEFORE ROAD SURFACE, EXIT 25 MPH, GARDEN STATE PARKWAY.

'Was it possible that we could do even better travelling westbound in the same area? We turned around and found an astounding pangrammic distance of only 1.3 miles: INTERSTATE NEW JERSEY 80, SQUIRRELWOOD RD, WEST PATERSON, PATERSON, EXIT 25 MPH, BRIDGE FREEZES BEFORE ROAD SURFACE, PASSAIC RIVER, NO TRUCKS IN LEFT LANE.' (from *Word Ways*, May 1990)

By the August 1990 issue *Word Ways* was able to report an even more compact alphabet. To quote Ross Eckler, 'Less than three miles from his doorstep, the editor on the northbound lane of Interstate 287 on an 0.8 mile stretch . . . [noted] WASHINGTON'S HEADQUARTERS, NO TRUCKS IN LEFT LANE, LAFAYETTE AVE, EXIT 20 MPH, BRIDGE FREEZES BEFORE ROAD SURFACE, and INTERSTATE NEW JERSEY 287.'

(The Pangrammic Highway was devised by Udo Pernisz.)

THE
FAN-TAN
SERIES

The Fan-Tan Series

The Chinese gambling game of Fan-Tan involves the placing of a number of small coins under an upturned bowl and wagering on the value of the remainder after that number has been divided by four.

This small series is based on that principle. Only the first game is suitable for children.

1 Fan-Tansy

Choose any simple subject such as flowers. Each player now writes the name of any flower on a piece of paper and places it face-down in the centre of the table. Players now guess at how many letters remain (none, one, two or three) after the total number of letters of all the words has been added up and divided by four. The winners collect points appropriate to that remainder; if they correctly identify a nil remainder they receive 4 points. (If you do not wish to think of a new flower (say) for each round, you can make do with two and permutate them as you wish.) If you choose long names, such as MICHAELMAS DAISY, write the total number of letters after it (15) to make the mathematics easier.

Misspelling can be taken into account on checking, if they affect the mathematics. Obviously, a dyslexic rendering of DAISY as DIASY does not affect the outcome of play, but ANTIRRHINUM is capable of being produced with a quite different numerical value.

2 Fan-Tangle

The expert's version of Fan-Tansy.

Each player in turn selects a particularly restrictive subject, such as animals with names beginning with the letter Z.

ZEBRA is obvious, but are any of the other players likely to produce ZEBU or ZHO? If not, you can be fairly sure that they will all have ZEBRA and you control the total. Admittedly, they have a free guess at the remainder and will suspect you of having produced a wicked example but they have no idea what. To prevent them bamboozling you, forbid plurals. ZEBRAS will change the mathematics and your probable control. Not all plurals need automatically be forbidden – a different subject might be a single word meaning the plural of domestic cows and bulls but not collective nouns such as 'herd'. The obvious answer is CATTLE. Can you think of another?

This is the point of the game. The person who suggests the subject imposes all the rules. He or she ideally selects a subject having only one very obvious example but which has at least one other, rather obscure, acceptable answer.

Whoever proposes the subject is the last person to state his or her guess at the remainder.

All other rules are the same as Fan-Tansy.

3 Fan-Tanagram

A game for two people without a choice of subject. Both players tell each other which everyday 3-letter word he or she has selected. The race is on to produce a genuine 6-letter word out of the two words.

4 Fan-Tandagram

An andagram is an anagram of a word plus an additional letter. For example CAT + S can make ACTS, CAST, CATS and SCAT; CAT + H gives CHAT.

Some words have an amazing potential for andagrams. It is possible to find 126 andagrams for the word STAINER, 132 for SATIRE and a mind-boggling 270 for ASTER. If you choose a basic 5-letter word containing two different high-frequency consonants (L, N, P, R, S or T) it is almost impossible not to have the basis of a set of andagrams.

In this game, one player selects a suitable 5-letter word as suggested above. He or she remains the scorer and umpire for that particular word. The other players (a minimum of two are required), in ignorance of the scorer's word, choose any letter they wish apart from S. All write down their word or letters on pieces of paper. Plurals are perfectly acceptable but only the scorer is permitted to include an s in the playing pool.

The scorer's bit of paper is placed face-down in the centre of the table. Each player now places his or her individual letter face-down beside it. This done, the scorer's word is revealed with one of the letters.

The race is on to write down andagrams within a brief spell of time – not necessarily a minute or any other arbitrary limit but as judged reasonable by the scorer. As a fair rule of thumb, once most people have signified that they have finished, the round ends. It is just hard luck on the busy little body who begs for more time.

Any players who have produced andagrams hand their pieces of paper to the scorer. He or she checks them whilst play continues with the next letter.

At the end of the rounds based on that particular word, the scoresheet is passed to the next player who assumes the responsibilities of the scorer. The former scorer is now a player. The whole game has each player acting as scorer an equal number of times.

(For a fifth Fan-Tan game see Shelling Peas with Gramps which is more conveniently placed in the Classroom Series. Gramps (page 194) is the Fan-Tan version of the contest, Shelling Peas.

The many examples of word play in Shelling Peas are perfect for Gramps.)

THE
BINGO
SERIES

The Bingo Series

A small series of games that are ideal for a large number of people. As it is pathetically easy to cheat you are advised not to gamble on the result unless you are prepared to check the winning claimant's 'card' against the letters called, as happens with commercial bingo. Children as well as adults will enjoy game number 1, whilst game number 4 is specifically for kids – of any age! One person stands down in each game to take the office of bingo caller. The caller is in charge of play.

1 Bingo

Three standard subjects are chosen – for example, animals, countries and girls' names. The players write down three 5-letter words, one being an animal, one a country and one the name of a girl.

The caller reads out the letters from the Bingo Letter-Frequency Table (see page 37) and the winner is the first person to mark off all of his or her fifteen letters. A player is not permitted to mark more than one letter at a time. Thus, if a player's words contain a total of seven ES, he or

31

she may delete only one of them on that letter being called out.

Misspellings do not matter unless you decide otherwise.

2 Ognib

Bingo spelt backwards – and that is the game. This time the players start off with a blank sheet and build up the three 5-letter words of the chosen subjects, as the caller reads out the letter.

Players may *not* change their minds about individual letters or the positions these occupy on their paper. This is a more skilful game than Bingo, described above, and all words must be correctly spelt.

3 Super Ognib

A standard subject is chosen – say, animals. The caller announces in advance how many letters he or she intends to call. As each line of the Bingo Letter-Frequency Table contains 24 letters so the number will be a multiple of 24. A minimum of five lines of the table (120 letters) is required if every letter of the alphabet is to be mentioned at least once.

The players try to use as many of these letters as they can to make up the names of animals, the winner being the one who utilizes the greatest number. Thus OX scores 2 points whereas the creature known as a THIRTEEN-LINED GROUND SQUIRREL will score 27 points.

The caller must not slow down despite any pleas from

the company and will maintain a steady flow of letters at a pace of: 'A and a B and a C and a D and, etc.'

The players use either graph paper or lined paper with it turned sideways so that it produces vertical lines, or at worst, blank paper with numbers running across the top to indicate the position of letters. Thus, once a letter is in a particular position in relation to the others, its position cannot be altered – for example, say a player has written ox in positions 1 and 2, he or she cannot subsequently add an F to turn it into FOX. To gamble on FOX one must have something like

1 2 3 4 5 6 7 8
. O X

or

F . X

or

F O .

already written down on paper.

Players may *not* write down letters at the side or bottom of the page for subsequent use. The letters have to be utilized as called or else ignored. For example:

1 2 3 4 5 6 7 8	
T . G E R	(hoping to make TIGER)
. O X	(hoping to make FOX)
B U L L	(with the options of such as BULLS or BULLOCK readily available)

Once calling has finished, the scores are totted up. In the above example only BULL will count, not OX. Similarly, had the player extended BULL as BULL . . KS (hoping for BULLOCKS) there would be no score for BULL.

To enable players to judge the situation it is recommended that the caller indicate every 24th letter. Thus, if 96 letters are going to be used then the caller should say: '. . . N and letter number 24 is U . . . Y and letter number 48 is T . . . E and letter number 72 is D.'

In family play one assumes that every player will be honest but, if the game is played as a serious competition amongst strangers, special rules need to be adopted.

1　The caller adopts a different method of announcing letters. Not just 'R . . . S . . . A . . . ' but 'R, repeat R; S, repeat S; A, repeat A . . .'

2　The players draw a line near the bottom of the page under which they write every letter they do *not* wish to use.

3　The winning submissions are checked by officials to ensure:

(a) that every letter called appears on the paper either above or below the scoring line. If any letter is adrift (omitted, repeated, illegible, crossed out or possessing any other sign of being a possible second thought) the submission is void;

(b) that every animal (or whatever) claimed for score is valid. Under these circumstances it must appear in a previously agreed dictionary.

This means that if the top three players are to be honoured, then the top six submissions are taken. First the words are checked for validity then all the letters are privately re-called and marked off bingo fashion.

By having the letters originally called 'competition style' no player can complain that he thought that, for example, a V was a B. Equally, if a caller made an error (even though he or she was being monitored by an official during calling) that same error would show up on all submissions. It would be wise in competition play to have the clearest voiced speaker as the caller.

Finally, when stating a subject make absolutely clear what is required. 'Animals' is vague. It could mean that words such as COD, FERAL, COWLIKE can all be claimed as being within the boundaries of acceptability. If you mean 'terms for mammals excluding man' say so. Obviously, all words have to be correctly spelt.

4 Bingo Cricket

A little bit of fun for a couple of youngsters who support different cricket teams. (Don't worry if you don't know how cricket works – this is purely words! But you do need to find out the names of some international cricket players.) Suppose one favours England and the other the West Indies. Each writes down the surnames of the players of his or her chosen team. If we assume that England is to bat first, then suppose that Gooch is the choice for opening bat to face the 'Windies'.

The West Indian supporter now reads from the Bingo

Letter-Frequency Table. Every letter, other than G, O, C or H, scores a run. As each letter of the surname, Gooch, is read out so that letter is crossed off. The England opening batsman will, therefore, survive four appeals for dismissal before the last letter of his name (be it G, O, C or H) is read out and he is dismissed. *Two* O's have to be called, not just one, for him to lose his wicket.

When England bowl and, say, Richards is facing the attack, then he will score runs for all letters other than those of his surname. The fact that the letter A will be called out quite a number of times before he is finally dismissed is of no consequence other than that first time, all repetitions being treated as non-scoring deliveries.

There is no need to have full teams of eleven players, otherwise boredom can creep in. Three or four might be sufficient, after which the team is presumed to have declared.

If Mum finds herself roped into play, choose Pakistan and have Qadir on your side. With luck, he will score her a lot of runs!

Each participant writes down three or four surnames and, as each one is dismissed, so the next batsman takes his place. Each surname produces different results and my money is still on Mum's Pakistan if she does a little quiet research in advance.

Players should be seated in an arrangement which inhibits cheating and enable errors to be corrected. Bowl in overs of six letters, taking a short break between them.

As each line of the table has 24 letters so that represents 4 overs. It is up to Dad how many overs he is prepared to call.

Bingo Letter-Frequency Table

Begin at any point and call out letters in a standard left to right, top to bottom sequence.

```
R S A R A C N E E D L R E P D O O R T W U L N U
I R Y N I S H A Z U J S E F O V E N G I G R Y T
A C D E S I L A M I N O R N I F E R K T A T E D
H O G A X I O B E I E W A I R T C M E L U B G S
T Q E P A S Z E L N O A R E S O F E O A I R T L
O E R A R I S A R E U N I R E C V F I R E S A J
T O S E P I D I D N U T A R K W E N T Y M N U G
E N U R M L T H E C A W B I X A G Y G I T D H S
P B O O G L E S S A D E N T I N D E D I N U R B
E S A T I P A D J E S O R O P I R L Y A G I T A
T E G U G E Z M U N G I S Y M E R A S U R I F S
E A R X E B V E Q O F E W K A R N O W L N E S H
O D A S T L R L T O R C I H A C R P G E H S C U
K I M E R S I T E S O D O V E E B X A O R O I P
R E Y U S G L S E U B L E R L C A I T N A Y I T
L N I D O A S F T O R Z E O G J T T A G D E N N
A H A S I R A N W E N I R U M R W A F E D Q E A
U N N D I G S E A H T I S A R A R S E N A I O L
B E S R O A M F C H O I G I T V T J Y B A I R S
D A E P U N D E G U L Y E S P O O W A E E N O L
N E R I S R E X T G R W T M I K T F U Z R L R E
D C R S E T U I E R P S I L G E O D P D E E D A
I R O Q O T K E R Y U V E U T G E A H I C F A Y
R S I X I L O A R O L E R O S A E R J A T A N W
N N I Z A F R G S C D S G B N B L S E W M I T M
U T A N H E N N O T A G C E N B G O I C H I T Y
M E S P R A B L I G E L A I N Z U F D S N W S O
O L N A H L E O T T E I W E T I Q U E E R T A V
U R K I R J R R E S R A P I D A M N E S A S E A
G O X U Y S R F E D D R N E S R Y S U O A R J E
R K A R L G H E W A I T A C E G L I B U R A F E
X Z S E G U I S E S I N M E D O P R R E A D D O
O F U P Q T B N C G T M T H A N E L I A S W E N
Y I I S O D V E T R N A T O L R N Q P U F D I D
M E N E S S A U G I N O O D L N W A E S L O N A
H E S Y X E B A T R F I G E E R T W I O H U Y G
A I R R A G E R K C N J R A E S S A O T M T S Z
E A R R R U B L E C O T I V D L E I T P E T E R
```

5 American Bingo

Unlike the Brits, the Americans play Bingo on a small card containing five rows of five numbers and, in addition to the universal horizontal line win, they also have a diagonal line and a 'four corners' winning sequence. So, if you wish to play Bingo with a Las Vegas flavour amend the game of Super Ognib and play on a small 5 × 5 grid with the winner being the first person to create a *valid word* of five letters in *any* horizontal or diagonal plane or a 4-letter word perceived in the corner squares commencing at any corner and read in strict rotation.

THE
CONSEQUENCE
SERIES

The Consequence Series

Two games, either for adults or children. As their senses of humour will differ, so it is better to have all children playing or all adults rather than a mixture of the two.

1 Consequences

An old favourite with a charm of its own. Many will know how to play it but, for those who do not, have available a boldly written list marked as follows:

1 adjective
2 girl's name
3 MET adjective
4 man's name
5 AT location
6 time and/or date
7 HE SAID TO HER whatever he said
8 SHE SAID TO HIM whatever she said
9 what he did
10 what she did
11 AND THE CONSEQUENCE WAS whatever it happened to be
12 AND THE WORLD SAID whatever it might choose to say

Each person now has his or her own long sheet of paper. Each writes any adjective suitable for describing a girl (WITTY, PRETTY, STUPID, SEXY, LUDICROUS or whatever) and folds down the paper to conceal what has been written and passes it to the player on the left. If you have five players then five pieces of paper will be passed on simultaneously.

Each person now writes the name of a girl, folds and passes the paper.

At the third stage, the word MET is written followed by a suitable adjective for a man.

So it continues with each person writing something, folding the paper and passing it on.

When all twelve stages have been completed each person now reads out the story which has been created. No winners, no losers, just a giggle for however many participate in the game.

2 Picture Consequences

Great fun especially as few people would call themselves artists.

As with Consequences, everyone has a piece of paper. This time it is a very long narrow strip – about two inches wide is about right.

At the top of the strip, using as little of it as possible, everyone draws any picture he or she wishes. It is not folded yet.

This picture is passed to the person on the left without comment: no apologetic statement on the lines of, 'It's supposed to be a cow eating grass' or any other such words may be uttered.

Each player now writes a description of what he or she honestly thinks has been drawn – if you think the 'cow eating grass' looks like a dog sniffing a worm, write that down.

The original drawing is now folded so that only the description can be seen by the next player.

He or she now illustrates what has been written. So the sequence continues until all the strips have been filled; the final item has to be a description. Those filled first are put on one side until all are complete.

The fun arises in the comparison of the original drawing with the final statement. You will be amazed at the eventual description of the 'cow eating grass'.

THE
DECK OF CARDS
SERIES

The Deck of Cards Series

A ten-game series with an unlimited potential for addition, it is patterned on popular card games. It is important to recognize that many people have their own versions of the basic card game used as a model for the word game and that the word games described below often merely approximate to the original. Few will prove suitable for children, even those children already familiar with the basic card game.

In addition to paper and a pencil for everyone, two other items will prove useful: a dictionary, naturally, in the event of any disputes over validity of words offered in play, and a crossword-solving dictionary for use by the 'dealer' in various games.

All these games are appearing in print for the first time.

1 Qop

The original card game has many names, of which the most descriptive is Thirteen-card Brag, and the peculiar name above, (pronounced 'cop') and its pronunciation are intended to be apt for the word-game version.

In the card game, thirteen cards are dealt to each player

who, after rejecting one of them, creates four sets of three cards arranged in a descending order of intrinsic value similar to that in poker. The idea is that players wager on the 'strength' of their sets, starting with their highest-value set, then the others in a descending order of value. The player who wins all four sets then scoops the kitty.

The word game will mirror the original in many respects but, for simplicity's sake, will be described in terms of a twelve-card version. A thirteen-card version for competitive wordsmiths will follow the basic description.

Using the crossword-solving book for convenience, the dealer (players take turns to deal) selects two 6-letter words which all players write down. Viewing these as a 'hand' of twelve letters each player, in secret, transposes them into four 3-letter words bearing in mind the necessity to match the card game in terms of value:

Three-of-a-kind The only 'words' of this type found in general prose rarely feature in dictionaries, these are interjections OOO (expressing surprise), MMM (content-ment) and ZZZ (sound of snoring). You are at liberty to consider these if general agreement to which might be deemed valid was obtained *prior to commencement of play*. Otherwise, stick strictly to the Aldhelm Rules (page xvi).

Run There are only a few words which consist of consecutive letters of the alphabet such as CAB, FED and the more esoteric, found only in certain dictionaries, MON (a Japanese family crest) and NOP (a mattress stuffed with woollen waste) but note that 'PON (as in ' 'pon my word') is invalid due to the apostrophe.

Flush Words which consist *entirely* of consonants such as CWM, CRY, DRY, etc., or of vowels like OUE, a word which can be discovered in one of the darker recesses of the *OED*.

Pair DAD, DID, DUD are examples of 'pairs', words containing two identical letters. ZUZ, as you will discover below, is probably the highest value 'pair' providing that this word, which describes an ancient Hebrew silver coin, features in the dictionary you are using.

High card Considering letters in alphabetical order to represent their 'numerical' value, then a word such as ZAP will be better than any other word (other than those previously described) which has, like BOY, a 'high letter' of lesser worth. In the event of matching 'high letters' like ZAP and ZED then the second 'highest' letter is considered; in this example the P of ZAP is superior to the E of ZED. The 'high card' principle is extended throughout the whole range of 'sets' so making the nonce word QOP the highest possible 'set' such that it would QOP the lot if it was deemed to be valid!

Suppose that the dealer provides the following words BRAIDS and ZOOEAL and three players – Tom, Dick and Harriet – produce the valid 3-letter words detailed below in descending order of value, could you determine the winners of each round?

Tom	*Dick*	*Harriet*
LOO	ZOO	BOO
BAA	ALA	ALA
RIZ	RIB	SEZ
SED	SED	RID

If you can, then you are halfway to becoming an expert at Qop. If you require a little assistance in determining values then I would suggest that you have a few dummy runs before attempting to compete. Notice that the double o features as the highest pair and that ZOO is deemed to outrank the other double o pairs by virtue of the Z. Similarly, with the double A pairs, Dick and Harriet have tied with their ALA outscoring Tom's BAA. Harriet has the top 'high card' word for the penultimate round; the last round is a Tom/Dick tie.

Each player commences with a notional sum of points – say, 25 – and places an agreed amount – say, 5 – in the kitty, then wagers points on each individual round as nerve permits. In the event of a tie – as with Dick and Harriet's ALA taking the second round – then the number of points staked on that round is added to the kitty for the first player to 'qop the lot'. Meantime, Dick collects all the first-round points and Harriet that of the penultimate round.

Variations on this theme   If the gambling aspect is too complicated for the company then devise a points-scoring system of your own, such as 4 points for the winner of the first round; 3 points for the second round; 2 points for the third; and 1 point for the last. Any unclaimed points go into a kitty for the first to qop out.

A thirteen-card version can be played by the simple expedient of providing 13 letters, the players having the option of discarding any one of them.

Or instead of two 6-letter words one can produce twelve letters in any combination – such as a 4-letter word and an 8-letter word. It is quickest and easiest if you have some sort of crossword-puzzle solving dictionary to find a word of, say, eight letters, but otherwise flick through the dictionary for such a word and supplement it with a simple, say, 4-letter word.

Finally, if you wish to include the non-dictionary sanctioned interjections for the 'three-of-a-kind' category then you might also consider adding the nonce word QOP in order to create a reasonable number of possibilities. But do get general agreement *before* starting the game as to which 'words' are acceptable.

2 Happy Families

Unlike Qop which has specific needs in its 'dealing' of 'cards', this is the first of various games which have what I term, for want of a better phrase, 'standard dealing'. 'Standard dealing' consists in reading aloud from any work of prose, words in the sequence in which they occur, one word to each player in turn who writes it down as the source of his or her letters for subsequent play. Obviously, one uses whatever prose is to hand: it might be a novel, a newspaper, or even road signs if one is playing on a car journey. The dealer may miss out certain 'difficult' words if the company includes a Simple Simon but, generally speaking, only non-words such as numerals or meaningless collections of letters which might form part of the passage in question will be ignored. Standard dealing gives each player very different hands from which to make his or her play. The object of this game is to create a 'happy family' of three logically associated words such as these:

COB, PEN, CYGNET
FOX, VIXEN, CUB
BULL, COW, CALF
DOG, BITCH, PUPPY
KING, QUEEN, PRINCE (or PRINCESS)
PRESIDENT, FIRST LADY, FIRST CAT
(or DAUGHTER or whatever)

and any of these is created, in the first instance, from one's existing stock of letters but will, in all probability, be completed by taking letters from the other players. The dealer will give each player (including him or herself) about half a dozen words irrespective of the length of each word. More may be dealt out in future games if six words prove to be insufficient for play.

Imagine that Snow White is trying to assemble DUCK, DRAKE, DUCKLING and can produce only such as DUC, RAKE, DUKLING, so she must now decide which of her 'missing letters' K, D or C she is most likely to obtain from the other players. Let us assume that she attempts to find an available C (as this might feature in another player's COB, CUB, CALF or COW: she asks the player on the left, Grumpy, for a C. If he has one *even if he wishes to use it himself* he must surrender it to Snow White. If he has no C then Snow may ask the next player, Doc, and so on round the table until at least one player or no one satisfies Miss White. Once she has had her turn then Grumpy may, if he so wishes, ask for a C knowing that Snow White has been given one. If Dopey gave a C in error the dealer may be called upon to check Dopey's sheet and correct the situation. Only memory can be employed to recall the location of the various letters as it is 'bad form' to write down the 'cards' of other players.

3 Rummy

A standard deal (as described in Happy Families) gives each player about half a dozen words. The dealer then reveals what the next word will be by writing it down on a sheet of paper left exposed for all to see.

This time the objective is to create a logical (if ludicrous) sentence or paragraph using *all* the words in one's 'hand'.

Snow White, who once again is the first to play, now has the option of reading aloud her 'statement' or else surrendering a complete word of her own for either the word on display or the unknown next word. To do this she deletes the word on the open sheet and replaces it with any word from her 'hand', making sure that she also deletes it from her own playing sheet. She now either announces that she has taken the 'top card' or else asks the dealer to tell her what the next available word is.

So play continues until one player makes a satisfactory declaration and wins the game.

Rummy niggles   If it is intended to play the game as a serious contest then the dealer should stand down from play to avoid accusations of cheating or general malpractice – but the ideal company to play this game is one that is slightly inebriated and not too serious. The dealer is the judge in any dispute which may arise as to 'quality' of declaration or the fact that Dopey failed to use all his words or even misinterpreted the meaning of one of them. If the dealer is also a player then the judge of his material is selected by general assent from among those who did not object.

4 Whist

A standard deal of half a dozen or so words to each player. As in Happy Families it is the indidivual *letters* with which one is concerned. These are now made into a collection of 3- and 4-letter words, each word now being viewed as a 'card'. The objective is to take tricks by the 'value' of one's 'cards'. Qop values are assigned to these words on the basis of 'high card' aspects. Thus ZEBU beats ZOOS on the strength of the second high letter, U being superior to S.

As an optional extra, 'trumps' can be such as proper names contained in an agreed reference book (supplementary to the dictionary).

The indefatigable Snow White is again the first to play and states her first 'card' (a 3- or 4-letter word of any 'value') and others must follow suit as far as possible by playing a 'card' which starts with the *same letter*, whether longer or shorter than hers. Naturally, a 4-letter word usually has the advantage over a 3-letter word, but ZAP will outscore a word like ZEAL (P is superior to L as a secondary letter), and such as OOZE is considered to have been 'thrown away' as it has a different initial letter.

The winner is the person with the greatest number of 'tricks'.

Variations on this theme As there are so many different forms of whist then it is up to you to introduce such as knockout whist by applying this basic technique to whichever form of the card game you are most familiar with. Without too much effort on your part you could organize a whist drive from among those already familar with the basic concept.

Whist niggles Dealers-cum-judges can always stand down from any serious event such as a whist drive but, wherever possible, restrict play to players of a matching ability to avoid unnecessary interruptions to explain the basic rules to Dopey or Simple Simon.

5 Cribbage

Only the basic concept is described below as there are so many possible variations that I leave it to true devotees of this amusing card game to adapt it to the game as they play it. Essentially, the idea is to score points on the basis of 2 points for creating a total of 15 (such as a court card + 5; 9 + 6; 8 + 7, etc.) and a point per card featuring in such as a run (Ace, King, Queen or 4, 5, 6, etc.) or a flush (three or more diamonds, etc.). The winner is the first to score *over* 120 points.

While the word game will have elements of Qop and the standard dealing described in Happy Families, the first thing to accept is that each letter has its own individual value on a basis of $A = 1$, $B = 2$ and so on up to $Z = 26$.

Half a dozen or so words are dealt to each player who now makes out of them, wherever possible:

(a) 3-letter words which correspond to the top three Qop hands (three-of-a-kind, run or flush), any one of which scores 3 points.

(b) Words of any length which total 15 on the basis of their constituent letters.

All unused letters are now available for the person whose turn it is to possess the 'box'. The dealer is normally the person who has the benefit of the 'box' and, as the deal rotates, so does this advantage. As the 'box' is very likely to contain letters from the higher end of the alphabet a knowledge of words utilizing such letters as U, W or Y will be a distinct advantage.

For the 'box' only, any multiple of 15 will also be valid for scoring purposes on a basis of 2 points per 15 multiple, and though this departs from the true card game it still makes sense for the wordsmith. Words from the 'box' can be of any length – even a 2-letter word such as YE will score (totalling 30, it is worth 4 points) so bear in mind, if it is your box, to discard potentially useful letters such as an E to accompany a Y which might well be discarded by another player.

Cribbage purists will despair at this further departure from 'their' game but I am ignoring such aspects of play as 'cutting the cards' for an additional card, scoring extra points for the Jack, and also scoring points by 'playing' out the cards prior to scoring values in the hand.

Once all players have made their decisions then scores are computed, after which the dealer is accorded additional time to make sense of his 'box' of discarded letters which are announced by each player in turn as he or she describes the results of his or her actions. The dealer writes the discarded letters on a separate sheet exposed for all to see.

One final point – it will assist in the smooth running of a session if the organizer draws up a table of letter values which is left on the table on open display.

Cribbage niggles What is a reasonable length of time to allot to decision making? For your first few sessions take your timing from the slowest player, thereafter you can speed things up by imposing arbitrary limits based upon experience. What if arbitrary limits are imposed, and Simon is in a mess? If it is essential to include him in your social activities, why did you consider him in the first place for an amusement way beyond his class? Play something else, even if it means getting out a pack of cards and teaching him the techniques of something like Snap! But, on a more serious level, simply ignore his letters both for his own scoring and, sadly, the dealer's 'box'.

6 Brandysnap

A 'card game' designed to accommodate Simple Simon but one with the potential for the competitive wordsmith to excel. This time dealing takes the form of a 'general knowledge' quiz with ludicrously simple questions such as: Name a creature which quacks.

The *obvious* answer is DUCK but a DRAKE also quacks and, according to the *OED*, so, too, does a FROG! Thus, despite the seeming innocence of the question, at least three possible answers exist. It is up to you to decide on such possibilities as EIDER (a breed of duck) or any other answer which might be given by a subtle player. In the event of dispute the dealer is the arbitrator – after all, he or she set the original question.

Players write their answers down on paper, and the game takes the form of players taking turns at reading out their answers. To see the game in context, let us suppose that Doc posed the questions: State the name of a president.

Those who perceived it as 'State, the name of a president' have little option but to write WASHINGTON, though most people will not have understood that a comma was implied so would name any president. Anyway, the play:

Sneezy	WASHINGTON
Dopey	NIXON
Happy	KENNEDY
Snow White	KENNEDY, *Snap!*
Grumpy	KENNEDY, *Brandysnap!*

Happy now has to delete KENNEDY from his list of answers; Snow White 'doubles' the subsequently detailed 'value' of her answer whilst Grumpy triples the 'value' of his KENNEDY.

When writing down one's answers one tries to have more than one answer if possible so that had she, say, written down both WASHINGTON and KENNEDY then she would have scored a point per letter in WASHINGTON but two points per letter in KENNEDY. Grumpy having, say, WASHINGTON, MONROE and KENNEDY has a score of 37 points for question number 1. Sneezy and Dopey both having, say, only one name each have scored 10 and 5 respectively whilst Happy, who also had, say, only one answer, scores nothing for that round.

Bearing in mind the fact that some people will require more time than others to answer questions – Dopey in order to think of one, but Grumpy to decide *which* to name so that he would have both a 'snappy' answer and at least one that was unlikely to be deleted from his score. The dealer should take his cue from a typical pi-man's writing action, once that pi-man has finished, move on to the next question. It follows from this that the dealer does *not* participate in any round in which he or she sets the questions and, as dealing rotates, so all players get the chance to compete.

Brandysnap niggles No additional answers may be written once the 'snapping' begins and anyone who does so has his or her whole series of answers declared void and, if possible, ignored for the remainder of the round. The dealer may request sight of any player's answer sheet at any time during the round he or she has control of play. Beyond brandysnap, double and triple brandies are accompanied by a cry of 'brandysnap' but only a triple score is awarded no matter how many 'brandies' have been called. Once a player has exhausted his answers to a particular question he automatically moves on to his next answer with subsequent players following his lead.

7 Snapdragon

A game of Snap for anyone other than Simple Simon. This time each player – a minimum of four is required – deals his or her own 'cards' by writing down any 8-letter word he or she can think of.

Dealing is not the only difference between this and the previous version of the childish game of Snap. The cries of 'Snap' and 'Snapdragon' will be given by players other than those who declare their answers.

The aim is to call 'Snap' when a word called contains at

least four of the same letters as the previous word. If those four similar letters also happen to coincide in sequence in both words then the cry is 'Snapdragon'. Any player other than the one who last spoke may cry 'Snap' or 'Snapdragon'. One point is awarded for each correct 'snap' and two points for each correct 'snapdragon', but a point is deducted for any false cry.

Play rotates but whoever spoke first is the arbitrator in the event of any dispute over such as who spoke first and word validity. Play continues with fresh 8-letter words until all have had the opportunity of going first.

(Snapdragon was devised by the writer Susan Thorpe)

8 Barbarianism

This game is based upon a card game I played as a child and knew as Pelmanism; it consisted of a complete deck of cards being arrayed face-down on the table in columns, from which one made random selections of cards in twos hoping to pick up a matching pair such as two queens, or two sevens, or whatever, keeping the pairs, replacing those that did not match. The name of the word game version is based on the discovery by the American wordsmith Chris McManus that every alternate letter in BARBARIANISM spells out the word BRAINS. Some of his other discoveries of this nature include POETESS in PROTECTRESSES, SEDATES in STEADFASTNESS and RIFLES in FRUITFULNESS. A classic word of this type – I am unsure who discovered it – is the remarkable TRIENNIALLY which, alternately, spells out both TINILY and RENAL. Logologists, who make a study of such wordsmithery, term word play of this nature an 'alternade'; Chris terms the word created in this way (e.g. BRAINS out of BARBARIANISM) a 'lend' (as LEND can be perceived alternately in ALTERNADE). The object of the game is the scoring of points for the discovery of 'lends' in words made available for play, with greater points available for alternades on the basis of one point per letter per valid word.

Using the dictionary or, better still, a crossword-solving word book the dealer reads out a selection of longish words which everyone writes down on their own playing sheets. A reasonable amount of time is now available to make alternate word discoveries not necessarily encompassing the whole length but each perception *must* be created from letters separated from each other by one other letter. Unless another player is prepared to make a copy of the selection for the dealer then he or she will need to stand down whenever dealing takes place.

This game can also be played as a form of Patience.

9 Grumpy

The model for this game is twofold; in the first instance I encountered it as a game played with *real* playing cards and my brother, David, told me that it was called by the German word for excrement as one was liable to utter expletives during the course of play; the second encounter was in the company of the lady to whom the game of Maggie (see page 162) was dedicated, in a book produced for a British television channel and co-written with a TV producer named John Meade. We played a commercially produced version with all manner of curious symbols instead of standard card designs, at the house of John and his wife Gill, and it had some curious Italian name which completely escapes me but, anyway, is of no consequence other than the fact that it had similar rules and also had the effect of inducing me to utter expletives. I have named the word-game version after the nickname Maggie's delightful granddaughter gave me.

The object of the game is to be the first to dispose of one's 'cards'. The dealer selects any paragraph from any work of prose and allots seven words, one at a time, to each player, taking note of where he or she finished in that paragraph. The dealer may participate if he or she so wishes.

Ideally, four or more players compete and each writes his or her words clearly on his or her playing sheet. The player on the dealer's left is the first to 'go' and selects any word on his or her list which is both announced to the company at large then *lightly* deleted from the playing sheet (lightly in the event of a subsequent dispute). Let us suppose that that first word is ROSE. The next player must now offer a word which begins with the last letter of the previous word – in this instance a word beginning with an E. If one has no such word on one's sheet then one may produce a suitable anagram from amongst the words that are there. The game continues in this fashion until a player is unable to make a move, at which point he or she has to be given a new word, the next word from the dealer's prose. A typical run of play to the point at which an obvious hiatus occurs follows:

ROSE – EXTRA – APPLE – EAR (from 'are') – RABBIT – TEAR (from 'rate') – RAP – PUTRID – DARN – NASTALIO.

To add 'grumpiness' to the game include various other penalty situations such as:

(a) After any word ending with any vowel the next person must miss a turn; but, *only* that next person.

(b) The playing of a proper noun *must* be followed by another proper noun, but this may be produced by anagramming. In this instance the last-letter rule no longer applies. Failure to produce a proper noun results in one being given two extra words.

(c) When one is down to a single word on the sheet one *must* announce this to the company at large by saying, 'Grumpy'. Failure to do so results in being given an extra word.

(d) Any other stupid rule you may wish to add of your own devising. Impose whatever silly penalties you deem appropriate, but *announce all such rules in advance of play*!

10 Dopey

This game is a little complicated to set up but, once done, it is simplicity itself. It is modelled on a card game known by various names such as Beggar My Neighbour or Strip Jack Naked. Type and photostat several copies of a poem containing enough verses for each player to be allocated one. Supply each player with two differently coloured marker pens. The object of the game is to retain as many of the words in one's own verse as possible, at the same time gaining additional words from one's opponents. Whilst it may seem, and is, a child's game, it is best played by a slightly inebriated gang of wordsmiths.

The first player reads aloud the first word of his or her verse. The second player now follows suit but, in order to gain an advantage, may, if he or she is capable, produce an anagram of that word. If no anagram is offered then that second player's first word is added to the stock of words available for winning by the first player who offers a valid anagram.

Play continues in this fashion until all the verses have been read out, then one tots up one's stock of words and the player with the greatest number of words is the winner.

Grumpy/Dopey/Niggles   Single-letter words such as A or 2-letter words such as AN or TO should be ignored in the dealing of Grumpy, and overlooked for both playing and scoring purposes in Dopey.

11 Ploo

PLOUGH and PLOW are, of course, the British and American spellings of the same word which had a late ancestral form of PLOO immediately prior to taking its two distinctive unvoiced endings. But PLOO is also an anagram of the two games, POOL and POLO, mentioned in the game of Mouse (page 70) which, if you are prepared to consider nonce words (and PLOO as a *game* certainly is) will add yet a third possibility to those previously discussed. However, it is a more common anagram of Ploo which is of greater relevance to this particular series of games. PLOO can be perceived as having arisen by 'looping' the ultimate letter of LOOP from the back to the front rather as one shuffles cards. And that is the basis of the game.

The dealer 'shuffles' letters in sequence; such that LOOP becomes PLOO, thence OPLO, thereafter OOPL, if you wish a full 'shuffle'; and now the question is *what was the original word*?

Was it PLOO? Or was it LOOP? Consider some other examples: INENUPT – is this the *Pine sabiniana*, the North American NUTPINE or could it be the PINENUT, a pinecone, especially one containing edible seeds? Contrast that with ALMNUTP – is this the Australian tree, *Cyces media*, the NUTPALM, or is there such a word as PALMNUT?

What are the rules? How does one play it? This time I leave it to you to devise your own rules and method of play. The pack of words is yours, I have merely shown you the rudiments of a shuffle, now you can either play a game of patience or else amuse others with a 'card trick''. The reader who thinks that he or she has come up with the 'PLOO perfect' competitive game is welcome to submit his or her version to me for possible inclusion in any future editions of this book or any others I might be tempted to compile.

THE
ESPIONAGE
SERIES

The Espionage Series

Three variations on a single theme, all appearing in print for the first time. Though the Cold War has ended, the intelligence services of the major powers have continued to function by the simple expedient of offering their expertise to other branches of the government. Russia's famed KGB, for example, now concerns itself with industrial espionage as does the French secret service, both of whom consider the commercial secrets of the West to be fair game for their attention. So incensed was the American Hughes Aircraft Company at this treachery by their former friends that they, on one famous occasion, withdrew from the Paris Air Show. By contrast, Britain's MI5 now concentrates its attentions on major crime. However, one visualizes the action as being between mutual antagonists such as wartime enemies.

1 Cat

A game for two players, both of whom agree a subject in advance – for example Cities. They now attempt to conceal the names of an agreed number of cities within a series of individual sentences. For example, 'Cosmo's cowardly attitude disgusted his colleagues' conceals MOSCOW in its first words: 'Cos*mo's cow*ardly . . .'

But, what about this sentence? 'Jump, Ari, surrender by twelve o'clock.'

Did you notice that it had *two* cities?

Having DERBY as well as PARIS in a single sentence now means that player can create a 'dummy' sentence to bring his or her total of sentences up to the agreed number of concealments (the assumption being one concealment per sentence). In this fashion one can bedevil the opposition in a perfectly legitimate manner.

Players now exchange workings and for an agreed length of time attempt to discover as many as possible of their opponents' 'secrets' as they can. Naturally, if one player 'beats the clock' then he or she not only wins outright but, if you are playing a series of this game, scores a point per city (or whatever) he or she has discovered and also a point for however many of his or her cities (or whatever) remain undiscovered by opponents.

2 Mouse

This is identical to Cat in many respects but with the difference that one has *anagrams* instead of *hidden words*. Subtle players, in a contest concerning Fruit could conceal both LEMON and MELON in the nonce transposal LOMEN. Note that it is not necessary to have a *genuine* word on one's sheet for the opponent to unravel, otherwise it becomes an exercise in pure wordsmithery. By this method one can add a 'dummy' transposal to this list.

Proceed and score as before.

3 Cat and Mouse

Simply a mixture of hidden words and anagrams with whatever limits players wish to impose. Ideally, the anagrams feature within sentences so that one's opponent is not given a clue as to what he or she is seeking.

However, a word of caution to the clever Dicks who might, in a contest on Trees, construct a sentence like this: 'Painters soak their brushes in turpentine.'

OAK is certainly one tree but as PAINTERS transposes to both STAR PINE and PINASTER *which are the same tree* it makes only *one* tree. Proceed and score as before.

Cat and/or Mouse for three or more players Before extending play to a tableful of competitors it is best that two players are fully conversant with the game and its rules (see also *niggles* below) so that both may assist the newcomers. Essentially, you make the targets and scoring system what you will but, obviously, adjust matters like timing to suit a convention of pi-men but do not lower standards of attainment. If Simple Simon wishes to participate then it is up to him to meet your standards not you to descend to nursery level. You can, of course, make it easy for him by choosing 'easy' subjects.

Cat and/or Mouse niggles The first question that arises with a subject such as Cities is, 'Does BOSTON score twice: once for BOSTON, Mass., and once again for BOSTON, England?' No! it only scores once.

'In clever Dick's sentence there were *other* plants, what about those?' BRUSH is defined in *Webster's* as a 'thicket of small trees and shrubs', *not an individual tree*; and though there is a 'turpentine tree' it is not known as the TURPEN-

TINE. (The turpentine tree is, in fact, the terebinth tree, *Pistacia terebinthus*.)

'If the subject was Plants and one used clever Dick's sentence, could one count not only the trees but also RUSH and RUSHES? And how about the North American plant the TURPENTINE SHRUB?' Obviously, the trees are acceptable as Plants even though the reverse is not true, but one cannot score both RUSH and RUSHES; one *can* however score both BRUSH and RUSH as brush also has another meaning as a species of plant. TURPENTINE still remains invalid as the prairie burdock (*Silphinium terebinthinaceum*), variously known as the turpentine weed or the turpentine shrub, as it is still not known simply as the 'turpentine', at least not in any reference book that is accessible to me. And *that* is the key. If a contentious word can be proved to exist in the previously agreed reference work – not necessarily a dictionary – then it scores.

'But, suppose that Dick did not intend to have both RUSH and BRUSH as plants – what then?' First let me explain that the sentence was *originally* constructed to disguise Trees and the phrase '. . . their brushes in turpentine' was a 'dummy' aspect to camouflage both PINASTER and OAK. Considering it as a construction for Plants only really adds BRUSH and RUSH to the score and, of these, only RUSH is concealed which, if BRUSH was not intended, could have been disguised by such as CRUSH or THRUSH. But, having made this 'error' does it score? Yes, but if you think that you have discovered a 'freak' continue to search until you have found all the words that you think were intended.

'Simon can only think of the names of two trees. What do we do?' Other than suggesting to him that he might refill the glasses, you could let him consult the book of trees in advance. Why worry? You'll still beat him.

'Which reference books should we use?' Basically, it is what you have to hand but a word of caution about books other than quality dictionaries and encyclopaedias: one of the crossword-solving 'dictionaries' marketed in the UK, which lists words by subject in groups according to the number of letters in each word is positively riddled with stupid errors such as including the Bombay duck (a fish) in its section on *Birds*! This is a pity as it would otherwise make a very useful wordsmith tool. Better ones exist so, if you have the one which includes bum(m)alo (or Bombay duck) in its list of birds give it to Simon and treat yourself to a better book. In the meantime, check its words in the dictionary and if Simon manages to conceal BOMBAY DUCK in a sentence give him brownie points for effort and score nothing yourself.

One final point: ensure that each player has plenty of paper to hand not only for passing round the table but also for secret rough working.

THE
CROSS PLAY
SERIES

The Cross Play Series

A series in which players take turns in calling out (if played on two or more sheets of paper) or writing down (if all players use the same sheet) letters or words of their own choice. It contains some of the greatest pencil and paper games. Only game 21, Pool, is appearing in print for the first time. Expert players are particularly recommended number 5, Words, and number 14, The War Game. All, however, are worthy of consideration. None are specifically children's games, but the brighter youngster should have no difficulties with games numbered 7, 8, 10, 16, 20 and 27.

1 Competitive Word Squares

A two-person game, each playing on his or her own 5 × 5 grid. Neither knows what the other is doing but both are trying to get the higher score. They take turns to call out a letter, putting them anywhere they wish on their own grids. For example, the first player calls out z. This z could be put into squares as varied as:

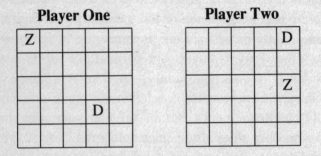

Player One   **Player Two**

The second player now calls out, say, D. These might be distributed in this fashion:

Player One   **Player Two**

As the object of the game is to make words running both horizontally and vertically, and to score points for them, so it is obvious that Player One is thinking of making two words beginning with Z whilst Player Two has a totally different plan.

Play could eventually finish as shown below. The numbers indicating the points scored. Only the longest word in a line counts. Thus, one cannot have, say, both BRA and ZEBRA scoring in the same line. The achievement of a 5-letter word is rewarded with a bonus point. A 5-letter word scores, therefore, 6 points. A 4-letter word, 4 points. A 3-letter word, 3 points, and a 2-letter, 2 points.

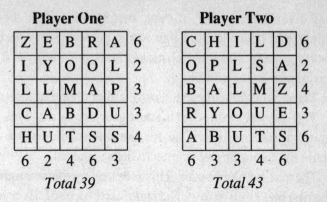

Player One

Z	E	B	R	A	6
I	Y	O	O	L	2
L	L	M	A	P	3
C	A	B	D	U	3
H	U	T	S	S	4

6 2 4 6 3

Total 39

Player Two

C	H	I	L	D	6
O	P	L	S	A	2
B	A	L	M	Z	4
R	Y	O	U	E	3
A	B	U	T	S	6

6 3 3 4 6

Total 43

Incidentally, the highest known score in this game is the 58 achieved by Sir Jeremy Morse versus his wife, in July 1961.

2 Chinese Crosswords

This is poker played with completed Competitive Word Squares grids. For three or more people to play the basic game, as happened at a convention of the American National Puzzler's League, makes it, to my way of thinking, less a game of skill and more a game of luck. With, say, four people taking turns to call out letters, one has almost no control whatsoever on the outcome. The Chinese, however, love to gamble, and by gambling on the results – for points, for pennies, or whatever – an interesting and stimulating challenge can be rescued from the frustration. The four players, therefore, complete their 5 × 5 grids as described in Competitive Word Squares. They compute their scores, but do *not* reveal them.

The top horizontal line is now considered. Each player

has a limited number of, say, matchsticks. If he or she thinks that his or her top line is a good one it may well be worth staking a few matchsticks on. If not, they need not participate in the gambling.

Those who do participate, now wager on the outcome.

The person with the highest-scoring word wins the matchsticks, but if two tie for the top scoring word they share the total number of matchsticks wagered.

There is no fixed stake. This is set by the person making the first bid. High or low. The stake can be a bluff. Everyone, whether he or she intends to gamble or not, must put at least one matchstick forward at the start of play. The first player (decided in advance by rota) now sets the stakes. Whoever participates must match the stake. The wagering continues until two players remain. The compare scores.

They must, however, first state their scoring word, and then reveal the contents of that top line. It is up to the other players to adjudicate on any disputed words and also, if they wish, to record what their opponents have written. These two players have now revealed parts of their future words, the less ambitious have not.

The second wager is on the extreme left-hand vertical line. The new first player will set the stakes for this.

So play continues, horizontal line then vertical line. The ambitious revealing more and more of his hand, the cautious still giving nothing away. The winner is the one with the greatest number of matchsticks at the end.

(*Note: both this and its parent game can be played with larger-sized grids. The bonus scores for words of maximum length in the other versions are 7 (6 × 6), 9 (7 × 7), 10 (8 × 8), 12 (9 × 9); 9 × 9 is known as Arepo.*)

3 Crossword

The world's first crossword puzzle was devised by Arthur Wynne, a journalist who emigrated to New York from Liverpool. His creation, which he called a word-cross, appeared in a Sunday newspaper, the *New York World* on 21 December 1913.

Since that time, crossword puzzles have spread not only around the world but have been used as the basis of many word games of which Scrabble® is the peer. Most of these games are commercial but there are also some excellent pencil-and-paper games of which Crossword is one of the most demanding.

A 9 × 9 grid is drawn and any 9-letter word is placed anywhere on the grid either horizontally or vertically. Assume that the word CROSSWORD has been chosen and placed as follows:

C	R	O	S	S	W	O	R	D

Players now take turns in adding any letter they wish providing that each letter they play creates a valid word. Each word they create scores points equal to the number of letters used.

Two examples of play follow. One having a couple of average players, Bill and Ben, the other a pair of experienced rivals, Jack and Jill.

(a) *Bill versus Ben:* Bill goes first. He scores 2 points for adding an O below an S to create the word SO.

Ben has three options of which two are obvious. Either score 2 points for a different 2-letter word – DO, perhaps – or score 3 points for converting SO into a 3-letter word. The third option will be discussed in the Jack and Jill game. Ben scores 3 points for SON.

Bill scores 4 points for SONG; Ben scores 5 points for SONGS. Their score at this point is 6 points to Bill and 8 points to Ben.

The remainder of their game will be equally basic.

(b) *Jack versus Jill:* Jack goes first and scores 2 points for SO. Jill immediately takes the third option and scores 4 points. She creates two simultaneous 2-letter words in this fashion:

C R O S S W O R D
O O

The Scottish word OO scores her 2 points and WO provides the other 2 points. (All 2-letter words mentioned in this game are defined in the Miniglossary, page 449).

Jack now scores 5 points from

<pre>
C R O S S W O R D
T O O
</pre>

2 points for ST plus 3 points for TOO.

Jill now scores 6 points from the following:

<pre>
C R O S S W O R D
T O O N
</pre>

2 points for ON plus 4 points for TOON (the Indian mahogany tree).

Ignoring the fact that STOON, an obsolete form of the word STONE, would give Jack 7 points, we can reasonably assume that Jill has forced him to move elsewhere. The most he can now score is 3 points.

Jack studies the board. Ideally he would like to have TOONS but, as yet, that is impossible as no such word as 'RS' is valid. Therefore, what he must achieve is a word ending in R which he can pluralize. To do this he converts ON into TON so that whoever plays such as TE/ER for 4 points will immediately give him 8 points for ERS/TOONS as shown below:

<pre>
T E
C R O S S W O R D
T O O N S
</pre>

This is the game played at its most tactical. The following section of the board will illustrate how important is the knowledge of the strangest 2-letter words.

ACROSS

1 SWAB needed AB, the W then inserted between S and AB

4 XI (see Miniglossary)

5 WAGER could have arisen in various ways such as W blank G thence WAG, WAGE, WAGER. But the existence of such words as WA, AG or GE give far greater opportunities for it.

7 This part of the base word, CROSSWORD

9 WOO arises from either WO or OO a well as W blank O

10 ELM from EL apart from E blank M

11 HIDE from ID or DE thence IDE or HID

	S	W	A	B
	E		X	I
W	A	G	E	R
A		L		D
S	W	O	R	D
		W	O	O
		E	L	M
H	I	D	E	

DOWN

1 SEA from EA

2 AXE can only have arisen from a very complex route which depended upon building up from the R of WAGER, R had to become IR, thence BIR (an obsolete verb 'to pertain'). The B had to become AB, the X was then inserted between the A and the E to create, simultaneously, AXE/XI. Thus, not even AXE was possible unless XI was also valid.

3 The nonce word, BIRDDOM, meaning the world of birds collectively depended upon both the creation of BIR (see 2 above) and D becoming DO then DOM. Finally, the D was inserted between BIR and DOM.

The remaining words were all created similarly, based on rare 2-letter words.

Naturally, all play is to Aldhelm Rules but the following also apply:

1   An erroneous word has to be removed from the grid either with a rubber or typewriter correction fluid. If you play one you get a double forfeit: 10 points are deducted from your score and you have to forgo the particular turn in question.
2   The game ends when both players agree that no further move is possible.
3   A player may not pass for strategic advantage. If a player claims that he cannot see a possible move he or she does not merely miss a single turn but *two* turns (i.e. The opponent makes three moves in succession).

4 Getaway

Two players each select the name of a geographical location of an agreed number of letters. For example, one player might choose a country such as ENGLAND or DENMARK, and his or her opponent might choose a city like BELFAST or GLASGOW. All four of these contain seven letters. Whilst both players know what *type* of location the other has chosen, they have no idea of its identity. The object of the game is its discovery.

A large-scale grid is drawn – say, 12 × 12 – and the players take turns in writing down any words they wish of any length. The only stipulation is that a 3-letter word *must* contain one of the letters of the chosen location – and it must be in the correct order.

Suppose that Jack chooses DENMARK, Jill chooses BELFAST, and they agree to 'get away' from the English prison of STRANGEWAYS. This word is now written in the centre of the grid and they build up a crossword from that base.

Jack is to go first and he decides to be cautious and constructs the word GOOD descending from the horizontal STRANGEWAYS. His reason for this is that he now has complete control of where his letter D (of DENMARK) is to be sited. It might be the first letter of such as DIP, the second letter of such as ADO or the third letter of, say, AND.

Jill decides to do two things. First to complicate things for Jack if he is trying any tactic as outlined above and, at the same time, do exactly the same thing herself. She plays the word BOMBING in this fashion:

```
S T R A N G E W A Y S
          O
      B O M B I N G
          D
```

The tactics are many and varied and the game can end in a variety of ways:

1. An opponent having discerned, say, DENM from the 3-letter words played, wins by calling out 'Denmark!''
2. One player has made a complete getaway.
3. A player cannot possibly complete the word due to lack of space. For example, DENMAR is already on the grid

but к cannot be contrived into a 3-letter word with a particularly cramped construction of words. He must now reveal that к to his opponent if she is equally frustrated. The winner is the first of the two to identify the location.

Note that as more and more 3-letter words are added it becomes increasingly difficult to remember in which order they were played. Therefore, players who wish to play a good, challenging game, are not permitted to keep notes as to the order in which their opponents played their words.

5 Words

The classic pencil-and-paper game, so great that pale imitations appear on British television and it is even marketed as a boxed game. It has long been a favourite pastime of British word lovers and devotees even form their own informal clubs, with leagues and knockout tournaments to play this truly addictive game.

You do not have to be an expert to play, but *don't* attempt to introduce it to someone who is baffled by the rudiments of Hangman and fails to obtain the simplest of words. Such a person would never appreciate the elimination skills so essential for success. It is a game for two players, both of whom hide their workings from each other. In the following example of play, Jack will use the Words Word Table (see page 431) and try to discover a particularly obscure word chosen by Jill and, for the sake of contrast, Jill will play a totally random game in an attempt to discover an ordinary everyday word chosen by Jack. In reality, two players normally start off by selecting ordinary words and progress to the obscure as expertise develops. They have no such visual aid as the Words Word Table – this represents Jack's experience with the game. Jill has never played it before, but she is nobody's fool.

All words for all games have five letters. Jack chooses the word BREAD. Jill chooses XENON. Neither tells the other what the word is, the object of the game being to find out the other's unknown word first. The winner will always emerge within twenty guesses at the opponent's word. The Jack and Jill example is rooted in normal play, it has *not* been specially contrived.

First, however, a word or two of caution. Players will make mistakes not in guessing but in replying. Such mistakes will be genuine and, for this reason, apart from any other, it is vital that you follow the basic instructions. Mistakes of this sort are very frustrating and misleading and, once discovered, the game is normally abandoned and a fresh pair of words chosen. Neither Jack nor Jill will make any mistakes in the example.

When playing the game, you will not need to write down anything other than what is shown below in block capitals. Some books on word games show 'working alphabets' in their instructions. The writers of those books have either never played the game or else used inferior logic. You will only ever need to write down the words which you say to your opponent and the words which your opponent says to you. The net result is that you will have two vertical tables of 5-letter words, one containing your opponent's guesses at your word, the other containing guesses at your opponent's word.

You base all your strategy on the developing table of guesses at your opponent's word. The table which develops under your own word will assist discussion over a possible 'mistake' – such discussion is quite frequent but usually groundless. It normally arises when a player has made a wrong assumption. This would occur if, say, Jill guessing at BREAD said 'TROOP' and was told that she had one of the letters correct but not *which* letter (the R) and, for her next guess, said 'BLOCK' and was again told she had a letter correct. As the O is common to both words she could easily assume, as many people do, that Jack's word has an O as the middle letter. Whereas, of course, it was the R and the B that he meant: two different letters not one.

Rules

1   You always say how many letters correspond directly in position with the original word. For example, if an opponent guesses 'BEARD' for BREAD, the response should be 'Two': only the B and the D share a common position.

2   You never give clues, you only ever state a number. You never impose limits on choice of word. You may have a tacit understanding to restrict play to 'normal' words, but that is for beginners only.

3   All guessing words (as BEARD for BREAD) *must* be real words. If Jack has already discovered . ENON but does not yet know the first letter (X), and has never heard of the word XENON, he may *not* make up 'funny words' such as 'AENON', 'BENON', 'CENON', etc. in order to discover it. He already *knows* . ENON so, to eliminate A, B

or C, he must say such as APPLE, BEAKS, CHASM or whatever. Only when he gets a reply of 'One' to such as XIPHS does he find out the word is XENON. A reply of 'Nil' to APPLE tells him that it cannot be 'AENON' and a reply of 'One' to BEAKS tells him it cannot be 'BENON' as he already knows that E is the second letter, so the 'one' *has* to be that E.

4   Whoever has the first guess must allow his or her opponent one last guess to tie the match if that first player should prove successful.

Jack and Jill are now ready to play and both mark the tops of their pieces of paper as follows:

Jack heads his columns *Me* and *She* and underneath *Me* he writes the word she is attempting to discover. Underneath *She* he puts five dots to represent the unknown letters. These are sufficiently widely spaced for him to pencil in the letters as they are discovered.

Jill heads her columns *Me* and *He* (or whatever other description suits her mood) and writes XENON under *Me* and five dots under *He*.

Jack is to guess first. We will follow his progress, knowing that experience will have him following the pattern shown by the Words Word Table. Jill's sound tactics, albeit random, can be discerned. Jack will use some very obscure words, but most of which are defined in the *OED*, and you may rest assured that no matter how 'funny' they appear all are completely genuine. We begin at the point where Jack has made his first guess. He is trying to discover vowels, beginning with the most common of all, hence the 'funny' word SEEER.

Me	*She*

B R E A D   . . . . .

                       S E E E R   1

Immediately Jill has to say, 'One'. So he puts a 1 beside
SEEER. He does not know which of the five letters it is, so
he will begin a process of logical elimination.

The next example is four guesses later, by which time he
has established that the second letter is E. Meanwhile he
has recorded Jill's guesses under the appropriate column.
He also records the numbers appropriate to both him and
her. X denotes nil.

Me	*She*

B R E A D   **E**

                       . . . . .

E A G L E   X   **S E E E R**   1
A S P I C   X   **S E V E R**   1
L O O P Y   X   **L E V E R**   1
C H A R T   X   **L O V E R**   X

As the only difference between LEVER and LOVER is the
second letter and LEVER scored one but LOVER scored nil so
E *has* to be one of the letters in her word. Her word almost
certainly has another vowel, so he will continue to look for
it.

We next study Jack's sheet at the point where he has
accidentally hit upon the consonant N in his logical pursuit

of the second vowel. Once again we are at the point when he knows for certain what it is.

	Me				*She*		
B R E A D				E N			
				. . . .			
E A G L E	X			S E E E R	1		
A S P I C	X			S E V E R	1		
L O O P Y	X			L E V E R	1		
C H A R T	X			L O V E R	X		
P E T E R	X			E X I N E	X		
S I N U S	X			A R A B A	X		
Q U E E N	1			B A N A L	1		
Q U E A N	2			C A N A L	1		
Q U A R T	X			C A B A L	X		

Whilst Jack knows *both* his letters, Jill is certain of only one, the A. However, she knows that the other is either E or N. She will soon catch Jack up. She did not guess wildly with QUART but, very sensibly, looked back through her guesses and combined the barren CHART with the fruitful QUEAN. Also notice how she very cleverly switched her vowels and consonants around in her first ever 'fishing expedition' for a starting letter. Jack is already beginning to suspect that the next word he chooses for her for their next game will have to be a 'swine' – CRWTH or LLAMA or something equally horrendous. Jack has yet to find that second vowel. True, it could be a word such as WENCH but the odds still favour a second vowel. We next see him lighting upon it but accidentally hitting and confirming a second consonant before he is certain of the vowel.

Me			*She*	
B R E A D			E N N	
			. . . . .	
E A G L E	X		S E E E R	1
A S P I C	X		S E V E R	1
L O O P Y	X		L E V E R	1
C H A R T	X		L O V E R	X
P E T E R	X		E X I N E	X
S I N U S	X		A R A B A	X
Q U E E N	1		B A N A L	1
Q U E A N	2		C A N A L	1
Q U A R T	X		C A B A L	X
A S P E N	X		V I V I D	X
W R E A K	3		S E N O R	3
B R E A K	4		T E N O R	3
B R E A M	4		T E N O N	4

To hell with it! Jill is *definitely* going to get a tough one next time! Jack is under pressure. He knows that Jill has BREA. but he is facing either TEN . N or . ENON.

The word he is trying to find cannot be TENEN (if it exists) as he has already eliminated E as a fourth letter (with LOVER). Equally it cannot be TENAN or TENIN and TENON is only worth 4. Could it be TENUN or TENYN? Doubtful. That leaves DENON (he has already eliminated the possibility of the first letter being A, B, C as well as E, L, S, T and V) but FENON, GENON, etc.? It is a race, and he can only tie at best. Jill is bound to come up with BREAD next time and she still has a move in hand. HENON? IENON? JENON? KENON? MENON? NENON? OENON? PENON? Surely never QENON – but she *does* know an awful lot of those peculiar Q words without a U, look how many times she used them in Hangman! RENON?

The result is immaterial, the game is great. I thoroughly recommend it. If you like word games, you will love this one.

(Note that Jack missed out BOOBY in the Words Word Table. He already knew the second and third letters, so BOOBY would be a complete waste of 'vowel hunting' time.)

6 Superwords

The author's own variation on Words for three or more players. Only those already familiar with the skills of Words should attempt it.

When playing with three players, each person has two words for the others to find, the winner being the one who finds *two* unknown words, one from each opponent.

For example, Tom, Dick and Harriet are to play a three-way contest.

Tom chooses IGLOO for Dick and MYRRH for Harriet. Dick chooses QWATE for Tom and YCLAD for Harriet. Harriet chooses ZYGAL for Tom and FLUFF for Dick. They play a mean game!

Each player now compiles four lists. Tom's will look like this:

	Dick		*Harriet*	
He	*Me*	*She*	*Me*
. . . . I G L O O	. . . . . M Y R R H

Each player now questions both of the others in turn. Tom will guess at Dick's word and write down the result. He will then guess at Harriet's word and write down the result.

Dick will then have his two guesses, followed by Harriet with her two guesses. Play continues in this fashion. Even if Dick and Harriet have both guessed Tom's words for them, he is still in the hunt until someone obtains both the hunted words. All that happens in this situation is that Dick and Harriet now ignore Tom and battle with each other whilst Tom (assuming he has not scored yet) still makes 'conversation' with them. Although I have never tried it with four or more players, I see no reason why it cannot be attempted.

Those who do will need wide paper.

7 Jotto

Jotto is similar to but should not be confused with the classic game, Words. Jotto is logical deduction for the hard of thinking. This time, instead of being told that one has found two of the letters in the mystery word, BREAD, if one has guessed BEARD one is told that all five have been found.

Obviously one is seeking an anagram of BREAD.

8 Jotto Variations

There are two. For the first one you make it even easier for the person guessing at BREAD with BEARD by saying, 'Two in the correct position and three in the incorrect position.'

The second, devised by Don Laycock, is more subtle. This time, any guess you make at your opponent's word must be accompanied by a statement as to how many of these letters also occur in your own word. This is not as childish as it may seem, and Laycock's Jotto is the only one of the three forms of Jotto worthy of adult attention.

9 Little Dominoes

Two players write down – but keep secret from each other – six valid 2-letter words. Thus:

Jack	AT	IN	ON	NO	TO	SO
Jill	BO	OB	GO	OO	TO	AT

Ignore the fact that BO, OB and OO are unusual words (they are defined in the Miniglossary, page 449) but note that the players have the words AT and TO in common. This is significant as no word may be repeated in play. How this is resolved will be explained later.

Jill is to play first and, on a mutual playing sheet, she writes the word OO in a little box. For fun she has it domino-style and writes it vertically. This is not necessary – all of the play is restricted to a horizontal plane – but makes for easier illustration in this example. Jill crosses OO off her secret list.

Jack now writes the word TO in a little box. This is in the accepted horizontal plane and has to be to the left of OO so that the letters in common are conjoined. Jack crosses TO off his list.

Jill plays AT. The position is thus:

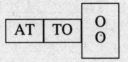

and now both of the words in common have been played. This was not contrived, but logical play in the circumstances.

Jack plays ON. Jill cannot make a move.

Jack plays NO. Jill plays OB.

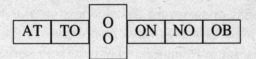

Jack's remaining words are AT, IN, SO. Though none fit as they stand he does have the letter A available for a link if he can contrive a valid 2-letter word from any combination of his six letters. Therefore, he plays the word TA.

Jill plays BO.

Jack has IN and SO remaining. How can he use the O? He cannot play ON, as it has already been played. He does not wish to play the exclamation OI as this will leave him an utterly unplayable combination of N and S. He chooses the word OS.

Jill cannot make a move.

Jack cannot make a move.

Jack wins on the letter count. He has only two letters (the word IN) left whereas Jill has four letters (the words GO and TO). The final appearance of the game is:

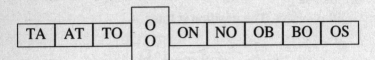

| TA | AT | TO | O
O | ON | NO | OB | BO | OS |

10 Clewlow's Dominoes

Two players agree upon a subject – Animals in this example. The object of the game is to force the opponent to surrender. No word may be repeated and no hyphenated compounds or two-word descriptions (such as MUSK OX) may be used. (See page 106 for word rules.)

Unlike Little Dominoes, play is in both horizontal and vertical planes. But, like Little Dominoes, there are only two ends open for play. Thus, only the T and R of TIGER may be used, but they may be either the first or last letters of any valid word. Therefore, if TIGER is the first word played, one has four options. Once the R, say, of TIGER has been used it cannot be used again. At all times there are two ends and four options. The skill lies in creating 'dead' ends. A fairly quick game might end thus:

CAT	TIGER	RAT	TAPIR	RATEL	LYNX

	C
	A
	L
	F

	F
	O
OX	X

O
R
Y
X

Whoever played the last 'X word' has won and if he knows that such as ASPALAX, HYRAX or ADDAX are still available keeps quiet about it. He wishes to force a surrender.

(The first of two games devised by Charles Clewlow.)

11 Clewlow's Super Dominoes

A strictly adult version of Clewlow's Dominoes with the playing format exactly as before. This time, however, both players write down the complete alphabet and the object of the game is to be the first to use every letter of the alphabet. (General word rules are on page 106.)

The letters may occur in any part of the domino played. Thus, if a player begins a game based on Animals with the word QUAGGA then he or she deletes the letters Q, U, A and G from his or her personal alphabet.

If an impasse should arise with both players agreeing

that no further play is possible or fruitful then the one with the greater number of letters utilized is the winner.

(The second of two games devised by Charles Clewlow.)

12 Simon Doe

Simon Doe is one of the many anagrams of the word DOMINOES. There are dozens.

This is a domino game in which the winner is the first to play an anagram of an agreed word or short phrase, let us say, DOMINOES. The only stipulation is that the anagram must have no fewer than two words.

A neutral word is agreed as the opening domino: ANAGRAM would make a perfect starting point as neither its first nor its last letters provide a link for any possible anagram of DOMINO. Finally, a subject is agreed – say, Birds. The words played must be either birds or else those which form part of one's anagram.

Only genuine words may be played and there is no objection to any of the three standard English single-letter words A, I or O. This means that anagrams like SO DEMON I or O MISDONE are perfectly acceptable.

The skills lie not only in playing out the dominoes but in retaining the flexible combinations of letters till later. It would be silly, therefore, to play MISDONE and retain the single-letter word O. Far better to play O and save the flexibility of MISDONE. An even better play would be either OD or DO and retaining letters capable of becoming EONISM, MONIES, or SIMEON.

The layout and rules (see page 106) are otherwise identical to Clewlow's Dominoes or else those of Chesterfield. The Clewlow formula tends towards 'wide open spaces' whilst the Chesterfield formula can lend itself to tactical play by restricting the opponent's freedom of access to essential space.

13 Chesterfield

Probably the most dramatically different and demanding of all the games in this book is The War Game. Chesterfield is but Stage One of that six-stage epic of word play for the truly competitive. However, the opening stage stands as a pleasant little game in its own right and the non-military title simply commemorates the fact that it was first played in that English town.

Graph paper is ideal, but not essential, for this two-person, twin-subject challenge of the domino genre. Unlike any of the preceding domino games, words are not in individual boxes and 'end letters' are written only once.

First of all, players agree on a pair of subjects acceptable to both, it might be Capitals and Countries. One player then writes a 'secret list' of six capitals whilst the other writes a similar list of six countries. In the course of play other capitals and countries will need to be used, but players are restricted to their individual subject. The aim is to be the first to play all of one's six chosen words. Henceforth, these six will be referred to as 'dominoes'. All other words used in play will simply be called words.

The full word rules appear on page 106, but the essential rules are that only subject words may be used in play and no word may be repeated. Finally, a pin is stuck in a book or newspaper and the nearest 3-letter word to the pin is written in the centre of the graph paper. For convenience, this is called the 'pinword' and it provides the two end letters from which play will begin.

Two examples of play are given below. The first illustrates the basic action. The second illustrates other aspects.

Example Number One   Player A selected Capitals. His dominoes were LONDON, BERLIN, AMSTERDAM, MADRID, ROME and VIENNA.

Player B selected Countries. His dominoes were ALBANIA, FINLAND, SPAIN, DENMARK, THAILAND and AFGHANISTAN.

The pinword was THE.

A spin of the coin had B going first. He played his domino, THAILAND, descending vertically from the T of the pinword:

```
                         T H E
                         H
                         A
                         I
                         L
                         A
                         N
                         D
```

His opponent then added MADRID:

```
                         T H E
                         H
                         A
                         I
                         L
                         A
                         N
            M A D R I D
```

The game ended thus:

```
                        V
                        I
                        E
                        N
                        N
            R U M A N I A                    L
            O                                O
            M                                N
        T H E                                D
        H                                    O
        A          A F G H A N I S T A N
        I          M
        L          S
        A          T
        N          E
M A D R I D        R
A                  D
U                  A
R          B E L G I U M
I          E
T          R
I          L
U          I
S P A I N
```

Example Number Two   In this game one of the players made a very significant error and the other failed to spot it. The subjects, Animals and Birds, agreed. A chose Animals as dominoes: TIGER, LION, HORSE, DZO, ELEPHANT and SNAKE.

B had Birds: MERLIN, EAGLE, FALCON, OSPREY, WIND-HOVER and KITTYHAWK.

The pinword was AND.

DZO was known to both and was no problem. WIND-HOVER, which was never played, might have caused difficulties according to whichever reference work one may have resorted to in the event of a dispute. *Chambers* dictionary has it hyphenated as 'wind-hover', but the *OED* shows it as a single word.

'KITTYHAWK' is where the trouble lies. It is not to be found in any dictionary or ornithological work. KITTY HAWK does appear, however, in the *Encyclopaedia Britannica*. It is the place where the Wright Brothers first flew an aeroplane! As both A and B are respected Scrabble players at the highest competitive level, B should have known this and A should have challenged.

What is signicant is that the players both had opportunities to utilize the N of MARTIN for their dominoes.

LION had to be rejected as this would have clashed with the A of YELLOWHAMMER and produced a nonsensical 'ALION'; FALCON could have gone through YELLOWHAMMER in this form:

```
        O           R
        W           T
        H           I
    F A L C O N
        M
```

but again had to be rejected as words cannot be interlinked.

Chesterfield has an intriguing twist. Unlike Clewlow's Dominoes, players may ask each other for help if they are stuck. Of course you help them – to a word which helps you!

The completed game is shown on the opposite page.

Whether as Stage One of the War Game or as an independent game, Chesterfield requires its contestants to choose naturally related pairs of subjects. Ideally, these should be ones for which you possess some reference work

```
                        D Z O
                        R S P
                        A   R
                        K   R
            S N A K E   E   Y A K
            K               I
            U               T
            A N D           T
                U           Y
                C       H   A W
                K I N E     A W
                    A G     L
                    L   K U D U
            H O R S E         U
            A               N
      G N U W               I
      E     K Y             C
      E A S S E             O
      S U H   L   M E R L I N
      E L K A L   A
        G O O S E O   R
            L   W   T
            E   H   I
            P   A   N U M B A T
            H   M         E
            A   M         R
            N   E     L I O N
          T I G E R
```

or works which can be consulted in the event of a dispute. But, any subjects can be grist to your Chesterfield mill such as:

Boys and Girls: forenames
Left and Right: political surnames
Time and Motion: months, zodiac signs/modes of transport
Work and Play: occupations/games
Here and There: home country cities/foreign cities
Wet and Dry: geographical locations or creatures
Soap and Water: soap opera characters/fishes
Nuts and Bolts: objectionable politicians/athletes
Fast and Furious: athletes/boxers

or any other combinations which have mutual appeal. Both players must agree *both* subjects as part of the skill lies in second-guessing what dominoes the opponent is likely to have.

Word Rules for Chesterfield, Clewlow's Dominoes/Super Dominoes and Simon Doe

1 All words used in play must be ones that can be confirmed in an agreed reference work such as an atlas or a dictionary in the event of a challenge.

2 All words must be within the category specied. For example, if the subject is Cities, both EDINBURGH and GLASGOW are acceptable; but if the subject is Capitals only EDINBURGH may be played.

3 An erroneous word must be removed and replaced with a valid word. If, however, it cannot be removed by virtue of having already been used it is deemed to be 'acceptable'.

4 If an erroneous word is also a domino an alternative domino must be added to the player's 'secret list'. First,

however, the offending word – say, KITTYHAWK – must be replaced – say, by KITTIWAKE – then the new domino chosen, with letters that cannot be used at either end of the chain. Thus, if the two ends have KITTIWAKE and TIGER with the T available, the new word may not either begin or end with the letters T or E.

5   Hyphenated compounds or two-word descriptions are not permitted. Thus, only SPARROW is acceptable not HOUSE SPARROW or TREE SPARROW.

6   All words must be correctly spelt.

7   Standard plurals using an S are not permitted. The reason is that no contest could possibly ensue if one player's dominoes were such as SWANS, SWALLOWS, SPARROWS, SKUAS, SHRIKES and SNIPES and his or her opponent had SHREWS, SNAKES, SERPENTS, SCORPIONS, SLUGS and SKINKS. Equally, if only one had plurals then he or she could pluralize every non-domino played (EAGLES, FALCONS etc.) and so create a totally unfair game. Plurals such as OXEN or GEESE may be used, however, as they can be fairly construed as being different words from OX or GOOSE. To argue that SHEEP in one play is singular and in another play is plural will not be accepted. GEESE, GOOSE and GANDER are all acceptable as are EWE, LAMB, RAM, TUP and SHEEP.

8   No incidental words even if within the acceptable category may be simultaneously created by the playing of any word. Apart from the natural connection, all words in play must be at least a one-letter space distant from any other word already written down.

9   It is the responsibility of the opponent to challenge any word used in play.

For Simon Doe and the two Clewlow games these exceptions apply:

(a) There is no objection to plurals.
(b) When an invalid word is played it must be removed and the opponent now has the option of either insisting upon a replacement word or else taking that opportunity to make a play for himself or herself.

14 The War Game

A saga for two wordsmiths with stamina.

The game is played in stages but, first, the battlefield will need to be drawn, ideally on stiff card. This is a 4×3 grid, divided as shown, and on a scale large enough to accommodate whatever (coins, buttons, etc.) you use as playing pieces.

You will require two sets of six pieces which are easily distinguished. For example, six blue buttons and six yellow buttons.

Stage One　Play a game of Chesterfield (page 101) to acquire the cannon fodder for the subsequent battle. This will consist of the dominoes you are able to play. For each domino played so you will gain a playing piece and the strength of these pieces will depend upon the total stock of individual letters contained within the played dominoes. No word, however, may consist of more than fifteen letters.

The winner of the Chesterfield stage will have six pieces but the loser must have at least one piece or else the contest is over at this point; the loser will usually have three to five pieces.

Bearing in mind what you will need at the battle stage, described below, you should select dominoes not only capable of winning that stage but of the greatest value for the battle.

Stage Two　As the battlefield is divided into territories of North and South, so the example will use these same terms for the combatants. Assume that North won the Chesterfield stage with the following dominoes: ALBATROSS, EAGLE, YELLOWHAMMER, TEAL, PENGUIN and SPARROW.

South managed to play the following: STICKLEBACK, CANDLEFISH, STINGAREE and STEELHEAD.

First of all, North will cover all of his home territory with, say, blue buttons and South having only four words will cover his tracts of territory numbered 1 to 4 with yellow buttons. South is not vulnerable to attack on tracts 5 or 6.

Players assign numbers to each domino, writing these down and leaving them on open display.

North has   1 TEAL
2 EAGLE
3 PENGUIN
4 SPARROW
5 YELLOWHAMMER
6 ALBATROSS

Additionally, North must arrange his troops in battle formation which consists of splitting each domino into 'regiments' of 4-letter words with 'reserve units' of a single letter. This is written down but kept secret.

1 TEAL
2 GALE E
3 PINE N, G, U
4 SPAR R, O, W
5 ROME, YELL, WHAM
6 BATS, ORAL S

Three is the maximum permitted for both regiments and reserves for any individual number. Thus, the longest possible domino consists of 15 letters. A player who miscounts at Stage One and has (say) a 16-letter domino which is successful, loses it completely at this point.

If a player either decides to, or can only, construct a number of regiments which produces a remainder of four letters (e.g. YELLOWHAMMER produces ROME, ELLA plus W, H, M, Y) then all four remaining letters have to be discarded;

only the two regiments are available for play. This means that words of 4, 8 or 12 letters must be divided into an exact number of regiments. It follows that neither a 2-letter nor a 3-letter word can possibly form a regiment. Therefore, such words may *not* be selected as dominoes for Stage One. There is no objection, of course, to 2- and 3-letter words being used in normal Stage One play. A player who, for whatever reason, selects, say, a 3-letter word as a domino is deemed to have transgressed rule 4 of Chesterfield and action is taken under that rule.

South, not having six dominoes, must assign two numbers to two of the words. Thus no. 3 might also be no. 5 and no.4 also no.6. This information is made known to the opponent on the open display sheet. South's strategic data is as follows:

1 DEAL, CHIN F, S (from CANDLEFISH)

2 KICK, SEAL B, C, T (from STICKLEBACK)

3/5 EAST, HEED L (from STEELHEAD)

4/6 TEAR, GINS E (from STINGAREE)

South's counters are placed on squares 1, 2, 3 and 4. (See diagram on page 112.)

The stage is now set for North to invade with any adjacent army. Square 6 **South** can be occupied either from 6 **North** or 5 **North**, 5 **South** can be occupied from either 5 **North** or 4 **North**. North *must* invade. The 'silver' army is on the march.

Stage Three   Have to hand your dictionary, your atlas, your book of children's names and anything else you can think of. You will be disputing words left, right and centre. This is war. The numbers assigned to each word relate to the square occupied by a counter. Thus, at the start of this example of play, North has three buttons capable of occupying either of South's two vacant squares. Each button is an army and its effectiveness depends upon the terrain where it operates. The three armies capable of invasion are located at 4 **North**, 5 **North** and 6 **North**. Power is always assigned according to the number of the square, so 4 **North**'s army, if it remains where it is, has the power assigned to 4 – in this example, SPARROW. But, the moment it occupies 5 **South**, its power changes and is that of YELLOWHAMMER. 5 **North**'s army is that of 5, YELLOWHAMMER. If it invades 5 **South** it remains as YELLOWHAMMER. But, if it invades 6 **South** it becomes ALBATROSS. 6 **North**'s army invading 6 **South** begins and remains as ALBATROSS.

Moves are made only in a horizontal or vertical direction and battles are fought against an opponent located horizontally or vertically. The initiative rests entirely with the attacker who, on moving an army, announces which enemy he intends to attack.

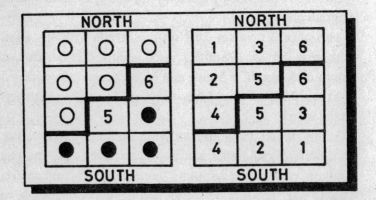

By attacking 3 **South**, North is facing the power of STEELHEAD.

By attacking 2 **South**, North is facing the power of STICKLEBACK.

The object of the game is to destroy the enemy letter by letter, word by word until he is either completely annihilated or else forced to attend a peace conference where he will lose the diplomatic arguments. It is a vicious battle of literary attrition.

All battles must be decisive. This means that one side must lose at least a complete regiment before a change of tactics is permitted. Reserves may be used in a battle or else held back for subsequent warfare. As casualties (the loss of letters) occur they are recorded on the open display sheets by the deletion of that letter. Players are advised, but this is not mandatory, to mark their own secret lists accordingly.

In the following example of a battle fought between North and South, the first engagement will be between a Northern army located at 6 **South** and a Southern army located at 3 **South**. Square 6 will give North the power of ALBATROSS which he has divided into two regiments. One is codenamed BATS, the other is codenamed ORAL. There is only one reserve, the letter s. Square 3 will give South the power of the regiments EAST and HEED together with the solitary reserve, L.

All battles are decided by your ability to construct anagrams. Each anagram you produce must be matched by your enemy or he will either lose a letter (providing that he has a reserve to take its place) or, failing that, the complete 4-letter word from which he was constructing those anagrams.

Obviously, the anagrams are made from the codename of a regiment. Equally obvious is the fact that it is not the potential of the regiment which matters but your own ability to utilize that potential.

Everything hinges upon your personal word power.

But the game is not a simple test of anagramming ability – it has as much to do with genuine game play tactics as any you will ever encounter. If you enjoy both words and games you will love this one.

North decides to invade 6 **South** from 6 **North**. It is now Force ALBATROSS versus Force STEELHEAD. Neither yet knows which regiment will attack or which will defend. The attacker opens the engagement by announcing the codename of a regiment – BATS, say – and the defender now replies with the codename of a regiment – say, EAST. A strict time limit is enforced, perhaps 10 seconds for each salvo. Failure results in the loss of a complete reigment.

North: BATS (Opening with the regimental codename)

South: EAST (Replying with the regimental codename)

North: TABS (First anagram of codename)

South: SEAT (First anagram of codename)

North: STAB (Second anagram of codename)

South: TEAS (etc.)

North: BAST

South: SATE

North: TABS

South: Repetition! Choose another word.

North: S is dead. (He deletes S from the display sheet) I am bringing in a reserve, a second S. I am now attacking with TABS.

South: EATS

North: BATS

South: ASTE

North: Challenge! No such word.

The dictionary is consulted and no such word discovered. South must now forfeit the complete regiment. This is deleted from the display sheet. The battle was decisive. As the winner, North has all the options.

1   He may continue with the same attack. Even though TABS and BATS have already been used in the reinforced regiment, they are still available for the next battle. This same attack may stem from either BATS or ORAL.

2   He may withdraw the depleted ALBATROSS and see what South decides to do.

If North withdraws, South may now move one of his own counters. This effectively changes his defences. These are his options and the results:

1   Advance the counter from 3 **South** to 6 **South**. This counter no longer represents the depleted STEELHEAD but now, if defending, is STINGAREE.

2   Move from 3 **South** to 5 **South** and it will remain as STEELHEAD if attacked.

3   Move from 2 **South** to 5 **South** and convert a strong defensive STICKLEBACK into a weakened STEELHEAD.

4   Waive the option of the move.

North withdraws. South remains in position.

North advances from 5 **North** to 5 **South**. He announces that he is attacking 3 **South** (now only HEED, L) with YELLOWHAMMER.

North: ROME

South: HEED

North: MORE

South: D is dead (D is deleted from his display sheet) and L is coming in from the reserves. HEEL

North: The regiment is completely wiped out (E, M, O, R deleted) but I am bringing in a fresh regiment. YELL

South: Surrender

The whole of STEELHEAD has been destroyed. STEELHEAD is both 3 and 5, so South has now been seriously weakened. Any of his counters on 3 or 5 (**North** or **South**) is powerless. A counter may be moved to one of these but it will be instantly annihilated if attacked. This effectively reduces South to defending his bottom line of 4, 2 and 1. North can move his armies around at will. South needs to remain where he is.

North retains a counter on 4 **North**. He does not wish South to have access to his territory other than by risking his forces crossing the deathtrap of the L-shaped 3/5 line. He has counters on 5 **South** and 3 **South** poised to attack. South does nothing. An attack is only made immediately following a move. South is prepared to wait.

North considers the situation. His 5 is weak. He attacks with 3. It is, therefore, PENGUIN versus CANDLEFISH.

North: PINE

South: DEAL

North: NIPE

South: Challenge! No such word.

The dictionary is consulted and NIPE turns out to be an obsolete noun and verb meaning 'nip'. There being no objection to obsolete words, South must now reply.

South: LEAD

North: N is dead. (It is deleted.) A fresh N from the reserves. PINE

South: DALE

North: NIPE

South: LADE

North: E is dead. G from the reserves. PING

South: LEDA

North: Challenge! No such word.

An encyclopaedia is consulted and LEDA is proved to be the wife of a Spartan king seduced by Zeus in the form of a swan. North must now reply.

North: GNIP

South: Challenge! No such word.

The dictionary gives it as an obsolete Scottish verb meaning, of a horse, to champ on its bit.

South: L is dead. F from the reserves. LEAF

North surrenders. He runs out of time trying to use his remaining reserve. The whole of PENGUIN is wiped out and the initiative is with South. South may now attack. He attacks 5 **South** from 2 **South**. (North has only YELL and WHAM remaining from YELLOWHAMMER. South has STICKLEBACK.)

South: SEAL

North: YELL

South: SALE

North: The regiment has been wiped out. A fresh regiment is taking its place. WHAM

South: LEAS

North has been shattered. He still has four armies to

South's three but now the 3/5 L shape is dangerous to both. South still has the initiative. What South does depends upon the position of North's counters. But, however they are placed, the only attacking and defending positions involve a border skirmish.

4 v. 4 is a certain skirmish. 6 v. 6 is only possible if North does not occupy the safe haven of 6 **South**, thus preventing South from venturing onto dangerous ground.

To attack a heavily defended frontier involves a sacrifice. Whoever mounts such an attack must first surrender a reserve or a regiment. South compared the potential of the two 4s. He considers STINGAREE to be far stronger than SPARROW. If North is of the same opinion then he will not attack. But, if South is to begin the skirmish he must sacrifice that valuable E (North has no idea of what he has) or rid himself of something else. What are his options? They include:

    (a) Keep TEAR, GINS and dispose of E.

    (b) Create TEAS, keep E and dispose of GRIN.

    (c) Create TEAS, GRIN and dispose of E.

Sensibly, he waits to see if North will attack, surrendering his right of the next move by saying, 'I stick'. North also passes, but South does not wish to attend the peace conference yet. If both players pass twice each in succession, then it is the peace conference and that is not until Stage Six.

 South sacrifices GRIN. The attack ends in a tie after twelve sorties.

South plays TEAS, SEAT, EAST, SATE, ETAS and EATS twice by virtue of the E; ETAS is challenged but accepted (*etas* are members of the lowest Japanese social class).

North plays SPAR, RAPS, RASP and PARS twice by virtue of the R. Then WRAP, WARP and PRAW. PRAW is challenged and discovered to be a Malayan boat. Finally, he plays PROW.

The battle has been fought to a standstall. No further fighting is possible.

(Note that in the above, final, exchange South could have played such as AETS and TAES and continued the warfare. For the purpose of illustration, however, unusual words have been kept to a minimum.)

Stage Four North has 21 letters remaining. These consist of TEAL, EAGLE, PROW and ALBATROSS.

South has 25 letters remaining. These consist of CANDLEFISH, STICKLEBACK and TEAS.

They must now prepare to negotiate from strength and the advantage has finally swung in favour of South. As he has the greater number of letters so his total is divided by 6 to determine the number of 'rounds' of negotiations which will be undertaken. Thus, four rounds ($6 \times 4 = 24$) will be the ultimate decider of the whole of this epic.

As the first stage, Chesterfield, is a game in its own right, so this final stage is equally capable of standing alone in circumstances where players are not handicapped as North now finds himself. It will, therefore, be shown as Conference and found on page 121. The rules of Conference are slightly different to those given below.

Negotiations take place on battlefield-shaped grids. To accommodate four rounds, each player draws four 3×4 grids side by side and keeps them hidden from the other's eyes.

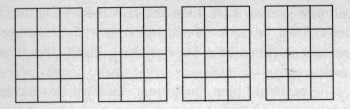

The stage is now set for the conference. However, as with all previous stages, one player can always resign, if he considers the odds to be hopeless. But North has not lost yet.

Stage Five Players take turns to call out any of their remaining letters, placing them wherever they wish on whichever grid they wish. Neither player knows where the other is placing his letter.

However, as each letter is called out so it is deleted from the open display sheet and this is a guide to the players' tactics.

Eventually, North runs out of letters but South may now add his remaining letters to any of the grids that he wishes.

Players tot up their scores. Only 3-letter words in the horizontal plane may be counted and only 4-letter words in the vertical plane may be counted. These score 3 points and 4 points respectively.

The winner of this epic word game is the one with the higher total.

Before attempting the complete War Game, you may well prefer to acquaint yourself with the essential skills of Stages One and Six. Stage One, Chesterfield, is described earlier, and Stage Six, Conference, also forms a separate game, described next.

Finally, it should be noted that the warfare stage could

end with just two 4-letter remnants of armies – say, PROW versus TEAS. A conference is still held with each player drawing his own solitary 3 × 4 grid. This could result in an honourable draw with neither player scoring a point, or else various scores of up to a maximum of 8 points could be produced.

The rule for the conference rounds is as follows. Divide the higher total by six and ignore any remainder. A minimum of one round is always undertaken if combatants have failed to settle the issue at any earlier stage.

15 Conference

This game is the sixth and final stage of the War Game, the epic battle of word power and tactical skill for the true wordsmith. However, played in the context of that very demanding contest it is normally an unequal struggle as players have fought through the preceding stages to gain the advantage at the conference table. As an independent game, Conference is not only a competition between equals but more than two may play. This basic description has a simple Jack-versus-Jill example with the rules for three or more players given subsequently.

Both players draw two 3 × 4 grids side by side on their personal playing sheets. These are kept secret. They now choose any two 6-letter words, which they write down on separate sheets and display quite openly. In this example Jack has DAMAGE and QUEENS, Jill has EXTRAS and SEEING.

They now take turns in calling out letters from their chosen 6-letter words. Jack calls out G. He puts this anywhere he wishes on either of his grids. He crosses out the G in DAMAGE. Jill also writes G anywhere she wishes on either of her grids.

Jill now calls out I. The procedure is exactly the same.

As play progresses so the players gradually formulate the final patterns knowing what to expect. But, with this subtle difference – not all of the letters will be called. Both players will leave out two of their letters. Thus, Conference has some of the villainy of its origin, the War Game. In the War Game all letters are used but unequal numbers are available and similarly incomplete grids pertain.

DAMAGE, QUEENS, EXTRAS and SEEING were genuinely chosen at random. Jack chose QUEENS to make it difficult for Jill (he controls the Q and the U), Jill chose EXTRAS for a tricky X in a combination of highly flexible letters.

However, if we now presume that Jill says the letter T in addition to the I which she has already stated, then Jack is in a position to display gamesmanship at its most devilish. At no time will Jack say the letter U. But, his final letter will be the Q! The reason for this will be obvious when their final grids are compared and scored.

The object of the game is to score points. Three points are awarded for every 3-letter word in a horizontal line, 4 points for every 4-letter word read from top to bottom in a vertical line. No other words count. The skill lies in maximizing the two-way potential of each letter.

First, we will score Jill's grid and see that she had to dump that frustrating Q where it gave her the least trouble:

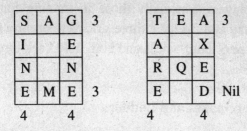

Jill scored 25 points. If Jack had said U instead of Q she could have scored an extra 3 points for either NUN or RUE. She merely stuck the Q in an available square.

Jack played a very different game and won with a score of 31 points. His masterstroke was the production of the unusual Q without a U words, QADI and QAT, well known to Scrabble players although Australian and American players are more familiar with the spelling QADI while British ones know if better by its alternative spelling of QAID.

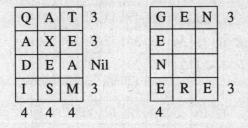

For three players, draw three similar grids. Still select two 6-letter words each and, again, each holds back two letters.

For four players, four grids, two 6-letter words each but, this time, hold back only one letter. Beyond four it will cease to be enjoyable.

123

Two players, especially those in training for the War Game, may care to try a three-grid version in which both select three 6-letter words and both hold back three letters.

16 Secret Snakes and Ladders

Great fun for all the family as the acknowledged expert can lose just as easily as anybody else – and doesn't that make a delightful change! True, there is a little more skill to it than throwing dice but the game is essentially the same as traditional Snakes and Ladders.

Draw a large-scale grid – 8 × 8, or larger if you prefer – and number the squares in the traditional Snakes and Ladders format:

A	64	63	62	61	60	59	58	57
B	49	50	51	52	53	54	55	56
C	48	47	46	45	44	43	42	41
D	33	34	35	36	37	38	39	40
E	32	31	30	29	28	27	26	25
F	17	18	19	20	21	22	23	24
G	16	15	14	13	12	11	10	9
H	1	2	3	4	5	6	7	8

Now add the letters as shown.

Assume two players for the moment, the rules for more will be given subsequently. Jack will play Jill.

They agree in advance how many snakes and how many ladders both will *secretly* arrange for the other. Naturally,

124

both will want a nasty big boa constrictor running from the top row to the bottom, but neither will want the other to know from where to where. So, a boa constrictor is agreed from A to H. The players now mark their own playing sheets with the chosen squares. Only square 64 may *not* be utilized. Hence:

	Jack	*Jill*
Boa Constrictor	61 to 1	60 to 1

Next they decide to have, say, a king cobra. This may have a descent of only five lines – perhaps drop from A to E, B to F, C to G, or D to H. They mark their sheets accordingly. Other snakes, and then the ladders are recorded. Their playing sheets now look something like this, after they have agreed that no one line may feature more than two heads of snakes:

	Jack	*Jill*
Boa Constrictor	61 to 1	60 to 1
King Cobra	62 to 25	40 to 2
Rattlesnake	32 to 2	58 to 33
Sidewinder	52 to 6	29 to 3
Puff Adder	46 to 17	53 to 25
Viper	20 to 3	24 to 4
Bandy-Bandy	21 to 4	31 to 9
Asp	16 to 3	18 to 10
Ladder (5 rungs)	2 to 33	17 to 49
Ladder (4 rungs)	31 to 49	2 to 31
Ladder (3 rungs)	47 to 62	34 to 49
Ladder (2 rungs)	8 to 9	7 to 10

Notice that both players have ladders that finish up on a snake. Jack's 3-rung ladder leads to his king cobra. Jill's 4-rung ladder leads to her bandy-bandy. The design rules are entirely up to you. Also notice that both players have ladders starting on square 2 – gambling on the opponent's greed, so missing it.

The rules are as serious as one wishes them to be but the essential rules are:

1   Words are limited to an agreed subject such as, say, Animals.
2   No word may exceed six letters.
3   The only bar to repetition is if the first player chooses, say, DONKEY, the second player may not repeat it immediately.

Jack goes first and chooses DONKEY. He moves his counter to square 6.

Jill must now choose a word beginning with any of the letters of DONKEY. What should she choose? A crafty word such as DZOBO perhaps? But a little word like KA, KY, OX or ZO might have its advantages. She chooses OX and giggles. Jack not only has to reveal that she has climbed a ladder, but he has missed a similar ladder himself.

Faced with OX, Jack chooses OTTERS (plurals are perfectly acceptable) and moves his counter to square 12, far behind Jill on square 33.

Jill's RABBIT puts her safely on square 39 but Jack's RHINOS has him on square 18 to be greeted by Jill's nasty little asp and back he goes to square 10!

So play continues, up ladders and down snakes.

The top line is the one to consider. One must land exactly

on square 64 to win. Obviously, if you can, you have a 2-letter word from square 62, a 3-letter word from square 61 and so on. But this may not always be possible. You might, for example, be forced to land on square 63. Either a tactically placed ladder or a word taken from a difficult combination of letters might do this. Under these circumstances, any chosen word has one counting both forwards then back again. Thus, one would go from square 63 back to square 59 by travelling forward one square to 64 then five squares back.

The other significant point about the top line is that if a player descends the boa constrictor quite a few of the significant squares become known, not least the boa constrictor. So, once a player descends a boa constrictor his or her opponent may now change as many or as few of the snakes and ladders as desired. Obviously, they must still conform to the agreed arrangement.

With three players, the game is exactly the same except that Jack would play to Jill's arrangement, Jill would play to, say, her mother's arrangement and Mother would play to Jack's.

Add another player and simply organize any logical pattern. Possibly the best, if the players are seated on each side of a square table, is to play to the arrangement of the person opposite.

No matter how many players there are, one always plays from the last spoken word whatever the pattern of playing arrangements.

Finally, when drawing the Snakes and Ladders board, stiff card is far better than paper, and the squares should be big enough for the chosen counters and boldly drawn.

17 Literary Battleships

If you enjoyed Battleships when you were young then this tactical, adult version should prove quite a challenge.

As with Battleships, draw a grid to personal taste and designate the horizontal and vertical lines with whatever system you once used. However, only one grid is drawn and, this time, you record your positions on your personal, secret, working sheet.

Agree a fleet with your opponent. As a child, the author played to the following navy:

– One aircraft carrier (designated by the letter A and placed anywhere on the then personal grid)
– Two battleships (B, B and placed in a formation horizontal, vertical or diagonal anywhere on that grid)
– Three cruisers (C, C, C in formation)
– Four destroyers (D, D, D, D in formation)
– Four submarines (S, S, S, S in formation)

The fleet might well have been dispersed in this fashion:

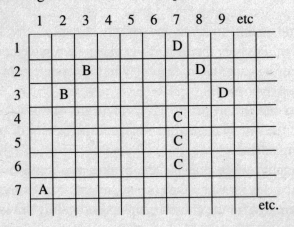

On the personal sheet, you record your positions by reference number and it might well take a form like this:

Aircraft Carrier	1–7			
Battleships	2–3	3–2		
Cruisers	7–4	7–5	7–6	
Destroyers	7–1	8–2	9–3	10–4
Submarines	12–1	13–1	14–1	15–1

The aircraft carrier, in this example being located at square 1 across and 7 down, the battleships at 2 across and 3 down and at 3 across and 2 down, etc.

Alternatively, you may prefer to draw a grid on your working sheet, placing your fleet in position for easier visualization.

The object of the game is to produce a legitimate crossword-type construction on the playing grid to sink as many of your opponent's ships as possible while leaving yours unscathed.

The winner is the one with the larger fleet still afloat when neither player can contrive any further legitimate words on the playing grid.

The first word played is always GO. This must be placed somewhere in the middle. If your opponent selects, say, square 6–7 for the G and square 6–8 for the O, you now announce that he or she has sunk a cruiser. (See illustrated example.)

Your literary problem is twofold. How do you defend the other two cruisers and simultaneously attack the enemy?

You are allowed a free choice of word but it must link to either the G or O, or even both, in some way. Obviously, a word such as STING would be stupid – you would sink your two remaining cruisers if you do that.

What do you do? Would ZOO protect, if written like this:

$$
\begin{array}{cc}
 & Z \\
G & O \\
 & O
\end{array}
$$

It might. On the other hand, would it not give the position away?

Suppose you turn GO into FOREGONE. Is not that an equal giveaway and is it not, at the same time, bringing play dangerously close to your aircraft carrier?

This game is more than Battleships, it is more than constructing a crossword. It is a true battle of wits using words.

You cannot expect the childish satisfaction of destroying a complete navy but, as in real-life naval battles, the remainder of the losing fleet steams away once it knows that it has lost.

The word rules are whatever you decide. But words must be correctly spelt and you may not have nonsense constructions such as 'ZQUEEN', the z being part of some other word. If, in this example, QUEEN is a defensive ploy the opponent must use a perfectly legitimate means of attacking the horizontal square immediately to the left of that Q.

18 Jack

This is like the British game of crown green bowling played with words. Three people are involved, but one of them stands down each particular game. Paper and pencil are needed for writing down whatever information might prove of value. Reasonable time-limits are imposed. The following example has Tom standing down whilst Dick plays Harriet to see who is the first to score 21 points.

Tom's task is to set the jack for the others to bowl at. He does this by choosing any 7-letter word he wishes – say, ENGLAND – and announcing only one of its letters – say, G.

The others have four 'bowls' each. These are 4-letter words of their own choice. It is not essential that their 'bowls' contain the letter G, but they can only score with words which have at least one letter in common with ENGLAND. Both choose to incorporate the G.

Dick bowls at the jack. He chooses the word SWIG. Tom says nothing – yet.

Harriet bowls at the jack. She chooses the word GOAT. Tom now announces that Harriet is nearer to the jack than Dick. (Only the G in Dick's SWIG is common, whereas Harriet's GOAT has the A and the G.)

Both Dick and Harriet have a problem. Tom has not announced a 'toucher' – a word containing four of the jack's letters – so what do they do next?

It is Dick's second bowl. He cannot say GOAT as Harriet has already used it, but there is nothing wrong with TOGA and he is certain to tie with Harriet. He chooses TOGA.

Harriet cannot use either GOAT or TOGA. What can she do? She knows that this combination must contain either two or three of the jack's letters. Two if Dick's SWIG only has the G but three if Dick's word contains two letters. She gambles on Dick's word only having one letter and decides to change one letter of the GOAT/TOGA combination. She says GATE. Tom announces that Harriet has one bowl nearer the jack.

Dick cannot think of an anagram for GATE. What can he do for his third bowl? Tom has not announced a 'toucher' so GATE must have three letters in common, and G and E must be two of them. Harriet must also have had two in GOAT. The A or the T? He fancies the T, so combines, G, E and T with another letter. He says GENT. Harriet also fancies that T. She says GERT. Tom announces that it is a 'measure'. This means that neither has the nearer bowl overall.

Dick considers the situation. GATE and GENT must both contain three of the jack's letters, but could GERT have three as well? If it does then G, E and T are common to all three. What 4-letter word can he think of? GETS? No. SWIG eliminated the S. This is his final bowl. He says GELT.

Harriet does not wish to say GETS (or its anagram, GEST) but she cannot think of another G, E and T combination which has not been used. Does she say GETS or try the other possibility – G, A and E? GAME? GALE? GAPE? AGED?

The following are the results of the game based upon three logical choices faced by Harriet.

GETS   The end is tied. The nearest bowl had 3 letters. It is a 'measure' so the results are compared. Harriet had GATE and GERT, both with 3 letters. Dick had GENT and GELT, both with 3 letters. The other words are immaterial.

The score, therefore, would be 0:0.

GAME It is a 'measure'. Though Harriet had three words with 3 letters, and Dick had two, it is still tied.
The score is Harriet: 0, Dick: 0.

GALE Harriet wins, but by what margin? She has the only word with 4 letters, GALE – the 'toucher'. It is now a 'measure' for the second bowl. As both had two words with 3 letters so that means the second position is tied. No further score is possible for Harriet.
The score is Harriet: 1, Dick: 0.

It is now entirely up to the players which option they wish to exercise. Dick and Harriet could continue until one of them is the first to 21 points. Alternatively, one of them could drop out – say, Dick so Tom and Harriet play. On this basis, three matches are played simultaneously: Dick vs Harriet, Tom vs Harriet, Dick vs Tom.

The only outstanding question is what would have happened had either player used the letter N. As there are two Ns in England, would N score twice in, say, GENT?

The answer is *no*. It is just rather unfortunate that Tom's jack used the same letter twice. To limit jacks to 7-letter words with every letter different is imposing something of an unnecessary task, but care should be taken to minimize difficulties.

Obviously, luck is an ingredient in this game – the skill lies in capitalizing on the luck. Scores of 1:0 and 2:0 should be obtained with a fair regularity but a 3:0 win is less likely when both players are equally skilful; 4:0 is still possible between skilful players as can be seen from the following scorecard kept by Tom:

Jack	*Dick*	*Harriet*
ENGLAND	SWIG 1	GOAT 2
	GOBY 1	TOGA 2
	GOTH 1	GLUT 2
	TUGS 1	LAGS 3

In this game all four of Harriet's bowls were nearer to the jack than any of Dick's.

19 Jill

Target practice with words using a similar format to that of Jack. The example is the same: Tom sets the 7-letter-word target, Dick and Harriet fire the 4-letter-word arrows.

This time the task is to discover the 7-letter word. Tom chooses the word, ENGLAND, and announces its 'bull' – the middle letter, L. The letters A and G will subsequently be described as 'inners'. By a delightfully confusing coincidence, the two NS are the 'magpies'. E and D are 'outers'. Dick and Harriet now mark their papers with such as '. . . L . . .' and try to discover the missing letters.

Dick thinks that the word could be something like TELLING so he fires off with GENT.

Tom says nothing until Harriet has fired off her quiver of four arrows. She sees possibilities in PRELATE, so she says RATE.

Tom tells Dick that his scores, in order of closeness to the bull, are inner, magpie and outer. He does not say which are which. He then tells Harriet that she has an inner and an outer.

The players now have the option of firing off a quiver or guessing at the word. They may not do both. Play continues until one player correctly identifies the word.

The 7-letter word is never spoken by a person guessing. He or she writes the guess down on paper and passes it across to the umpire. Comment is reserved until all (more than two may participate in the action) have completed a round of firing. Thus, if Dick guesses he has to wait until Harriet has either also guessed or fired arrows.

Tom will only tell Dick if he is right or wrong. He makes no comment as to accuracy.

Tom's own target looks like this:

so that he can make quick comments. Dick and Harriet write on their own paper whatever they wish.

20 Forescore

The proverb, TOO MANY COOKS SPOIL THE BROTH, makes an ideal basis for a game of pencil-and-paper golf.

Two players, Jack and Nicholas, begin by writing the numbers 1 to 18 on their respective pieces of paper. These are written vertically down the left-hand side. Next, they design the 'course' with 'holes' that are par 3, par 4 and par 5, so that both have identical targets including a 'short par 3'. Finally, they write beside each agreed par 3 hole either the word TOO or the word THE; each par 4 hole either MANY or COOK (singular); and each par 5 hole either SPOIL or BROTH. (Played at a more complex level, described later, the par 5 choice is COOKS (plural), SPOIL or BROTH.) Neither knows the words chosen by the other and their cards could look like this:

		Jack	*Nicholas*
1	par 4	MANY	COOK
2	3	TOO	TOO
3	5	SPOIL	BROTH
4	4	MANY	MANY
5	4	MANY	COOK
6	3	TOO	THE
7	5	SPOIL	SPOIL
8	4	MANY	COOK
9	3	THE	TOO
10	5	BROTH	BROTH
11	4	COOK	MANY
12	4	COOK	COOK
short 13	3	THE	THE

14	5	SPOIL	SPOIL
15	4	MANY	MANY
16	4	MANY	COOK
17	3	THE	TOO
18	5	SPOIL	BROTH

total 72

The object is to guess at the opponent's choices of words in a manner which produces logical golfing scores.

Guessing is by constituent word. For example, the word MANY comprises the single-letter word A, such 2-letter words as AM, AN or MY or such 3-letter words as MAN or MAY. The bigger the word, the greater the gamble. Thus, the more letters at risk, the more one will go either above or below par.

Consider hole number 1. Assume that both players begin cautiously. Jack guesses with the single-letter word A. He is wrong. Nicholas's COOK does not contain the letter A. Naturally, Jack now knows that the word *must* be COOK but he has to wait until Nicholas has had his tee shot. (This particular convention is only essential at the complex level which reflects, more truly, the game of golf.)

Nicholas guesses with the single-letter word A and is correct.

Jack now says the word COOK and is one over par. Par for that first hole being 4 so his score is 5 and he writes this down beside hole number 1 on his sheet of paper.

Nicholas now says the word MANY and has made par. Par being 4, he scores 4. Nicholas is now leading by one stroke after the first hole.

By contrast, had Jack guessed with a 2-letter word, say AN, he would have been two over par and scored 6 (par + 2). But, had he guessed with the Scottish word OO he would have been one under par and scored 3. Similarly, a guess with a 3-letter word, say MAN, would have put him three over par for a score of 7, or else, he might have guessed COO, and that would have put him two under par for a very remarkable score of 2 for the first hole. He may *not* have a 'tee shot' of a full word – that is only permitted at the short 13 hole.

The three single-letter words are A, I, and O. But, it is important to note that O is common to both SPOIL and BROTH on the par 5 holes and it may not be used when guessing is being undertaken at these holes. Thus, on a par 5 hole, one is only permitted to say either the single-letter word I, or else any longer word. Equally significant is the fact that the word THE does not contain a standard English single-letter word so the choice is between the caution of the exclamation O or a larger word.

A sample list of guessing words:

TOO	O,	TO	
MANY	A,	MY,	MAN
COOK	O,	OO,	COO
SPOIL	I,	IS,	OIL, SOIL
THE		HE	
BROTH		OR,	ROT, BOTH

The possible scores for the basic game are thus:

par 3	3 or 4,	2 or 5	
short par 3	3 or 4,	2 or 5,	1 or 6
par 4	4 or 5,	3 or 6,	2 or 7
par 5	5 or 6,	4 or 7,	3 or 8,	2 or 9

Therefore, one can play with relative safety by sticking to single-letter words, or else swing a mighty club and take the consequences.

On the basic game, par for the course is a reasonably easily obtained 72.

A more difficult game can be played by having the word COOKS as a third option for the par 5 holes. Under these circumstances both O and SO are disallowed for guessing purposes as the scoring has already taken on an added complexity without coping with the ambiguities presented by these two words.

If, however, one is correct with a first guess (the tee shot) the rules are exactly the same as before. But it can now take two guesses to be certain of the word, which means the approach to scoring on the par 5 holes must be amended. Finally, one even has to state the correct word when making the final 'putting' shot as it is not impossible that one has made a wrong deduction. The penalty points are shown by type of word:

Single-Letter Word   An error carries a penalty of one stroke. Write '+1' on your scorecard. For each incorrect guess with a single-letter word continue adding '+1s' until correct. The score for the hole will be par plus accumulated penalties.

2-Letter Word   An error carries a penalty of +2 on the scorecard. When correct it is 5 plus penalties.

3-Letter Word   The penalty is +3. When correct, 5 plus penalties.

4-Letter Word   The penalty is +4. When correct, 5 plus penalties.

Now try getting an albatross if you dare!

Finally, one can have a true championship golf course by naming the two cooks who spoil the broth, MAY and LOIS – MAY from MANY, LOIS from SPOIL. MAY is now a third option for the par 3 holes and LOIS is the third option for the par 4 holes. Penalty scoring exactly as given above, except for the differences in par.

The par 3 words being: TOO, THE or MAY

The par 4 words being: MANY, COOK or LOIS

The par 5 words being: COOKS, SPOIL or BROTH

A revised sample guessing table would be:

TOO	O,	OO	
THE		HE	
MAY	A,	AM	
MANY	A,	MY,	MAN
COOK		OO,	COO
LOIS	I,	IS,	OIL
COOKS		OO,	COO, COOK
SPOIL	I,	IS,	OIL, SOIL
BROTH		OR,	ROT, BOTH

Your proverbial golf course is now truly realistic and the 'Cook's Tour' of the rough will make par 72 a real achievement.

In effect you have a choice of three games. One on the Putting Green, one on a Pitch and Putt Course and, finally, one on a Championship Golf Course.

21 Pool

Mary, Queen of Scots, is alleged to have been a champion of billiards, the ancestor of both snooker and its sister table sport, pool. In the Snow White household, Grumpy claims the honour of being the champion of its literary derivative, having defeated not only every vertically challenged person in Hollywood but even the mighty Minnesota Fats. Dorothy, returning from a whirlwind romance in Oz, was keen to do battle with the ill-tempered wordsmith.

First, the 'balls' were 'racked', Grumpy and Dorothy achieving this by taking turns to nominate words commencing with the constituent letters of POOL. These were written on the single playing sheet and Grumpy opened with PORT for the P. Dorothy suggested ORANGE for the first o, and their full table layout took this form:

> **PORT**
> **ORANGE**
> **OUTWARD**
> **LEMON**

The object of the game being the isolation (and scoring) of the initial or primary letters by the utilization of the 'secondary' letters (i.e., the ORT of PORT and the EMON of LEMON).

Grumpy, having won the toss to open the play had to 'break up the pack' by creating a new word from amongst the secondary letters of at least two words. Hoping to isolate the P of PORT, so being credited with having 'potted' it, he took the W from OUTWARD and the O, R and T of PORT to create WORT (defined by *Webster's* as 'a plant or herb – usually appearing as the last element of a compound word, e.g. *milkwort*'). Now, having 'potted' a letter, he 'continued his break' with DRONE which, by *not* isolating a primary letter, gave the initiative to his opponent. Smiling sweetly, she 'potted' the very obvious RANGE of ORANGE thereby scoring the O. Not wishing to end the game in a stalemate with an unplayable single letter (the U) by scoring an L from constructing MAT she, very sportingly, deleted the AT of OUTWARD so enabling Grumpy to 'pot' two letters simultaneously by his construction of MU (see Miniglossary, page 449) for the last remaining primary letters, O and L. Grumpy positively glowed at his successful victory of the primary letters P, O and L to Dorothy's single O.

Desiring revenge, Dorothy called for a second game which, naturally, meant four new words. These were:

PARTRIDGE

OLIVE

OXEN

LIKE

and, going first, Dorothy commenced with a brilliant VIXEN to score the O of OXEN. This, she achieved, with the aid of the V and I of OLIVE so simultaneously denying Grumpy an easy LIVE (or any of its many anagrams) once he was 'back at the table'. KEEL from LIKE and the residue of OLIVE gave her a second score (OLIVE's primary O) in her continued 'break'. DIG from the I of LIKE together with D and G from PARTRIDGE scored her a third 'ball' in a row. She now had O, O and L to Grumpy's zero! Finally, she pulled off a master stroke: ARTIER from the residue of PARTRIDGE gave her a brilliant 4 to nil victory over the crestfallen wordsmith.

When last seen, Grumpy was applying for a bit part in Paul Newman's *The Drowning Pool* whilst Dorothy was the toast of Tinseltown.

Pool Niggles In keeping with the mainstream of competitive word games, single-letter words such as the previously mentioned U which has a single-letter word definition in the Miniglossary are *not* permitted in Pool. When a stalemate pertains the game is restarted with four new words and the previous scores are ignored. It was only generosity of spirit which made Dorothy refuse the opportunity of a drawn game by stalemate in her first encounter with the ill-tempered wordsmith.

22 Base Words

A game for two, three or four players, but the more there are the more difficult it becomes to score and the more frustrating the whole exercise. A swear box fills very rapidly with over two players.

The game is best played on lined paper turned so that the lines are vertical. Each player conceals his or her workings from the others but is honour bound not to cheat.

All write the same word, BASE, in the following form:

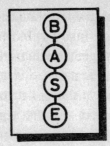

The top and bottom letters, B and E, constitute the extremities of available height, but the width is as wide as time permits. Play is for an agreed period of time.

Each player now adds two horizontal links from any two letters in either direction. For example:

Tom   Dick   Harriet

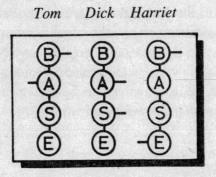

A subject is chosen – Animals in our example – and players try to make the greatest number of animals they can.

Players take turns in calling out one of two things, either any letter of their own choice or else the word 'Link'. When a letter is called it *must* be placed in a 'bubble' from an *existing* link. At this point Tom may use only B or A; Dick A or S; Harriet B or E. If, as will happen, no link is available a player has to miss out on that letter and wait until either he or she or somebody else

144

says 'Link'. The letter may *not* be added later.

If 'Link' is called, it may be drawn from any letter in either direction and may be horizontal, diagonal or vertical. No links may cross each other.

As words occur in the construction they should be written down at the side of the paper for subsequent scoring. There is no objection to the same letter featuring in more than one word, nor to the same word being repeated and a word such as FOX which is both OX and FOX may be counted twice. However, one may not have both FOX and FOXES from the same basic FOX.

A word may be read in any direction and twist and turn, however it may, but no letter may be used more than once in the *same* word. For example, if the subject was Food and Drink a player who wished to score with TARAMASALATA would need six individual A's to achieve this.

Now, back to Tom, Dick and Harriet's game. Tom, seeing the possibility of constructing the word BAT, chooses the letter T. Dick also realizes that he can have BAT so makes a similar construction. Harriet rejects the combination BT as unsuitable for any likely future word, but can see possibilities for TE. Hence:

Tom   *Dick*   *Harriet*

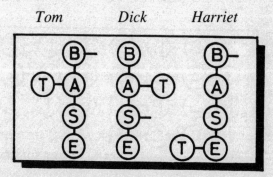

Dick, seeing the potential for CAT, now says 'Link' ready for his next turn. Tom decides to put that link to the S, without any particular creature in mind, but Harriet – seeing the chance to make STEER – links the S and T diagonally.

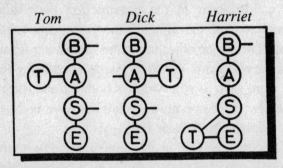

It is now Harriet's turn and she says 'Link' in order to pursue her STEER. A player in a similar situation might very well jump the gun and say 'E'. If so he would have to accept his misfortune (the other players might well have already written it down) and must *not* both write a link and follow it with an E in a bubble or even write the E in advance, planning to join it up later. He must use the only existing link, the B. Whilst he may swear, he is on his honour to suffer the consequences.

When the time expired, this was how the players ended up:

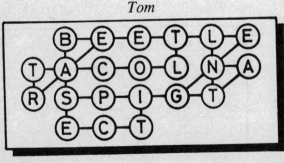

He swore a few times, being forced to waste good links on letters he did not wish to use but only once found himself unable to play a letter. An L in Dick's POLECAT. He scored 34 points for the 34 letters of BAT, CAT, BEAR, BEE, RAT, BEETLE, NEAT, GNAT and COLT. He was aiming for TIGER when the time ran out. He failed to spot the word PIG so lost the score for that word.

Dick

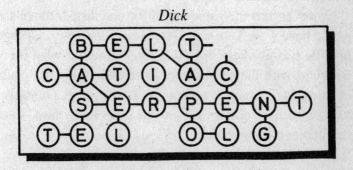

He also swore a few times but played a more open game so was never prevented from using a letter. He scored 29 points from BAT, CAT, APE, SERPENT, PEN, POLECAT and CAT. He was heading for a third CAT when time expired.

Harriet

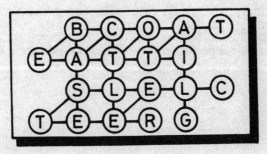

She played the tightest game of all and, in consequence, was forced to forgo the opportunities of using P, N and L. These were called when she had no available links. She scored 33 points for STEER, BAT, CAT, BEAST, COATI and, simultaneously in two different directions, EELS and EEL. This was the final call of the game and it was she who called the link. Thus she finished one point behind Tom but four points ahead of Dick.

However, had the game lasted for one further move she would have won. Tom would have been forced to call for a link, he had nowhere to fit a letter. No matter what he or Dick did with their links, they would lose. Harriet could immediately obtain 5 points for OTTER or 6 points for CATTLE or 8 points for a second and third EELS simultaneously produced:

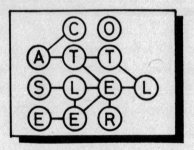

(Note that CATS would give only one point, CAT having already been scored.)

The tactical permutations of Base Words are a joy – but don't forget the swear box!

23 Double Base

The two-person, single-sheet version of Base Words. Graph paper is ideal for this game as people's writing styles are so varied that its horizontal and vertical lines will be helpful.

The game is not played to a time limit but a size limit. This is agreed in advance on a basis of the numbers of vertical lines either side of the base word. Thus, if players agree to 'Three either side' this will give seven vertical lines with the original word in the centre. Whoever is the second to play chooses the initial 5-letter word, which is written in the centre of the paper with horizontal links either side.

An example of play follows. Jack is playing Jill, he is to go first and the word of her choice is BREAD. They have agreed on Animals as the subject.

A player may make *either* a link or else write a letter in a bubble. Jack studies the base word. He sees the chance to make ZEBRA by a circuitous route, and Z is a safe enough letter to play at this stage. He puts a Z to the left of the R.

Jill makes a mistake that neither notices. She puts an R to the left of the A.

Jack, with his thoughts on ZEBRA, also makes a mistake. Jill will not only capitalize on this but realizes her error with the R and uses both to her advantage. Jack writes A to the right of the R of BREAD.

This is the picture he leave his opponent:

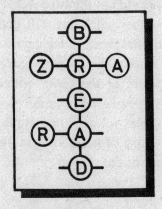

Jill pounces immediately. She writes B to the left of E and scores 4 points for BEAR.

By making a score, she is entitled to another turn. She writes a second B to the right of that E and scores 4 points for a second BEAR. Total 8 points.

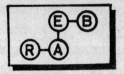

Another score entitles her to yet another turn. She now makes a diagonal link from the E upwards and to the right, to the A pencilled in by Jack. This gives her two simultaneous scores, a third and fourth BEAR for 8 points. Total 16 points.

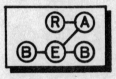

Jill now sees another aspect of her mistake which Jack (too concerned with a possible ZEBRA) also missed. RAT or RAM should have been taken by Jack. Jill makes it RAT for 3 points. Total 19 points.

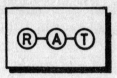

The addition of the T now opens the way for yet another scoring move. Jill links B to A for BAT and 3 points.

Jill has now scored 22 points in just one turn. BABE is

possible and the fish, DAB has been accidentally created but neither word really falls into the category as both understand it. She cannot see anything else, so what now? Does she block with a spoiling letter such as Q? Does she play a safe but useful letter? She decides to add a safe link from the T.

This is what the sheet looks like now that it is Jack's turn:

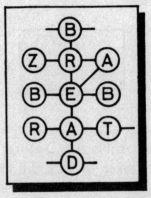

What does he do? If he links Z to E, Jill can then link B to R for ZEBRA.

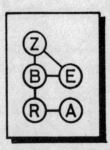

If he writes E to the left of the original B, Jill will link Z to E for a different ZEBRA.

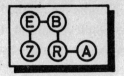

Then he spots it. One that Jill missed and could have obtained very easily. BARB, a swift kind of horse. He links the second B pencilled in by Jill vertically upwards to an A for 4 points.

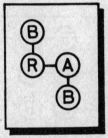

Now he spots another she could have got, BAT. 3 points for a link. Total 7 points.

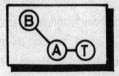

Jill's 'safe' link from the T is no longer safe. Jack now uses it for an S which complicates scoring. This simultaneously produces BATS, BATS and RATS.

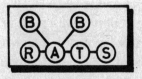

Irrespective of who scored the original BAT, BAT and RAT it is Jack who made the clever plural. Unlike Base Words, everything is scored again in full. 12 points for Jack. Total 19 points.

Jack cannot see anything else so he puts a U to the right of the original B to provide a potential ZEBU/ZEBRA simultaneous combination if and when the chance arises. This is what Jill now faces:

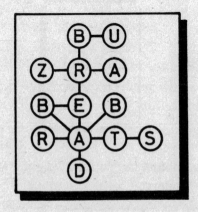

Bearing in mind that no lines may cross and that the same letter may not be used twice in the same word (the 'Taramasalata Rule' given in Base Words) what should Jill do next?

At least 17 points are available, using the names of animals already mentioned. If you can spot them, then Double Base is the game for you. You must, however, stick strictly to the rules and the answers are not published here.

When playing you may well need to add certain rules of your own to combat 'spoilers'. Taken to a logical defensive conclusion both of you could produce an utterly silly opening picture which looks like this:

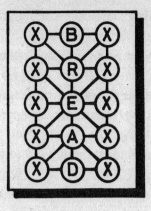

Under these circumstances you would have to impose restrictions on the number of times any particular letter may be used *in a non-scoring situation*, or else insist that, from the base word, a vowel must be written adjacent to a consonant and vice-versa. This, too, should, however, be limited to non-scoring play.

Do stick to categories – if you allow *any* words it will cease to be fun. No matter what the reasonably popular category you select, you will soon discover that you know more, say, animals than you could name off the top of your head. Finally, impose time limits for a move – as with all games of this nature, play with someone of equivalent mental agility. There is nothing so frustrating for a quick thinker as a contest with a deadbeat. Admittedly both Jack and Jill are quick thinkers and make mistakes, but they do *enjoy* the contests.

24 Square Bashing

A stimulating two-person challenge rather like the simple pencil-and-paper game of Boxes – but far more subtle.

Graph paper is ideal (though not essential) for a basic grid visualized as five squares by three, or any other agreed layout.

Players take turns to add any word to a word already in play. Thus, if CLIMB is the first word written down on the imaginary grid in, say, a horizontal plane, the opponent may now use either the C or the B to begin or end any other 5-letter word. The immediate object of the game being the completion of a square of 5-letter words and thereby claiming it. Thus

```
C L I M B
H
E
E
R A N D Y
```

would be claimed very easily with a host of words such as BADDY, BAGGY, BALKY, BALLY, and so on, by the player who makes that particular completion. He or she would then have the bonus of another opportunity of writing a linked word.

Obviously, one does not give away squares easily and, in the above example, the player facing the construction of CLIMB/CHEER would not have written RANDY as his or her move. Instead, that first player would have utilized any of the three available letters in a far more sensible fashion like:

```
        T                                   S
        H                                   O
        U                                   N
        M                                   I
   C L I M B   C L I M B   T U N I C L I M B   C L I M B
        H           H               H           H
        E           E               E           E
        E           E               E           E
        R   L O V E R               R           R
```

Once a box has been completed, the successful player claims it by writing within that box his or her personal identification. In the example overleaf this will be shown by the numbers 1 and 2.

The skills lie in creating difficulties for one's opponent and the following example of a genuine game shows how both players deliberately used such inflexible letters as Q in order to force their rivals to give them 'easy' boxes. At least three squares are still available to be scored with fairly 'normal' words – can you spot them?

```
S N I P S T E P S        Z E B U S T I F F
    K     T                      T
    I  2  O                      T
    N     O                      U
Q U I N S H E E P H A S E M B E R H O M B
U     P           X         E           O
I  1  A           T  1      C  1        U
N     C           R         A           N
T H I N E     Q U O T A H E A P L A I D
H           U         B       L         I
I           A  1      A  1    U  2      Z
N           F         F       M         Z
K       Q U I F F I R S T H U M B U S T Y
```

The rules are that no word may be repeated and each word played must be capable of being validated, if challenged, in a dictionary.

If a player cannot think of a suitable word he or she has to surrender that turn to the opponent. If neither can produce a word the game ends at that stage. This was true of the above genuine game. Player number one was leading by 5 squares to 2 squares and it was his move. He could not see a possible move and offered his opponent the chance.

In theory, he was handing victory on a plate. The final eight squares are ready to be taken in one fell swoop. A typical sequence would be the top left-hand box, S to Q, followed by the top right-hand box, F to B, then the top pair of boxes in the order Z to E, S to Z. Finally, the bottom four boxes in the order P to Q, E to Q on the horizontal, E to Q on the vertical and, last of all, K to Q. Such a run of moves being possible due to the bonus granted on completion of a box. There is no limit to bonuses.

Player number two also surrendered and so missed a chance of a face-saving 5–5 draw.

The final moves? There are no fewer than seven different words available in a standard dictionary to make the z to E move. Of these the most common is defined as, 'An American interjection expressing surprise and pleasure'. For the F to B move and the S to Z move, make logical guesses.

(Square Bashing was devised by Tom Wright.)

25 Twinset

Two players select an agreed number of versatile 3-letter words, ideally those which can feature either side of other equally valid 3-letter words to form a genuine 6-letter word. For example, PET. This can be prefixed by CAR to form CARPET or suffixed by TED to become PETTED. Each 3-letter word secretly chosen by an individual player must be different.

The object of the game is to be the first to play all of his or her 3-letter words, either as part of a 6-letter word or, less effectively, as a single 3-letter word. As neither player knows the other's words, so the basic ploy is to lead with a word which one can readily convert into the 'twinset', hoping that the other is incapable of so doing. In this event one gains the advantage, as the person who completes the 'twinset' leads off with the next 3-letter word. Sometimes neither player can complete a 'twinset' and the advantage is lost.

The following example is a genuine game between two

wordsmiths, known simply as 'He' and 'She'.

He chose ARC, ARM, ASS, BEL, CAP, DOG, ERS, GED, HER, LET, LOW, MAN, ORT, PAS, PET, RED, ROT, TED, TEN, TOR.

She chose BAR, BED, BOB, CAN, CAP, CAR, DID, DON, ERS, FAG, FOR, GET, GOT, HAM, LET, PAR, PER, RED, SON, TED.

Both players had twenty words with CAP, ERS, RED, and TED in common. A spin of the coin had the lady going first and she wrote down the word RED. He converted this into MANRED and began the next potential 'twinset' with ROT.

The game ended when he had used all of his 3-letter words and she still had CAR and HAM unused. The full play is given alongside, with the original 3-letter word featuring the central unbroken column. His final word was PET and the only other unconverted 3-letter words (DOG and GOT) had to have both players passing before a new 3-letter word could be written down.

```
M A N R E D
      R O T T E D
      B O B B E D
C A N D I D
      F A G G E D
      P A S T O R
B A R R E D
      C A P E R S
      A S S O R T
      A R C H E R
      B E L L O W
      T E N D O N
A R M L E T
      D O G
      P A R T E D
      C A P E R S
      P E R S O N
      F O R G E T
      G O T
      P E T
```

(Twinset was devised by Julie Titchener.)

26 Crosspatch

Two or more players each with individual playing sheets compete in constructing crossed words in such a way that as many words as possible are perceived in as many directions as possible. A pivotal letter is mutually agreed; after that players take turns suggesting 5-letter words which feature that letter as the third or 'middle' letter. As words are stated – a total of twelve words is required – each player writes them either horizontally or vertically on his or her sheet. For example, if I is the central letter and a player nominates TRIBE as one of the requisite dozen then TRIBE may either 'cross' an existing word or form the basis of a new 'crosspatch' as illustrated below in a Jack versus Jill contest where both had TRIBE as a horizontal word.

```
      Jack            Jill
       S               T
       P               R
   T R I B E       T R I B E
       C               P
       E               S
```

Jack had two 'straight' words, SPICE and TRIBE, together with three 'bent' words, SPIRT, TRIPS and TRICE. Five words, 5 points.

Jill has *three* 'straight' words, TRIPS, SPIRT and TRIBE, together with those same three words repeated through right angles. Six words, 6 points. The winner will now be decided on a total score basis of all six 'crosspatches' created.

> *(Crosspatch was developed by the author*
> *from a concept by David Morice.)*

27 Maggie

This game originally appeared in *The Countdown Quiz Book* as a tribute to a brilliant word player and charming lady, Maggie Warburton. As she constantly defeated me and I know of no other people who have ever played it so she can justifiably be called the 'Maggie champion of the World'! It is a two-person game but *three* pieces of paper are required; one for each player and a common sheet. Both players secretly write down a word like MAGGIE which has a double-letter in the central third and fourth positions. The object is to force one's opponent to write down *either* player's 'secret' word. The player who does so loses.

In a Jack versus Jill contest, suppose that Jack's 'secret word' is LITTLE and Jill has written down CATTLE. Further, suppose that it is Jack who opens the proceedings.

Jack now writes on the open sheet of paper placed before both players *any* 3-letter element of a 6-letter word. He may, if he wishes, select either element of his own word; either LIT or TLE of LITTLE. Alternatively, he may choose something entirely different – such as the MUD or DLE of MUDDLE – so as to disguise from Jill his own word to stop her forcing him to complete his own word. In this instance Jack decides to play TLE. He knows of no word prefixed TLE so it is a fair gamble that Jill may just prefix it with LIT thereby creating LITTLE and – by having written *his* word – losing the game!

Jill now has two tasks to perform. First, she must complete Jack's word with any valid 3-letter element. Jill, nobody's fool, confounds him by adding TUR to create TURTLE! For her second move – suspecting that Jack has a -TLE word –

immediately sets a trap for him by writing down TLE.

As TURTLE has already been played Jack cannot use it but, taking a leaf from his opponent's book, he turns it into MYRTLE.

With words such as SUBTLE, BEETLE, CANTLE, MANTLE, GENTLE, PINTLE, KIRTLE and HURTLE to draw on, they could continue in this fashion for quite a while before either is drawn into the dangerous area of the 'double T' words such as BATTLE, WATTLE, FETTLE, BOTTLE and CUTTLE. However, play is unlikely to follow a pattern of pursuing TLE to the death especially as both players had TLE words to begin with, so it will not be long before one or the other changes tack and attempts to force a victory with his or her prefixing elements of LIT or CAT.

28 Foxo

Noughts and Crosses played with the word FOX. One player is X, the other is O. Both players must, however, write the word FOX each time they play.

A 5 × 5 grid is drawn; it is O's turn to go first and he writes FOX in a descending diagonal line which puts O in the centre square:

It is now the turn of X to play. He has two options: he can write the complete word FOX anywhere he chooses; or he can utilize any existing letter or letters on the grid along with one or two of his own to produce the word FOX.

Once three Os or three Xs are produced in a horizontal, vertical or diagonal sequence these are drawn through and credited to that player. In this respect Foxo is the same as Noughts and Crosses but, unlike Noughts and Crosses: (a) the game does not end with the first person to make such a credit; and (b) the same letter may be used as many times as the player can create different combinations containing that letter. For example, a line of five Os has the central O occurring in three different combinations, each of which is counted for the score.

Scoring opportunities occur very quickly. If the above, with FOX written diagonally, is continued for just two further moves thus:

	F			
	F	O	X	
			X	

Move no. 2. X utilizes the O by writing F and X either side of it.

	F	F	O	X
	F	O	X	
			X	

Move no. 3. O blocks an upward line of Xs and simultaneously creates the threat of a diagonal line of Os.

It is now the turn of X to play. He has three opportunities for a run of three Xs. Notice that on one of them he would give away a run of three Os to his opponent – by writing the complete word FOX as in the illustration.

	F	F	O	X
	F	O	X	
F	O	X	X	

However, if he used the existing FO of the central vertical he would achieve the same effect without helping his opponent. The opponent could still score these same three Os but at only the cost of a move. If X chose the vertical Xs of the fourth column he has still failed to provide a defence against O scoring on the diagonal.

What should he do?

That's Foxo.

THE
POLYOMINOES
CONCEPT

The Polyominoes Concept

In 1954, Solomon W. Golomb, a Californian mathematician, introduced the concept of squares linked together as a simple game of shapes. This makes an admirable basis for an enormous number of word games which can be played by any number of people at any level of linguistic ability. However, I have included in this book only the merest sample to illustrate the potential for any inventive reader will be able to add to their number. Of the three games I have chosen one is a solitaire amusement, one involves two or more people challenging each other, and the third is for a group of players.

The shapes suggested for each game are purely illustrative and there is no reason why they should be rigidly adhered to. For simplicity's sake all three games are shown as pentomino games (played with shapes created by five squares linked together in varying formations) but, again, they could just as easily be hexomino games (six linked squares) or any other combination which appeals.

1 Fives

A solitaire challenge to score the maximum points possible with a single word. The five shapes selected have the potential for scoring progressively more points providing that, in each case, you can create valid 2-letter and 3-letter words.

Let us assume that the word TEARS has been chosen. This is written crossword fashion in the lowest-scoring shape:

T	E	A	R	S

One word of five letters gives us 5 points.

For our second play we create from TEARS two 3-letter words to give us 6 points:

	S	
E	A	R
	T	

The third play has a shape with the potential for scoring 7 points. It has two 2-letter word spaces and one 3-letter word space. How many points can you score from TEARS? All seven? Five? Four? Try it.

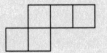

The shape for the fourth play can produce 8 points – if you can create four 2-letter words from TEARS.

Finally, 9 points. Three 2-letter words and one 3-letter word.

The maximum score is 35 points. Did you make it? If not, could you have done so if any of the chosen shapes had been twisted around? For example, the fifth one. Is this a more acceptable arrangement:

Or would either of these have been easier:

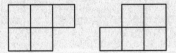

Ignoring the factor of twisting a shape around (which is very significant in word play) one has a choice of twelve basic pentomino shapes. There is only one 5-points shape but there are five different 6-points shapes:

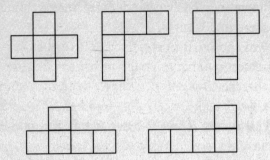

four different 7-points shapes:

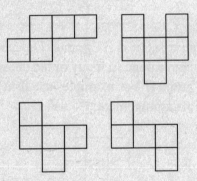

but only one 8-points shape and only one 9-points shape:

Your solitaire challenge with TEARS using all twelve shapes (however you wish to twist them) brings the possible score to 80 points.

TEARS was chosen, incidentally, solely on the basis that it has the greatest number of anagrams of any 5-letter word. Despite what the *Guinness Book of Records* may tell you, it is not the word with the greatest number of anagrams of *any* word (ANGRIEST is the supreme anagram) and it may or may not have the potential for scoring the greatest number of points in any re-run which must utilize *different* words for each shape. For example:

A	S	T	E	R		S	T	A	R	E		R	A	T	E	S

would each score 5 points in a second, third and fourth run at either the 35-points version of Fives or the 80-points version of Fives which, for convenience, may be termed Great Fives.

The rules for Fives are as follows:

1   Five different-scoring basic shapes are chosen. Once 35 points has been achieved, a re-run using any five different-scoring basic shapes may be selected in any attempt to achieve 70 points.

2   Thereafter, providing one has succeeded in obtaining the maximum points, additional re-runs may be undertaken until a failure ends the consideration of a particular 5-letter word.

3   All words must be genuine and abbreviations are not permitted. Note, however, that ST is a valid word in its own right (see the Miniglossary, page 449) even though

most people will regard it as an abbreviation for either street or saint.

4   In re-runs ST, for example, may be repeated in the same shape if the other word or words are different:

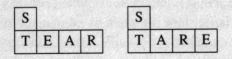

but twisting the shape and having identical words is invalid:

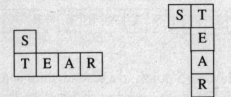

In Great Fives the rules are the same.

Which word has the potential for scoring the maximum possible in
   (a) Fives?
   (b) Great Fives?
   (c) Fives and Great Fives?

The challenges for Sixes/Great Sixes, Sevens/Great Sevens etc. are equally possible, all you have to do is design the requisite polyominoes in advance of the task.

2 Panic

Tom is going to play Harriet in a fast-moving game of pentomino decision. They agree in advance a total number of moves – say, twelve. Dick is the taskmaster, timekeeper and referee. Dick selects any 5-letter word he wishes and Tom and Harriet have one minute in which to record it in any pentomino shape they wish. There is no need to draw squares so long as it is clear which shape has been selected in the event of any subsequent dispute. Dick chooses the word FIRST.

As they only have a minute in which to record their results which shapes will they choose? Play safe and score 5 points for FIRST? See the potential for 6 points with such as:

```
S T I R        F           F R I T
     F  or   S I T   or        S
             R
```

Or gamble that RIT is a genuine word (it is!) and try for 7 points with:

```
        S
      R I T
      F
```

Once Dick calls time, they tear their results off the top of their scrap pads and hand them to him. At the end of the twelve similar moves, the papers are checked. Let us assume that RIT is challenged but not found in the pocket dictionary they have to hand. Despite the fact that both IF and ST are perfectly valid and worth 4 points, *no score whatsoever* is given for that particular play. If, however, a good dictionary was available then the word would have been accepted and the full 7 points scored.

Whoever, Tom or Harriet, has the higher score is the winner and is awarded 2 points. If they tie it would be a point each.

The points scored in play are ignored as the object of the exercise is to see which of the three of them over an agreed number of games is the winner, and some words have a far greater potential than others.

Tom will now play Dick, with Harriet in charge of proceedings; then Dick will play Harriet with Tom in charge.

In order to ensure fair selection of words any book or newspaper is used as the base. One merely opens up at any page, selects a paragraph at random and calls out 5-letter words in the order they occur. If this means that a particular word is repeated, so be it.

Six-letter or 7-letter words are just as suitable for this game.

3 Golomboes

The twelve basic shapes originally described by Golomb are drawn on paper (see page 177), and a photocopy made for each contestant.

(See **Lipograms**, page 254)

The challenge is to fill all twelve shapes using as few different letters as possible. However, unlike Fives or Great Fives, no individual word may be repeated in any of the pentominoes. In addition, the arrangement of the shapes is established, and they cannot be twisted to suit.

The ideal of utilizing only five letters will, for all practical purposes, prove impossible.

As a letter is used, it should be shown on the paper as a separate entry. Perhaps the easiest way of doing this is to have a complete alphabet typed in advance at the top of the page and, as each letter is utilized, so it is ringed.

Finally, note that the solitaire challenges (Fives and Great Fives) and the classroom contest (Golomboes) are mutually interchangeable. This will also prove true of some of the games described in the Classroom Series and Solitaire Series which follow. Essentially it is a question of the level at which you pitch the degree of attainment.

THE
CLASSROOM
SERIES

The Classroom Series

Whilst adults can, and do, enjoy these games, they are excellent for enlivening an English class, encouraging the children to think by adding a touch of sport.

Other games suitable for an English class are found elsewhere in the book but all of the following are ideal for this purpose.

1 Word Ladders

These were devised by Lewis Carroll, who called them Doublets, and first brought to the attention of the public in a letter of his published in *Vanity Fair* in 1879. The example he gave was turning HEAD into TAIL by changing one letter at a time. Carroll's solution was:

HEAD
HEAL
TEAL
TELL
TALL
TAIL

Any logical pair of words can be changed in this fashion. CAT to DOG for example:

CAT	CAT	CAT	CAT	CAT	CAT
COT	COT	CAG	CAG	DAT	DAT
COG	DOT	COG	DAG	DOT	DAG
DOG	DOG	DOG	DOG	DOG	DOG

The CAT/COT changes are obvious but the CAT/CAG changes are just as valid, a cag being a keg and dag has various meanings. The third possibility of CAT/DAT can be ignored as it uses an obsolete Scottish form.

Not that Scottish words can be dismissed, as any child north of the border could change Carroll's HEAD to TAIL in fewer steps, by the use of HEID (head) and HEIL (heal). Another way is to use TEIL, the lime or linden tree, in this ladder:

HEAD
HEAL
TEAL
TEIL
TAIL

Perfect solutions are not always possible. Carroll's APE to MAN is particularly tricky as the vowels have to become consonants and the consonant a vowel. Carroll took six steps whereas the journal, *Scientific American* has published several solutions shorter than Carroll's including the one shown to the right of the original:

APE	APE
ARE	APT
ERE	OPT
ERR	OAT
EAR	MAT
MAR	MAN
MAN	

In setting the company any test of this kind have your own solution to hand. But be prepared to arbitrate on some of the results obtained. To illustrate this point, consider the following transformations first published in 1893. Both are imperfect and both can be bettered quite easily. The HAND to FOOT perfect alternative uses a Scottish past tense and the BLACK to WHITE imperfect alternative has a word no longer considered to be of polite usage:

HAND	HAND	BLACK	BLACK
HARD	FAND	SLACK	BLICK
LARD	FOND	STACK	SLICK
LORD	FOOD	STALK	SLICE
FORD	FOOT	SHALE	SLITE
FORT		WHALE	SHITE
FOOT		WHILE	WHITE
		WHITE	

FAND is a Scottish past tense of the verb FIND.

BLICK is the iridescence appearing on gold or silver after the refining process.

SLITE is a rare verb meaning to slit or split.

The impolite word, incidentally, is perfectly valid for the UK Scrabble Championship.

(The name 'Word Ladders' was coined by the late Dmitri Borgmann, the modern American master of word play, and is far more apt as some of the following games will show.)

2 Build Up

Word ladders as the basis of a very different contest. Play with 4-letter words and challenge the company to create a much larger word. To make it fun, set them a task such as to 'Build a battleship from a cart'.

First of all they write the word BATTLESHIP at the top of their individual sheets of paper. Now they write the word CART directly below it. As the letters A and T are common to both words so they now delete the A of BATTLESHIP and one of the Ts. The challenge is to see who can be the first to use each of the remaining letters in a ladder of valid words. For example, six different contestants might begin as follows:

1	2	3	4	5	6
CART	CART	CART	CART	CART	CART
CARS	CARE	HART	PART	TART	CARP

No. 1 Deletes the S of BATTLESHIP.
No. 2 Deletes the E of BATTLESHIP.
No. 3 Deletes the H of BATTLESHIP but *not* the second T.
No. 4 Deletes the P of BATTLESHIP but *not* the second T.
No. 5 Deletes the second T of BATTLESHIP.
No. 6 Deletes the P of BATTLESHIP.

As one of the contestants might begin by changing CART

to BART this is pointed out in advance as being invalid as the word is an abbreviation of 'baronet'.

It is entirely up to you as to what limitations you impose. Are you going to permit such as the names of countries (e.g. MALI in a sequence running CART, CARE, MARE, MALE, MALT, MALI) or common personal names?

If, in the classroom, the winner's solution is written on the blackboard, might it not be easier to insist that every word used must be found in the dictionary? In this way no one can dispute some of the weirder names that are sometimes inflicted upon children, and any 'funny' words can be shown either to exist or not exist as the case may be. Quick finishes to each of the above examples imposing the limitations of words found in the dictionary could be as follows:

1	2	3	4	5	6
CART	CART	CART	CART	CART	CART
CARS	CARE	HART	PART	TART	CARP
BARS	HARE	HARP	TART	PART	HARP
BATS	TARE	HARE	HART	PARE	HART
BETS	BARE	HATE	HALT	HARE	HARE
BITS	PARE	HALE	SALT	HIRE	BARE
PITS	MARE	BALE	SILT	SIRE	BALE
HITS	MALE	SALE	MILT	SILE	SALE
HOTS	MILE	PALE	MILE	BILE	MALE
LOTS	MILK	PILE	BILE		MILE
	SILK	PILE			

Note that only no. 5 has the absolute minimum run and this contained the Northern England dialect word, SILE, found only in larger dictionaries. All of the other examples involve at least one 'non-deletion' move, these occurring at the ends of the different runs with only one letter requiring utilization. Perhaps you may care to find the perfect minimum run, not only for building a battleship from a cart without resorting to dialect but for any construction you decide to use.

3 Other Ladder Games

Pangrammic word ladders – those comprising *every letter of the alphabet* – made their debut in print in the August 1988 issue of *Word Ways* with this brilliant construction by Sir Jeremy Morse: FOXY, FOGY, BOGY, BONY, BONE, BANE, CANE, PANE, VANE, WANE, MANE, MARE, MARL, MAIL, HAIL, JAIL, SAIL, SAID, SKID, SKIT, SUIT, QUIT and QUIZ.

Four-letter word ladders are the recommended size for anyone new to the concept though there is no reason why the adventurous should not attempt 5-letter-word runs or even something larger. Equally, why not 3-letter words?

An alternative challenge for a junior classroom is to set simple tests to see who can first find a particular letter. To provide a suitable starting word – cheat! Begin with the letter you wish them to find, then work backwards a couple of steps. You can now pose the task of finding the X, giving them ICED (ICED, ACED, AXED), or the Z from LIME (LIME, LAME, LAZE) or any other suitable apparently difficult letter.

A different ladder game has been devised by Kyle Corbin of Raleigh, North Carolina, USA, and was first published in the May 1988 issue of the magazine *Word Ways*. This he called Minimal Word Ladders as it consists of changing one letter at a time to end with a word in which every letter is different. A 3-letter word, therefore, undergoes three changes and a 4-letter word four changes to qualify as minimal.

Kyle has discovered that up to 7-letter ladders can be produced quite easily without resorting to unusual words. These are some of his examples:

ANY	SOAP	ELATE	BRAVER	CANNONS
AND	SWAP	PLATE	BEAVER	CANTONS
AID	SWAY	PLACE	BEATER	CANTOS
KID	AWAY	PEACE	BETTER	CANTERS
	AWRY	PEACH	SETTER	CASTERS
		PERCH	SETTEE	MASTERS
			SETTLE	MASTERY
				MYSTERY

Others include ACORNS to SOAKED and PICKLED to BALLOT, which you may care to try for yourself.

The most frustrating of ladder-game amusements must be this one. Who can get to PARADISE with the minimum difficulty? The word PARADISE can be divided into any number of two 4-letter words – such as PEAR and SAID, and to construct it from *any* pair of 4-letter words is the target. The first step of the ladder is the word QUIZ repeated as a pair. The contestant must now write QUIZ twice and begin two separate ladders which end *simultaneously* with, say, PEAR and SAID. Thus a typical pair of ladders might begin:

QUIZ   QUIZ
QUIT   QUIN
SUIT   RUIN

at which point the first column has the S and I of PARADISE whilst the second column has the R and I of PARADISE. Two moves later:

QUIZ   QUIZ
QUIT   QUIN
SUIT   RUIN
SLIT   RAIN
SLAT   REIN

and, now, the first column has the S and A of PARADISE with the R, E and I in the second column. A rather nasty little rule needs to be mentioned – a word may *not* be repeated in the same column. This means that having achieved, say, SAID in one column too soon for combining with such as PEAR, PARE, REAP or RAPE one may not juggle the column in this fashion:

SAID
SAIL
SAID
SAIL
SAID   etc.

but must now begin to change SAID to something like DAIS, or even abandon that particular split entirely.

PARADISE has many combinations of two 4-letter words. Can you get there?

This game can have any 8-letter word as its destination so long as this word can be divided into two 4-letter words. For example, RICHMOND might prove easier to get to than PARADISE:

QUIZ	QUIZ
QUID	QUIN
QAID	RUIN
RAID	ROIN
LAID	COIN
CAID	CORN
CHID	MORN

though the fairly obscure words such as QAID (an alternative spelling of CAID, an alcade or Spanish/Portuguese magistrate) and ROIN (an old verb meaning to growl, found in Spenser's *Faerie Queene* with the spelling 'royne') make the attainment of CHID and MORN (Richmond) relatively simple.

It is not necessary to restrict oneself to QUIZ and QUIZ as the opening but they form as challenging a pair to begin with as any.

4 Guggenheim

There are two explanations for the name of this game of which the better know is that it was first played by the Guggenheim family. The other – first mooted by Frank Scully in his book, *Fun in Bed* (published in 1934) – has the game originally entitled Categories but changed to commemorate a malapropism. According to Scully, a category of Printers was included in a session played by Jerome Kern, Howard Dietz and P. G. Wodehouse, and Kern wrote down GUTENBERG. Apparently Wodehouse had never heard of Gutenberg and would not believe Kern's assertion that Johann Gutenberg (*c*. 1400–1468) was the first printer. When, some months later, Dietz suggested another session of Categories, Wodehouse is supposed to have said: 'All right, but no more of your Guggenheims.'

To play, choose any word of any length: a 5-letter word is reasonable. This is written, as individual letters, across the top of the competitor's sheet of paper. A series of categories is chosen and players now have to write down examples of these beginning with each letter of the original word.

A session of Guggenheim based upon the word SOLVE, with its first two categories being Birds and Countries might look like this:

	S	O	L	V	E
Birds	swan	owl	lark	vulture	eagle
Countries	Sweden	Oman	Libya	Venezuela	Egypt

When played in the classroom, ensure that answers to all

letters are feasible. For example, can you think of another country beginning with O or would the children have heard of a vireo?

The game is not as simple as it first appears.

5 Wordsworth

Any longish word is selected but the ideal ones are those which have a wide variety of any of the following letters: A, E, I, L, M, N, P, R, S, T. The reason for this will shortly become evident.

Suppose you choose TERMINAL. The object of the company is to discover it from the clues which you give to the individual letters.

First of all, create a number of words from its constituent letters, such as MERIT, MENIAL, MINE, MENTAL, etc. Now devise clues for each word – a simple dictionary definition is as good as any.

Announce to the competitors that they are trying to find an 8-letter word of which the third, seventh and first letters mean a large rodent ('rat'). Continue giving clues of this nature until the word is discovered.

(I presented an adult version of this game on local radio with cryptic clues. It was a phone-in programme and the lines were busy even before I had covered every individual letter in any of the chosen words. With clues matched to your classroom's level, you should have an equally intelligent response.)

6 Hidden Words

Compile a list of words each of which incorporates, say, the name of a creature. Examples include KNEEL, WRENCH, TAPED, BATH, BENEVOLENT, SEALED, CHART, BEHIND, SNAG, CROCK, TRAIL, KAYAK, COLLIER, ESCARPMENT, SHAKE, PLANTER, SHARED, GRASPING, BOAT and CLASP. Now add a twist: BULLION, SCOWL, CATCHFLY and FOXGLOVE.

The list is read out to the company and, apart from being a spelling test, is the basis of a fun puzzle. Each person writes the words down and is then challenged to discover the hidden creatures. Twenty-four words and, logically, there will be twenty-four creatures. But study the twist!

7 Classroom Back to Front

The Back to Front verbal games (see The Logomotion Series, page 361) can be adapted as a pencil-and-paper game played by a group. Compile your own Back to Front journey ensuring that it consists entirely of two-word phrases. The SCHOOL to COLLEGE example used in the Logomotion game has but four simple stages:

SCHOOL TIME

TIME LOST

LOST ART

ART COLLEGE

and these can be used as the basis of a classroom challenge. Take each constituent word (SCHOOL, TIME, LOST, ART and

COLLEGE), shuffle them around and dictate the result of that shuffle to the contestants. Now challenge them to reassemble in a logical order.

Obviously, a four-stage journey is far too short for a competition. However, consider this one: SCHOOL–WORK–BACK–BREAKING–DOWN–TOWN–HOUSE–PARTY–TIME–LOST–ART–COLLEGE.

Note that this eleven-stage journey also contains not only the basic four-stage journey but two five-stage journeys:

SCHOOL–PARTY–TIME–LOST–ART–COLLEGE
SCHOOL–WORK–TIME–LOST–ART–COLLEGE

a six-stage journey:

SCHOOL–HOUSE–PARTY–TIME–LOST–ART–COLLEGE

as well as the potential for breaking down with such as:

SCHOOL–TIME–LOST–ART–WORK–HOUSE–BREAKING–DOWN–TOWN.

The concept has as much potential as your wit. The task is simply to get from SCHOOL to COLLEGE. The rules of the game are whatever you care to make them, within the time limits you care to set.

To keep the action going, you can award, say, 4 points for the bright spark who spots the four-stage journey and tell him or her to win yet more points for other possible journeys whilst the others are still struggling to make a first logical word association. The wittier you are in the original compilation, the more fun and frustration for everyone else.

8 Shelling Peas with Gramps

(a) *Shelling Peas*   A game as easy as shelling peas – or is it?

The contestants write down a short list of ordinary words read out by the organizer. These will be such as:

        1   I T
        2   AT
        3   TO

and they are told that the object of the game is to see who can add the greatest number of P's to these words in order to change them from one genuine word into another. They are given the example of the first word, IT. By converting this into PIT they score one point and, if they have TIP as well as PIT, they will score 2 points. Most contestants will then score 6 points for the remaining two base words with APT, PAT, TAP and OPT, POT, TOP. A total of 8 points.

However, if the list continues with:

        4   ALE
        5   TOE
        6   DEAL

this is where the fun really begins! ALE not only has ALPE, LEAP, LEPA, PALE, PEAL, PELA, PLEA but it also has the double-P words APPLE, PAPLE and the triple-P word PAPPLE: 14 points.

TOE not only has PETO, POET, POTE, TOPE but EPOPT and POPPET: 9 points.

DEAL not only has PADLE, PALED, PEDAL, PLEAD but APPLED, DAPPLE, LAPPED, PALPED and PLAPPED: 15 points.

And these scores ignore the wealth of material provided by the obselete words!

Even a simple little word such as AS has PAPS as well as ASP, SAP, SPA, the obscure PAS and PSA and the dialect word APS. LA can score even more: it has ALP, LAP, PAL and LAPP, PALP, PLAP. There is no need to work out all the answers in advance. Simply choose any word containing at least one P and, once the P or P's are removed, see if the remaining letters produce a valid word. For example, PEPPERPOT. Removing its four P's leaves a sterile set of five letters. However, as PEPPERPOTS (not every dictionary hyphenates it or treats it as two words) it has a base word of STEREO. Can STEREO plus any other combination of P's create a word? Essentially it does not matter as you have already provided a challenge worthy of standing alone. OPPRESS can be reduced to ROSES or SORES. In SORES the word SPORES is immediately obvious and, in ROSES, PROSES (prose as a verb) is equally apparent and POSERS follows that quite logically. If a contestant submits SOPPERS this can easily be confirmed as being valid. PIPER provides an excellent example of the valid and the invalid. As the base word IRE it has (apart from PIPER) PIER and RIPE together with the obscure word PIRE. But what about 'PIPPER'? Logically it would describe one who or that which pips in any sense of the verb and a far more likely word than PIRE. But not even the *Oxford English Dictionary* records such a seemingly sensible noun.

To avoid the tedium of constantly consulting the dictionary keep the contest within the bounds of knowledge

– not guesswork – by making clear from the outset that any words which provide invalid result in a loss of points on a basis of one point per P. Thus 'PIPPER' would mean a penalty of a three points' deduction, and guesses based on STEREO plus fewer than four Ps would be held in check.

To lull the unwary into assuming that they are meant to add only a single P to most (if not all) base words, consider SEA and EDITOR, originally selected because they can be converted into other words by the addition of just a single P. SEA, designed to produce APES, APSE, PEAS (with SPAE as the 'clever' word), might well have a competitor providing the Scottish word for popes, PAPES. At the most advanced level of competition, with EDITOR as the base for five 'clever' words – DIOPTER, DIOPTRE, PERIDOT, PROTEID and the obsolete (but valid at this level) TORPIDE – could well have a wordsmith supplying PTEROPID!

At the classroom and adult fun levels, a simple list of only eight little words is ample for a wide variety of scores. Knowing that IT, AT, TO, AS, LA, ALE, TOE and IRE have the potential for more than fifty points without resorting to obsolete words (which may be deemed valid only at wordsmith level), a reasonable time limit can be imposed. Under these conditions the winner is much more likely to be the one who first appreciates the 'ordinary' words such as APPLE, PIPER and POPPET rather than one who has heard of obscure words such as LEPA or PETO. Even such obvious words as APT, OPT and PLEA will be overlooked by the cleverest of players who, having discovered the double-P and triple-P aspects, miss the points which others obtain.

Basically all you need for the competition is a single 'multi-P' word, say, POLYP. As LOY you can see that it can become PLOY. If a competitor comes up with a lucky guess, the perfectly valid LOPPY, that is his good fortune, but that same gambler is just as likely to fail with PLOPPY and fail to spot your 'clever' word POLYP. Couple that with APPLE (as ALE) even if you only appreciated PALE as the obvious disguise and the remaining half-dozen words can be of the IT, AT, TO type.

For an advanced level competition you would have the larger words such as DEAL, STEREO, EDITOR and, if you reduce APREST to, say, STARE, the expert can score at least 30 points from just that single base word! Do not, however, refrain from giving the serious-minded adults little words – AS is ideal for them – and, if you would care to indulge in a little bit of fun, test yourself with AY. Deduct points for any wrong guesses you make.

(b) *Gramps* Gramps is the two-person, face-to-face version of Shelling Peas, in which any letter is added to any small word in ignorance of the potential. Essentially it is a Fan-Tan not a Classroom game but, for convenience, it is given here.

One person writes a letter – say, P – on a small piece of paper which is then placed face-up in the centre of the table. The other player then chooses a small word – say, ALE – and the game is on. Both players now have to try to make as many words as they can from ALE plus as many P's as they wish. Neither tells the other what he or she has written down and another letter and another small word are similarly chosen for the next round.

The 12 points attainable with ALE plus P's has already been discussed but now consider an absurd example.

The small word is AA (it will be defined below) and the letter is K. These are the possibilities in an 'impossible' combination:

AAK: an old spelling of OAK and still retained in dialect

AKA: any of several species of New Zealand woody vines

AKKA: the Egyptian piastre, a small coin which circulated in the Ottoman Empire; British servicemen's slang, it is sometimes spelt ACKER

KAA: an alternative spelling of KA in its sense as a verb. Meanings include 'of a partridge, to utter its cry'. Now only dialect

KAAK: a verb of a crow, to utter its cry. No longer extant

KAKA: a New Zealand olive-brown-coloured parrot

KAKKAK: a species of bittern on the island of Guam

These combinations give a total of 13 points. AA is a cooled cindery substance consisting of sand, earth, stones and melted lava.

Basically, however, one player will suggest 'sensible' letters such as L, M, P, R, S or T whilst the other will provide highly flexible base words such as AT, IN or EAT. (If, for example, T is suggested for EAT then assume EA as the base word and score a point for every T including the one in EAT.) Players take turns in coming up with words and letters, with the person providing the letter in charge of the time allowed for that particular round.

Four rounds constitute a set and the whole game is played to an agreed number of sets. Once a set has been completed, players take fresh sheets of paper for the next set. This is necessary as there is no objection to a player adding words to an earlier round in the current set and, if too many combinations were available for play, it would cease to be a fun game of interaction and be more like a Shelling Peas contest. Therefore, a player may not return to the workings of a previous set.

At the end of the game players check their opponent's results, not merely to confirm scores but – they hope – to deduct points for invalid submissions.

> *(Shelling Peas with Gramps was suggested by the stage, television and film actor, Maxwell Caulfield, as a tribute to his grandfather, Thomas Newby.)*

9 Squaring Up

Essentially this is Competitive Word Squares (page 77) played *en masse* using the Bingo Letter-Frequency Table (page 37).

Each member of the company draws a simple grid, 5 × 5 is ideal, and the leader calls out letters which people are free to place in any square of their own choosing.

Scoring will not be as high as the 35 to 45 points average with Competitive Word Squares, but a sufficiently wide range will be produced.

10 Strike

Tenpin bowling played with words. The basic description fits the concept exactly, but the game can be scaled down to any desired level. First a word about tenpin scoring.

Ten pins are bowled at. If, say, 6 are knocked down with a first bowl and, say, 3 are knocked down with a second bowl, this produces a score of 9 for a frame. A total of ten frames are played. However, if, say, 6 are knocked down with a first bowl and 4 with the second bowl, this does not result in a score of 10. It results in a score of 10 plus whatever the next bowl knocks down. Thus, the first bowl of the next frame scores twice. If it is, say, 7, then the total for the *first* frame is 17 and the 7 will be counted again in the second frame. The standard term for such an achievement is a 'spare'.

The best possible achievement is a 'strike'. This is all of the pins knocked down with one bowl. Under these circumstances, the next two bowls are added to the 10 and that total represents the score for the first frame. If one's first three frames are all strikes, then the score for the first frame is 30, for the second frame it is 20 plus whatever the next bowl is and, for the third frame, 10 plus whatever the next two bowls bring. In the event of a spare being recorded in the tenth and final frame, one final bowl is permitted. If a strike is recorded in the tenth frame this gives two extra bowls. The maximum possible score, therefore, is 300, produced from 12 strikes.

The tenpin word game has twelve combinations of ten letters written down in this form:

1	A A A I L N R S T U	7	A A G I L L M N R Y
2	A A C D E G L O T U	8	A A G I N N O S T T
3	A A C E I M N O R T	9	A B D E E L N O R S
4	A A C H I M N O R S	10	A C D E E I L N R T
5	A A D E E H M R S T	11	A C D E I I M N O T
6	A A D E I I M N N T	12	A C E E N N O R T U

Contestants now bowl at this collection. Number 1 represents frame number one. If a player can produce a 10-letter word in a frame, it is a strike; if a player can produce two words which total ten letters, it is a spare.

A player who achieves a spare in frame number ten may now attempt to do the best he or she can with the letters of frame number eleven to produce one word only.

Frame number twelve may only be considered by a player making a strike in frame ten and a strike in frame eleven.

A player who fails to make a strike or a spare in frame ten may go no further.

In this example, each frame contains a minimum of two 10-letter words, and three of them contain three 10-letter words, these three being frames six, nine and ten. All the words in this example are fairly well known.

The point is not the discovery of these anagrams but the finding of one 10-letter word per frame in order to gain a strike. Failing that, to do the best one can. When scoring a spare, the better of the two words obtained in the next frame is deemed to be the next bowl.

To scale down to an easier level, one has two choices. The first is to have 10-letter words all of which end with -ING or have some other equally recognizable element common to all. Any words suffixed -SHIP or prefixed OVER- would suit the purpose.

The other choice is to have similar words and smaller maximum scores.

The game is yours to play at whatever level you wish. If you require the definitive list of strikes for the above or would like to have the anagram concept as a permanent feature, you will find 35,000 words each with at least one perfect anagram in the *Pears Advanced Word-Puzzler's Dictionary*. It also defines any of those words which are unusual.

11 Shot Putting

Until 1988 no one had exceeded 23 metres in putting the shot though both men and women had exceeded 22 metres. This game, with each individual *additional* letter considered as a metre, has a theoretical but, for all practical purposes, impossible maximum of 26 metres. The 'world record' can, however, be broken.

The game is based upon the concept of andagrams (see Jargon, page xxvii)

The technique of word selection will be given shortly, but a basic, highly flexible, word is selected and this is considered to be the shot. The task is to throw the shot as far as one can. The method is to run through the alphabet adding a different letter each time and making just one andagram for each different additional letter. Each andagram with a different letter is a metre. How far can the competitors put the shot?

The game can be as easy or difficult as you wish to make it. Essentially, the smaller the shot the easier it is to throw.

Take a very simple example, the word TEA. The letters B, D, F, G, H, K, L, M, N, P, R, S and T will give, respectively, such as BEAT, DATE, FATE, GATE, HEAT, TAKE, LATE, MEAT, NEAT, TAPE, TEAR, SEAT and TEAT. A '13-metre throw' almost anyone can produce within a very short space of time. The outright winner, therefore, will need to use letters like C, V, X, Y and Z for CATE, TAVE, EXTA, YATE and ZETA, all of which are perfectly valid.

Even 18 metres is not a champion's throw for TEA. Anyone prepared to delve into the *OED* will bring E, J, O and W into play with such as ATEE, JEAT, OATE and WATE and, now, all that remains are the 'easy' letters A, I and U plus, of course, the Q. The *OED* may well have words to cope with these.

A '20-metre throw' based on NASTIER, for example, and comprising reasonably well known words, is possible from the *Pears Advanced Word-Puzzler's Dictionary*'s 126 andagrams of that word.

Neither TEA nor NASTIER are exceptional. Whilst, for example, the 6-letter word SATINE has slightly fewer andagrams (121) than NASTIER, it is still capable of being thrown the 'world record' distance of 23 metres – only J, Q and Y failing to be utilized.

The supreme andagrammable word is ASTER. This has at least 270 andagrams. These range, alphabetically, from the archaic adverb ASTARE to ERSATZ. How many metres can it be thrown? That is up to your contestants.

To produce a highly flexible word select, without duplication, from the following letters: *vowels* – A, E, I;

consonants – L, N, E, A, T; and combine them in the required length of 2-letter, 3-letter, 4-letter or whatever 'weight' of shot is suitable for the company.

The contestants begin by writing the complete alphabet down the left-hand side of their pages. They tackle the letters in any sequence they wish but are *not* advised to ignore such difficult letters as X and Q. With SEAT as the shot, they could easily discover TAXES and with SAT you never know but one bright little spark might well have heard of the perfectly legitimate QATS. Have a very good dictionary handy!

(If you require a mnemonic for those highly flexible letters, choose between ENTRAILS and LATRINES.)

12 Denby Dale Pie

The history of Denby Dale Pie began, in 1788, when this Yorkshire village celebrated the return to sanity of King George III with the biggest meat pie in the world.

From time to time the village has baked bigger but not always better pies. One nineteenth-century pie, for example, had an additional ingredient of game which went off and the whole thing had to be buried in quicklime. On another occasion the pie was so big and heavy that it crashed through the floor. The latest pie was baked in 1988 and voted a huge success. Its ingredients included meat, onions and gravy.

This contest brings game back into the pie.

The company suggest suitable ingredients for the pie. When sufficient have been named, a halt is called and the challenge is to produce the biggest word one possibly can from the words which have been accepted.

For example, a 'recipe' of DRIED PEAS, SALT, ONION, MEAT and FAT is more than ample for such blockbuster words as DEPARTMENTALISED or even DEPARTMENTALISATION, so keep it fairly simple.

13 Alpha Raise

The latest 'anagram-solving dictionaries' have adopted the system of alphomes (see Jargon, page xxvii) as a convenient system of logical assembly, and this classroom challenge to produce as great a number of anagrams as possible uses that same technique as a convenient reference. (Incidentally, some of these so-called 'dictionaries' are better than others but none can claim omnipotence, not even my own *Pears Advanced Word-Puzzler's Dictionary*.)

Offer the company an alphome such as AEINRST and find out why it is the Scrabble players' favourite rack of letters, achieved by the careful pruning of letters until this group has been created. One now has access to a host of premium-scoring 7-letter words of which the most easily recognized are NASTIER, RETAINS, and RETINAS though there are many others such as ANESTRI and RETSINA which are not 'everyday' words. Irrespective of official word source, AEINRST is supreme for Scrabble even though, for Championship play, competitors do not have access to the thirty detailed in the *Pears Advanced Word-Puzzler's Dictionary*. If your classroom limits activity to one (small) dictionary, how many 'AEINRST words' can be discovered? In essence, *that* is the challenge you set the class. *Full* words are required from the alphomed sets – witty teachers, aware that THE CLASSROOM and SCHOOLMASTER utilize exactly the same letters, have only *one* full word if they decide to offer a challenge based upon ACEHLMOORSST! But those who know that CARTHORSE and ORCHESTRA contain exactly the same letters can offer the class the alphome ACEHORRST and the race is on to see who can be the first to produce both (assuming that there are only two) of its words. To test yourself on the difficulties or otherwise of this task try the 'supreme anagram' AEGINRST, and see how close to the limit of some forty-odd sensible words you come. Which of your discoveries can you expect the class to match? The geographical proper name of TANGIERS is not a 'dictionary word', whilst the class might find it tricky determining such as ANGRIEST (not all dictionaries detail adjectival comparatives and superlatives) and does that same classroom dictionary stipulate GANTRIES as a plural of GANTRY? An awareness of the limitations facing your contestants will be helpful in determining performance ratings. Naturally, according to the age of the class members, you should limit the 'size' of the alphome and, to give them an easy starter, consider EILV. To start you off, does your classroom dictionary contain either of the two spelling forms of a word describing a shallow pool, VLEI or VLIE? A word of Afrikaans origin it is now found in some English dictionaries as having been (like AARDVARK) 'assimilated' into English. Another transposal of the alphome is the biblical name LEVI which, though a valid anagram, is not likely to be found in the smaller reference works. Do you accept it? If you permit 'open sources' then the obvious answer is 'yes' but if you are basically concerned with an intelligent appraisal of the classroom dictionary then you would have to disallow it.

However, be aware that – like the ACT of a CAT – some alphomes are words in their own right, of which the longest known is that of the anagrams SPOILAGE. SPOLIAGE and PELASGOI which, alphomed, becomes a word of various meanings, AEGILOPS.

Two final thoughts for you. First, if 6-letter words are considered a 'reasonable size' for your classroom then the alphome AELRST is a superlative in that particular category. Second and finally, if you desire to provide the classroom with a selection of alphomes from which to meet a taxing challenge then you could always add a touch of devilment with OPRSTTUVYY which, to my knowledge, transposes solely to TOPSYTURVY!

THE
SOLITAIRE
SERIES

The Solitaire Series

Some of the games mentioned elsewhere are quite suitable for a personal challenge and equally entertaining are some of the Classroom games such as devising your own perfect solutions for a pair of Build Up words (page 184), other solutions for the complete alphabet challenge discussed in Other Ladder Games (page 186) and discovering the most ingenious baseword for Shelling Peas (page 194). Even the Back to Front series of spoken games can be adapted for solo pencil-and-paper activity and your results used as a basis for another's verbal task.

However, anagrams apart, this series is concerned with concepts not covered elsewhere and it begins with one of the oldest known examples of word play.

1 Anagram Word Squares

The most famous of all word squares is written in Latin and has been found carved or scratched on stone at Roman sites as far apart as Cirencester, Pompeii and Dura-Europos in Mesopotamia:

```
R O T A S
O P E R A
T E N E T
A R E P O
S A T O R
```

First of all, it reads the same in all directions. Secondly, if AREPO is presumed to be a personal name, then the whole translates as 'The sower, Arepo, controls the wheels with care.'

The third and most fascinating thing of all is that it may have an esoteric significance. Certainly it could prove to be a secret sign of a Christian community because the whole thing is a most remarkable anagram. Consider this construction:

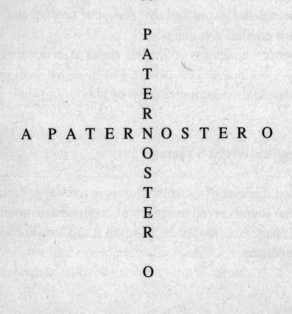

```
              A

              P
              A
              T
              E
              R
A  P A T E R N O S T E R  O
              O
              S
              T
              E
              R

              O
```

Paternoster is the Lord's Prayer 'Pater noster' – 'Our Father' – it's opening words. A and O stand for Alpha and Omega ('I am Alpha and Omega, the beginning and the ending, saith the Lord'). Finally, this anagram can only be constructed in the shape of a cross. Other solutions have been suggested but none match this for ingenuity.

To play with anagram word squares begin with a 3 × 3 construction. If you have never before devised a word square you will find out that it is so pathetically simple to produce a 3 × 3 that it is not worth bothering with, unless it has some additional challenge.

There are various anagram challenges worth trying. The first is to construct a single 3 × 3 square in which every word is an anagram of the other five words. My own solutions to this task are given below. But maybe you can devise better ones which do not necessitate the use of rather obscure words?

```
EAR     TEA     SPA
REA     ATE     ASP
ARE     EAT     PAS
```

A different type of anagram word square is one which contains exactly the same letters and mirrors the same pattern of at least one other square. Consider the following eighteen squares. They begin with one very simple square with the same words running both horizontally and vertically, then come no fewer than seventeen anagrams of it. Unfortunately, they contain a plethora of unusual words and ENA, of course, is the feminine personal name.

```
TAN   TAN   RAN   NET   NET   TEN
ARE   ERA   ATE   ERA   ENA   ERA
NET   NET   NET   TAN   TAR   NAT

TEN   TEA   TAE   RET   REN   RAT
ETA   ERN   ARN   ENA   ETA   ANE
NAR   ANT   ENT   TAN   NAT   TEN

NAT   NAT   ENT   ENT   ANT   ANT
ARE   ANE   NEA   NAE   NAE   NEA
TEN   TER   TAR   TER   TER   TAR
```

A third type of anagram challenge is to take a 9-letter word and make 3 x 3 square of it. For example, GALENGALE. This aromatic rootstock of certain plants of the ginger family is not only capable of providing the basis for a square but even that square has anagrams:

```
NAG   LEG   LAG   LAG   GAL
ALE   ENA   ALE   ANE   ANE
GEL   GAL   GEN   GEL   LEG
```

In each case the pattern of the same words running both horizontally and vertically is maintained. Quite a few additional anagrams can be produced by utilizing the christian name of LEN, the slang word GAN and the obsolete word NEG apart from any others which may well exist.

The challenges are to find better examples than these, as well as taking the whole concept a stage further by considering larger squares.

2 Supersquares

The construction of word squares up to 5 × 5 is such an easy task that it is not even worth having a go at unless it has some degree of entertaining difficulty. However, if the anagram word square holds no appeal, try to create an ever-increasing square which, at each progressive stage, consists entirely of genuine words.

Begin with a single letter which is a word in its own right – A, I or O are common English words but such geographical names as E, a Scottish river or Y, an American town, are equally valid. The task is to commence with a nominal 1 × 1 then convert it into a 2 × 2, thence 3 × 3, 4 × 4, etc. The example below, admittedly using the occasional obscure word, builds up to 5 × 5.

```
                              R A T A S
                    R A T A    A F A R E
           F A R    A F A R    T A P E R
    P E    A P E    T A P E    A R E A R
A   E A    R E A    A R E A    S E R R Y
```

Can you produce an example without the use of obscure words or else create the world's first ever 6 × 6 progressive word square?

The above concept is original but the ultimate challenge is the classic palindrome square exemplified by the Latin ROTAS/SATOR discussed in Anagram Word Squares. A few examples of English palindromic squares follow. These were produced without resorting to a computer though computer-generated squares of this type exist. However, for those 'sweat of the brow' squares:

```
A S S E T    D E D A L    S T R E W    L A T E S
S L I V E    E N E M A    T R E V E    A R E D E
S I R I S    D E W E D    R E F E R    T E N E T
E V I L S    A M E N E    E V E R T    E D E R A
T E S S A    L A D E D    W E R T S    S E T A L
```

However, if you prefer to attempt squares larger than 5×5 without any restriction, the superlative is the 10×10. Only two wordsmiths have ever produced reasonably satisfactory squares of this dimension: Jeff Grant of New Zealand (he who gave the world samorael bats) and the founder of recreational 'logology' the late Dmitri Borgmann of Dayton, Washington. Dmitri's square contained a mass of the most obscure words imaginable. Other experts, even with the aid of computers, have failed to match his achievement.

Borgmann's 10×10 is a traditional square, having the same words running both horizontally and vertically. Specialist word-play magazines carry pleas from computer buffs for assistance in the construction of a 10×10 double square (see Jargon page xxvii) in their attempts to achieve a 10×10 'first'.

But even Borgmann's 10×10 is imperfect as he was forced to repeat the words ANDOLANDOL, NGOTANGOTA and GALANGLANG in the same plane both horizontally and vertically. He admits that no fully satisfactory 9×9 square has ever been produced either, as the best of these required a dialect word in order to ensure completion.

The 8×8 traditional or double square may, therefore, be regarded as a supersquare and even the best of these will require an explanation of some of the words used.

The 7×7 is regarded as the first of the higher orders of squares and, like the 8×8, is really the province of the expert.

This leaves the 6×6. To construct one of these is a worthy accomplishment and, whilst it cannot be considered a supersquare, nevertheless it is a challenge worthy of being undertaken.

Of the two forms, the traditional is easier than the double.

3 Word Oblongs

An easier task than supersquares and one where you begin with a pair of logically related words and see how far you can take them as ever increasing acrostics.

For example, the words THE and END. As triple, quadruple, quintuple and sextuple acrostics one could have, with the aid of an obscure word or two, something like:

What is the best pair of words to consider and what is the

```
THE    THEE    THERE    TRAISE
HEN    HERN    HERON    HERDEN
END    EYED    ENDED    EXTEND
```

ultimate acrostic which can be built up in this stage by stage fashion?

4 Cryptarithmetic

There are two totally different approaches to this unusual conjunction of words and mathematics; that of the American Crytogram Association which is concerned with your 'cracking' the numerical values of letters chosen without reference to literary sense, and those of the wordsmiths who are more concerned with making a witty or factual statement capable of mathematical 'proof' by substituting numerals for the individual letters. These latter which, for want of a better term, I name 'literary crytarithms' are – unlike those of the ACA – often flawed by having more than one mathematical 'solution' but they do, at least, have the virtue of being literal statements expressed in mathematical terms. They are surprisingly easy to 'solve' but are far more difficult to construct! Each different letter represents a different numeral. Try and solve one or two then attempt to construct your own. The best of all have a single solution. Do any of these?

1 W R O N G	2 F A C E T	3 N I N E	4 B R A Z I L
+W R O N G	+ F A C E T	+N I N E	– T R E E S
R I G H T	+ F A C E T	+N I N E	D E S E R T
	W H O L E	H E L P	

5 $\text{PI} \times \text{R}^2 = \text{AREA}$

6 $\text{NINE} \times \text{FOUR} + \text{FIVE} = \text{FORTY-ONE}$

The first four are mine, and, unfortunately, do not possess single solutions, though that does mean that, for example, there exists more than one way of 'proving' that two WRONGS equal one RIGHT. Number 5 is by Eric LeVasseur and has only one solution which, for a mathematical statement, is apt! Equally aptly unique is Leonard Gordon's number 6. Number 3 is not mathematical, by the way, as 999 is the British freephone number for the emergency services.

5 Definitive Fun

A solitaire challenge to run through the alphabet producing witty definitions.

At its simplest, a punning alphabet which begins:

> A for ISM
> B for PORK
> C for YOURSELF

At its best, one can make a compilation after the style of the masters of the subject, Ambrose Bierce or Gordon Bowker. These are examples of their terse gems:

ALONE	In bad company (*Bierce*)
BORE	A person who talks when you wish him to listen (*Bierce*)
GAY	To be thoroughly bent on pleasure (*Bowker*)
HOOKER	A fisher of men (*Bowker*)
LAWYER	One skilled in the circumvention of the law (*Bierce*)
MOONIE	A lune with a view (*Bowker*)
TOY PISTOL	A gun-of-a-son (*Bowker*)

The puns, of which Bowker produces the best, are much easier to devise than the satire of Bierce whose *Devil's Dictionary* was published at the turn of the century and is still in print.

For a 'directory of famous people' you might care to rephrase the following classics of graffiti:

ARCHDUKE FERDINAND FOUND ALIVE: FIRST WORLD WAR A MISTAKE

LEDA LOVES SWANS

YOU THINK OEDIPUS HAD A PROBLEM — ADAM WAS EVE'S MOTHER

PINOCCHIO IS A SWINGER

SOCRATES EATS HEMLOCK

And, in so doing, develop your own satirical or punning style.

6 Things

Things are adult rebuses, though one British newspaper prefers to call them dingbats. Rebus is the Latin for THINGS and became part of the English language several centuries ago, applied usually to pictures/word puzzles.

Anyone can produce an adult rebus; a witty challenge for others to solve and confined entirely to letters, words, numerals and symbols.

The following examples are all my Things, some of which have featured as fun clues in my cryptic crosswords.

To solve a Thing, study its construction:

YOB

YOB is BOY written backwards. As a Thing it means, therefore, 'backward boy'. To place a Thing within the confines of a box gives one the additional scope of position, as two of the following will show.

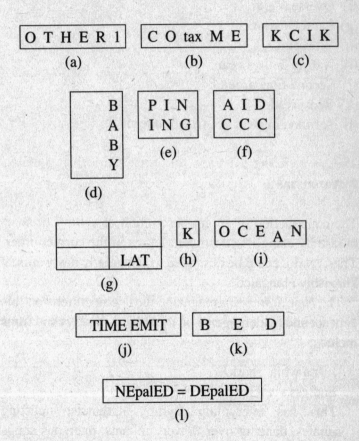

The solutions follow but, if you wish to work them out for yourself, then do not turn this page.

Answers
(a) One after another.
(b) Income tax.
(c) Kickback.
(d) Side issue.
(e) Underpinning.
(f) Overseas aid.
(g) Latin Quarter.
(h) Weekend.
(i) A drop in the ocean.
(j) Second time around.
(k) Bedspread.
(l) A friend in need is a friend indeed.

7 Acronyms

The construction of an apt description of a word or short phrase by using its constituent letters in the correct order. Thus, SNAKE could be described as 'singularly nasty animal knavishly elongated'.

The *New Statesman* magazine runs competitions on this concept and readers' gems on the subject of plays and films include:

'Just a white shark'
'Endless vivacity in the Argentine'
'This has everything: syrupy outbursts, uplifting nannies, dancing over flowery mounts, unctuous songs involving children'

Set yourself a theme and see what you can produce.

8 Poetic Licence

Limericks, clerihews and all manner of verse forms are worth emulating.

A classic limerick was once inserted in a newspaper by Monsignor Ronald Knox in a most unlimerick like form. It read:

> Evangelical vicar in want of a portable secondhand font, would dispose of the same for a portrait (in frame) of the Bishop-elect of Vermont.

The clerihew is a four-line versified biography invented by Edmund Clerihew Bentley (1875–1956). His masterpieces include:

> The digestion of Milton
> Was unequal to Stilton.
> He was only feeling so-so
> When he wrote 'Il Penseroso'

Even shorter verse fun can be achieved by taking a well-known line of verse and adding a second line of your own. For example:

> I wandered lonely as a cloud –
> I did look ghastly in a shroud.

Or:

> I wandered lonely as a cloud –
> Offensive smells were disallowed.

A programme on British television (*Countdown*) featured a sequence of tiny 'poems' which needed incredibly lengthy titles in order to make sense of the resultant rhyme. The smallest of all were created by John Meade, the producer of the programme, and by me. Mine was, 'The marine clairvoyant's reply to a query concerning her occupation.'

I
Eye

The 'world's shortest poem' is still waiting to be written, all it needs is a suitable title.

9 Man's Laughter

If MAN'S LAUGHTER means nothing to you then FORGOT HIST AS KIN SO LIT AIR ESK ILL.

CAT CHIN THEMES, SAGE looks equally weird but, correctly punctuated, tells you that this has a CATCH IN THE MESSAGE!

This challenge is to produce a longer or wittier statement.

10 The World's Longest Word Game

Begin with a letter which is also a word, say, A. Convert it into a 2-letter word – say, AT. Now continue with such as HAT or ATE and see what is the longest possible word you can create in this fashion.

Alternatively, try to build the tallest possible vertical column with overlapping words in the way that the top Scrabble players score their 7-letter words.

Faced with, say, LIMPETS already in play and having the bonus-scoring adverb AHEIGHT on his or her rack the top player will automatically consider what 2-letter word combination gives the best score. For example:

(a)   A H E I G H T
   L I M P E T S

(b) L I M P E T S
          A H E I G H T

(c) L I M P E T S
      A H E I G H T

All create valid 2-letter words, and the choice of the third option, other things being equal, would be made almost immediately.

For this solitaire challenge ignore the first option and see how you could build up, say, the second option. It might develop in this fashion:

      L I M P E T S
          A H E I G H T
      V I N T A G E
         S W I M M E R

assuming that you limited yourself to 7-letter words.

But you may care to give yourself greater flexibility and build up at either end with words of any length and see just how tall a construction you can produce. With LIMPETS as the base, the run below ended with two 5-letter words, GALAS and SITES, one 6-letter word, STANKS, and one 7-letter word, DUNITES. Apart from a result of a 7-letter word, one could view the personal attainment as being, say, 23 points by combining the total number of letters in all four words so constructed.

```
        D I D
        G U N
  M A N       A S
        L I M P E T S
  C A T       A I M
        S E R V A N T
          S O    K E L P
        C L A S S
```

Even the average Scrabble player aware of the basic technique of simultaneous horizontal and vertical scoring can devastate masterminds when they face each other in competition. For example, the Scrabble enthusiasts' magazine, *Onwards*, reported a contest between a team of quite ordinary members of a Scrabble club and MENSA members. No Scrabble player was surprised at the result – MENSA was sunk without trace.

11 Triplets

The name is not only a pun on the word TRIP as one takes 'trips' with words but is intended to be an advance on Lewis Carroll's concept of Doublets (see Word Ladders page 181) which Carroll himself attempted to take a stage further with a positively dreadful 'game' he named Syzygies. The idea is to progress from word to word by the technique of either inserting or deleting a letter to form another equally valid word. There are all manner of different Triplets but the technique is the same with each type and a working knowledge of the words listed in the Miniglossary (page 449) will prove invaluable.

(a) *Triplets, pure and simple* This follows the mainstream of word play by making witty or logical statements such as turning WATER into WINE or making a NO into YES. The simplest way of achieving this is to descend to a single-letter word and build up again from that base.

NO	WATER
O	WASTER
OY	ASTER
OYE (same as OY)	ASER (obsolete spelling of AZURE)
OYES	ASE (obsolete spelling of ACE)
YES	AS
	A
	AI
	I
	IN
	WIN
	WINE

227

A more difficult version of this is the construction of a 'word shape' such as that associated with ancient magic practices. In the example below I began with a single-letter word which I built up to the largest word I could – with acknowledgements to Jeff Grant who improved on my original 'diamond' – thence descended to a different single-letter word whilst sticking to the basic rules of never repeating a word in a 'column' and always using genuine, valid words.

```
            A
           A N
          R A N
         R A I N
        T R A I N
         S T R A I N
      R E S T R A I N
     P R E S T R A I N
    P R E S T R A I N S
    P R E T R A I N S
     R E T R A I N S
      R E T A I N S
       R E T A I N
        R E T I N
         R E I N
          R I N
           I N
            I
```

A different 'shape' one can attempt is such as this literary 'egg-timer':

```
          S A N D
          A N D
          A N
          A
          A D
          S A D
          S A N D
```

Note that, apart from the two terminal SANDS it stays strictly within the rules of no repetitions.

If typeset artwork is not to your taste you may prefer simply to 'doodle' by going on a 'trip' from, say, HOME via HOE, OE, O and then such as OI to I thence to any location one desires.

(b) *Triplets-in-parallel* This is more difficult than it seems at first glance as it is bedevilled by the need to harmonize mathematically between the original 'pair' and the concluding two words. First, an example of 'mainstream' word play; going from the LOG CABIN to the WHITE HOUSE.

```
          LOG      CABIN
          CLOG     CAIN
          COG      AIN
          CO       IN
          O        I
          IO       IO
          I        O
          HI       HO
          HIT      HOE
          WHIT     HOSE
          WHITE    HOUSE
```

Now a parable of sorts which transforms one well-known palindrome into another. The *OED* was consulted to confirm the guesses that VIL and INNE are obsolete spelling forms and that a verb 'to inn' also existed. Notice that the second and third columns had to be artificially lengthened in order to coincide with the minimal changes of the first and last columns so that perfect symmetry was maintained.

LIVE	NOT	ON	EVIL
LIE	NO	ONE	VIL
LE	O	DONE	VI
E	OA	DOE	I
EN	A	OE	IN
ENS	HA	E	INN
DENS	HAD	EA	INNE
DENIS	AD	ENA	INNED
DENNIS	AND	EDNA	SINNED

(c) *Siamese Triplets* This considers the elements of a large word as separate entities for 'tripping' and, by confining all action within a rectangle, creates interesting lexical patterns. In addition to the standard rules of no repetition of a word in the same 'column' and always using valid words, two other strictures must be met. The first of these is that the original elements must be words in their own right, and the second is that one must avoid internal 'crashes' which produce 'non-words'.

```
BLACKBIRD
LACK      BID
LAC        ID
LA          I
A          AI
AI        AIS
I        DAIS
IT        DIS
HIT       IS
WHIT     FIS
WHITEFISH
```

For convenience, I will refer to this original example as a rectangular triplet.

To demonstrate the practicality of rectangular limitation, six examples of the conversion of 10-letter words to their anagrams follow. Interestingly, the first of these, RANGER-SHIP/SPRINGHARE, mutually transpose to REPHRASING!

```
RANGERSHIP      STONEBRASH
RANGE   HIP     TONE    RASH
RANG     HI     ONE      ASH
RAN       I     ON        AS
AN       AI     O          A
AIN       A     BO        AR
PAIN      AE     BOA      OAR
PIN      ARE     BA        OR
SPIN    GARE     BAS      TOR
SPRINGHARE       BASE    TORN
                 BASSETHORN
```

```
MATTERLESS          STINKSTONE
MATER      ESS      SINK    TONE
MATE        ES      SIN      TON
ATE          E      IN        ON
AT          ED      I          O
A          LED      OI        OE
TA        LIED      O          E
TEA        LIE      NO        E S
TEAM        LE      NOT      ESS
STEAM      LES      KNOT    NESS
STREAMLETS          KNOTTINESS


OPENSTITCH          STITCHWORK
PEN    TITCH        TITCH   WOR
PE      ITCH        ITCH     WO
PIE      ICH        ICH       O
PI        IC        IC       PO
I          I        I       POI
IN        OI        OI       PI
PIN        O        O         I
PINT      ON        OW       IC
PIT      ONE        TOW     SIC
PITH    TONE        TROW   SICK
PITCHSTONE          THROWSTICK
```

Apart from the fact that the phrase OPENSTITCH STICKWORK provides a link between the final two examples, a neater connection lies in their termination in rustic missiles! Notice the original perceptions of the words RANGERSHIP, STINKSTONE, OPENSTITCH and the mathematical relationship between all pairs of intermediate words.

The perception of RANGERSHIP as RANGERS + HIP is just as valid as my own RANGER + SHIP. The same is equally true of STINKSTONE and OPENSTITCH; it is purely a matter of taste. Unlike their close relatives, rectangular triplets are not bedevilled by the need to harmonize mathematically as they do it of their own accord. Words of an odd number such as BLACKBIRD automatically devolve into pairs of words with an odd total. Even-numbered words such as STINKSTONE give rise to pairs with an even total. Either way, successful conversion is merely a matter of word power, not mathematics.

11 Wordsmithery

Whilst some of the earliest known English Language riddles are the work of Saint Aldhelm (*c*. 640–709) and we owe our affection for the collective noun to that magnificent nun, Dame Juliana Berners, whose classic work, *The Boke of Saint Albans*, was published post-humously in 1486, and Shakespeare was not averse to using the odd pun in the most unlikely of settings, it was really Lewis Carroll who began the play on words which has now embedded itself in literary anecdote. Since Carroll's time, two men have been pre-eminent in creating the sorts of literary trivia which get quoted so frequently without acknowledgement that their efforts are assumed to be in the public domain. Sadly, both have died in recent years: they are the American all-round good egg, Dmitri Borgmann, and the ingenious English palindromist, Leigh Mercer. This section owes much to what they either pioneered or else made, in the case of Mercer, a special study. The first section of Wordsmithery is devoted to Mercer's palindromes. Just how many of them have you heard before?

(a) *Roger G. M'Gregor* is a palindromic pseudonym which Mercer adopted when he joined the American National Puzzler's League in 1952, after which he submitted his 'running back again' constructions to their journal, *Notes & Queries*, for the remainder of his life. From over a hundred of his little masterpieces I present, below, a mere soupçon:

Rise to vote, sir.

Was it a rat I saw?

Ban campus motto, Bottoms up, Macnab.

Live not on evil.

Sir, I demand – I am a maid named Iris.

Are we not drawn onward, we few, drawn onward to new era?

'Tis Ivan on a visit.

Harass sensuousness, Sarah.

A man, a plan, a canal: Panama.

Sums are not set as a test on Erasmus.

Nurse, I spy gypsies, run!

Niagara, O roar again.

Did Hannah say as Hannah did?

(b) *Afterberners* is the name I gave in honour of Dame Juliana to a variation on the theme of collective nouns. Her original creations and collection of traditional expressions have, essentially, three bases of construction: alliteration, onomatopoeia or a characteristic inherent in the object being described, whereas my nonce creations are all anagrams of the object to which they relate. Whilst they are trivial by comparison with her poetic recordings they may, hopefully, amuse you and inspire you to continue the theme. Here, again, is but a small selection of previously published material (*Word Ways*, August 1991):

A triteness of interests.
A shower of whores.
A niceness of incenses.
A cluster of cutlers.
A streaming of emigrants.
A measuring of geraniums.
An assertion of señoritas.
A greatness of sergeants.
A mischance of mechanics.
A bluster of butlers
A slough of ghouls.
A brisance (explosive effect) of carbines.

For more on Dame Juliana Berners and true collective nouns see 'Bringing to Boke' (page 275).

(c) *Listen to the mocking word* is the title that William Tunstall-Pedge of Dundee, Scotland, gave to an amusing little piece in the February 1989 issue of *Word Ways* in which he had a series of statements followed by natural replies which were (unconsciously) mocking. He is interested in making a collection of them and if you can add to his short sample given below then any letters to him can be addressed to him c/o the author, via the publisher. Anyway, William's 'mocking words':

I wish you would stop apologizing!
Sorry.

Will you stop asking rhetorical questions?
How can I when I don't know what 'rhetorical' means?

Why do you keep answering questions with other questions?
Do I?

If there's one thing I hate it's your pedanticism!
The word is 'pedantry'.

Please stop arguing!
I am not!

You don't catch on quickly, do you?
Who doesn't?

Will you please stop agreeing with everything I say!
OK.

(d) *Chandlerisms* In his Kickshaws column in the February 1989 issue of *Word Ways*, David Morice, a cartoonist and poet as well as an ingenious wordsmith, discussed the metaphorical style of Raymond Chandler and quoted some of the examples which he and his Iowa City chums tossed off whilst considering the work of that hard-boiled detective writer:

'He was the kind of person who could make a catalog librarian drop a drawer.'

'She was the kind of gal who'd make a dogcatcher get the rabies.'

'She was the kind of redhead that could make a Communist salute.'

'She was the kind of dame that could make a bricklayer lay bricks.'

'She was the kind of customer that could make a grocer grosser.'

'She was the kind of lady who makes a linguist speak in tongues.'

'He was the kind of guy who could make a nun kick the habit.'

Dave then posed the question, Have you Chandlerized someone lately?

(e) *Deductive reasoning riddles*   This is a little concept of mine which, hopefully, is self-evident from the name – what you do is strike out the letters common to both words and shuffle the remainder to create an appropriate word.

1 What is the difference between a DICTIONARY and a DIARY?

2 Between a NUDE and a NUDIST?

3 Between a DOWAGER and a WORD?

4 Between a CARTHORSE and an ORCHESTRA?

The answers are 1 a TONIC; 2 the SITE; 3 AGE; 4 nothing!

(f) *Chain gang* Elsewere I discuss various ways of changing one word to another by a logical process, a concept originated by Carroll. Here is a sampling of various methods. Unlike Carroll's Doublets which require both the original and the terminal words to be identical in size, the following all transform words of unequal size, going from FIRST to LAST:

First Dmitri Borgmann's Synonym chain (of which more below) FIRST — HEAD — CLIMAX — TOP — EXTREME — LAST.

The rest are all my original ideas:

Triplet: FIRST — FIST — FIT — IT — I — AI — A — AT — LAT — LAST.

Logomotion: FIRST — BORN — FOOL — HAPPY — MEDIUM — TERM — TIME — OUT — LAST.

Cast off: This one is a rather curious little idea whereby one perceives a word (FIT) in the original (FIRST) and adds letters one-by-one from the target word (LAST) to make transitional linking words. Two examples follow:

FIRST — fit — fLit — fiAt — fiSt — fiTt — LAST.

FIRST — it — Lit — Ait — Sit — Tit — LAST.

By combining Dmitri's idea of synonyms with the ancient art of anagrams I came up with:

Anagram/synonym chain: FIRST/RIFTS = GAPS/GASP = GULP/PLUG = STOP/OPTS = ELECTS/SELECT = RARE/REAR = LAST.

(g) *Synonym chains* In his book, *Beyond Language* (1967), Dmitri Borgmann presented two examples of brilliant word play which captured the imagination of others in just the same way as Carroll's Doublets (Word Ladders) seized the imagination of his fellow wordsmiths some eighty-eight years previously.

Borgmann turned BLACK into WHITE, and UGLY into BEAUTIFUL simply by the use of synonyms:

BLACK — DARK — OBSCURE — HIDDEN — CONCEALED — SNUG — COMFORTABLE — EASY — SIMPLE — PURE — WHITE

UGLY — OFFENSIVE — INSULTING — INSOLENT — PROUD — LORDLY — STATELY — GRAND — GORGEOUS — BEAUTIFUL

The potential for this form of solitaire amusement has been demonstrated by a research scientist in the USA who, with the aid of his computer, has constructed several thousand synonym chains using *The New Collins Thesaurus*.

A. Ross Eckler has drawn attention to the fact that these chains are not necessarily reversible but that the opposite journey can still be achieved. His examples include TRUE into FALSE/FALSE into TRUE and LIGHT into DARK/DARK into LIGHT:

TRUE — JUST — FAIR — BEAUTIFUL — PRETTY — ARTFUL — ARTIFICIAL — SHAM — FALSE

FALSE — UNWISE — FOOLISH — SIMPLE — UNCONDITIONAL — ABSOLUTE — POSITIVE — REAL — GENUINE — TRUE

LIGHT — BRIGHT — CLEVER — CUNNING — SLY — FURTIVE — SECRET — HIDDEN — OBSCURE — DARK

DARK — OBSCURE — VAGUE — VACANT — EMPTY — FOOLISH — SIMPLE — EASY — LIGHT

Finally, should you wish to try these yourself, let me change the emphasis from WRITER to READER:

WRITER — SCRIBE — CLERK — SCHOLAR — ACADEMIC — LECTURER — READER

(h) *Self-referential English* The word FOUR is unique. It is the only number which contains letters equal to its value, its intrinsic quality of describing itself making it an example of a self-referential word.

The words **nonhyphenated** and **polysyllabic** are equally self-referential but **uppercase** and **lix** only become self-referential when specially contrived. Written as UPPERCASE it qualifies, but lix (a seventeenth-century word for a Roman camp follower) would only be self-referential if it were used for a 59-year-old Roman camp follower! The discovery of words such as these produces little more than personal satisfaction – unless one happens to be Douglas Hofstadter.

Hofstadter is the master of self-referential prose and his column in *Scientific American* sparkles with such as:

This is not a complete. Sentence. This either. You have, of course, just begun reading this sentence which you have just finished reading.

For his book, *Beyond Language* (1967), Dmitri Borgmann devised a related form which requires no explanation of an individual self-referential word. These he termed suggestive words and examples include 'war', with the letter A in the shape of a missile rising from a silo, or the arm of the letter T taking the shape of a bow tie in **bow tie**.

The English author, Darryl Francis, conceived yet another form of these words which has a greater potential than Borgmann's concept as it does not require artwork and can therefore be reproduced in any publication. Darryl described them pedantically as 'aberant forms of self-referential English' but has since accepted my suggestion that they be renamed 'Qwaints', under which name they occur as the next item.

(i) *Qwaints*   Qwaint is more than just a Middle English spelling of the adjective, quaint. To the twentieth-century reader it possesses the quality of *looking* quaint and thus reinforcing meaning of the word. Furthermore, in the days when it was spelt 'qwaint', it had the additional meaning of 'ingeniously designed'. Thus (bearing in mind that 'quaint' has also served as a noun) we have the perfect word to describe what have been described as 'unique varieties of self-descriptive word-like letter-sequences'. A Qwaint may, therefore, be defined as 'an ingeniously designed self-descriptive word-like letter-sequence possessing the quality of the word suggested'.

Darryl Francis's Qwaints: twogether, Decembrrr, HUMiLity, mispelling, neverendin, unsofisticated, millionaire$$, defectiv.

Anthony Sebastian's, Renée Merriam's and Ivy Dixon-Baird's Qwaints: vwliss, exxxxcess, sur++++, underscored, SP O RAD I C, endnsd, TEARDR P, close harmony.

Peter Newby's Qwaints:- greeed, exc!amation, SP CE, anoise, slowth, inelastick, Judoh, jaIIIl, dynamight, dysxelia, ampers&, shorthnd, booob, mi££ionaire, INLeT, fffreezing, metricat10n, CAMel, Rnst Vinvnt Wright, psighchoanalysis, prufe reeder.

Apart from playful coinings such as the above, genuinely accidental Qwaints also appear in print. For example, there is a British geographical feature named

odness and a long-obsolete nonce word meaning 'thrice terrifies' occurs in the 1618 publication of Joshua Sylvester's *Complete Works*: 'Destroyeth, Buildeth; Confounds, Confirms; Ter-Terrifies . . . '

Finally, one which has appeared in literature ever since it was first coined in the sixteenth century, which has appeared in both the singular form – **lithp** – and the plural – **lithpth**. Which reinforces the case for having an historical word to describe this delightful form of word play.

(j) *Hectowords* Philip M. Cohen of Pennsylvania collects mathematically defined words which have a metric base. Below are some of his best, all of which have been devised by readers of the American journal, *Johns Hopkins Magazine*:

1 mentality $= 100$ centimentality
2×10^6 pinpricks $= 1$ MHz
3 camp beds $= 1$ tricot
3 unicorns $= 1$ triceratops
1 magnum opus $= 10$ grand opera
2 tribes $= 1$ diatribe
10 glassfuls $= 1$ decanter
$1\frac{1}{2}$ dice $= 1$ trice

To which he has posed the question: 'Should the amount of suspense in a mystery novel be measured in whod units?'

(k) *Silly pess* (or *Zu game*) These two 'terms' are playful anagrams of the technical terms, syllepsis and zeugma, which mean roughly the same thing though this may depend upon which dictionary you consult. The *OED*, for example, defines syllepsis as 'a figure by which a word, or a particular form or inflection in a word, is made to refer to two or more other words in the same sentence whilst properly applying to or agreeing with only one of them'. It gives a similar definition for zeugma whilst stating 'more properly syllepsis'. Paul Hellweg, writing in the February 1993 *Word Ways*, quotes other dictionaries which gave him the impression that the words have slightly different grammatical and rhetorical senses but have a tendency to overlap each other, and, needing to choose one, he selected zeugma as the term to describe his examples. It was this confusion that led me to anagram the terms to express my perplexity. Anyway, whether one is drawn to 'silly pess' or wants to play the 'zu game', the result is delightful word play. I quote below first Paul's examples, and then some from another American word-smith, Vernon MacLarent.

He took the doctor's advice and two aspirin.

The accident sank our yacht and our dreams.

The soldier kicked a landmine and the bucket.

Wearing a negligee, she turned on the lights and her husband.

He swallowed his pride and two goldfish.

Snow White bit a poisoned apple and the dust.

The boy scout hiked up his trousers and a mountain.

She bore an illegitimate child and a grudge.

The prospector struck gold and his camp.

The Internal Revenue Service taxes my income and my patience.

and now, Vernon's:

The vampire ate his sweetheart's neck and his heart out.
The stickup man beat the shopkeeper and a hasty retreat.
The suicide bought an overdose and the farm.
The fastidious diner chewed the tough steak and the chef.
The cabby drove fast and his passenger crazy.
The careless boater drowned his wife and his sorrows.
The nurse felt the wound and sick.
The active child frayed his clothes and his mother's nerves.
The flirtatious pickpocket pinched her bottom and her wallet.
The conman ran a scam and away.

(l) *Circulars* These simple statements are, technically, self-referential word-order palindromes as, in either direction, they are self-descriptive. These idle doodlings with words originated with my chancing upon the word HEREBEFORE in the *OED* and had me wondering what I could do with such an 'interesting' word, one of whose meanings is 'earlier in this document'. Perhaps, you could add to the two given hereafter . . .

Start from HERE to read HEREBEFORE; HEREBEFORE is HERE before BEFORE. Before BEFORE, HERE is HEREBEFORE. Herebefore, read to HERE from START.

HEREWITH is HERE with WITH. Without OUT, WITHOUT is WITH. WITH is without OUT without. With WITH, here is HEREWITH.

(m) *Initial reactions*   Whilst the concept is mine, many of the examples given below come from the writer Susan Thorpe. The object of this exercise being the isolation of well-known sets of initials within a reasonably apt word or, if necessary, a short substantive phrase. Of all the examples of wordsmithery given herebefore, this is the easiest to attempt anywhere, anytime.

FeDeRal, ChInA desk, UpStAges, NoisY, LunAcy, PaX, OvErDiffuseness, MisSive, CoOrDination, SwAtS, dIaRrhoeA, inDispeNsAble

It is even possible to define one set of initial reactions with another: TeDium, an Irish MugwumP. Certain words carry obvious sets of initials but, as in the case of the palindromic word which describes a type of smoking mixture used by certain American Indians, KinniKinniK, the link is decidedly unsatisfactory. Now *there's* a word! UnSatiSfactoRy

(n) *Sumwords*   On average, the letters B, G, or V will occur once each in every hundred letters of standard English prose. By contrast, those same hundred letters will include 13 Es, 9 Ts, while on the other hand K, Q, X, J and Z will, in all probability, be completely absent. Assigning individual letter values on this basis and including decimal points up to 0.5 (beyond that they become letters of higher value) we have the following table:

A	8.5	H	6	O	8	V	1
B	1.5	I	7.3	P	3.1	W	2.3
C	3.5	J	0.2	Q	0.4	X	0.3
D	4	K	0.5	R	7	Y	2
E	13	L	4.5	S	6.5	Z	0.1
F	3	M	2.5	T	9		
G	1.3	N	7.5	U	3.3		

and the most fascinating study of words is now available.

Take a simple example, the 3-letter words. TEE (9+13+13) totals 35, whereas the Hebrew coin, the ZUZ (0.1+3.3+0.1) is, at a total of 3.5 a tenth of the 'value' of a golf peg. But, is there a 3-letter word to outscore TEE or one which can undervalue ZUZ? Equally, do either of these have a numerical 'anagram', a word possessing the same value?

If we assume TEE to be the ultimate high scoring 3-letter word, what is its superlative sumgram (sumgram being a numerical 'anagram')? When I posed this question to the Chairman of the Nottingham chapter of Pears Word Games Society, a lecturer in Scrabble at the Basford Hall College of Further Education, she studied the problem for a short while and produced a magnificent answer, the 9-letter word QUIZZICAL. Can you find a better sumgram than Mrs Ivy Dixon-Baird's QUIZZICAL?

Perfect sumgrams have no letters in common with each other, otherwise all anagrams would be automatic sumgrams and this would reduce the personal contest to a pure word study which renders the mathematical aspect superfluous. However, if one tolerates a degree of imperfection then a broad approach to the quest is retained.

What are the superlatives in every sensible category of

work length and what are their superlative sumgrams? Questions like these are for the pure wordsmith but the fun player can turn to irony and make all manner of discoveries. Scotland has a tiny river with the smallest known name. It is simply the river E. E is the highest-value Sumwords letter. Contrast this mere freshwater trickle with the mighty river OB which runs for 2,600 miles through Siberia. We now have the ludicrous fact that OB (9.5) is 'smaller' than E (13).

For even greater fun we can turn to adjectives and discover such as the SEXIEST women in the world. Which women have names which total the same as SEXIEST (55.6)? How about the world's LARGEST (49.8) insects or UGLIEST (44.9) men? What are the relative values of saints and sinners? Which saint and which sinner equate mathematically? Can we discern ideal partners? It is hardly surprising that ROMEO (38.5) and JULIET (37.3) are star-crossed lovers – who would have been a better computer match for either?

Sumwords' letter values, however, have their greatest potential in all manner of different combative pencil-and-paper games. Consider a written form of Wimbledon in which Jack plays Jill with the subject Birds. They limit themselves to, say, six birds each and set about the task of making the *lower* of the two scores. Essentially, therefore, they are looking for words with lots of Qs and Zs in them and as few Es as possible. Jack is to go first and the pinword is THE, thus he is stuck with a high scoring letter E to commence the name of his first bird.

Jack: EMU
Jill: URUBU (a South American vulture)
Jack: UMBRE (the hammerkop, a storklike bird)
Jill: EYAS (an unfledged hawk)
Jack: SKUA
Jill: AUK
Jack: KIWI
Jill: IBIS
Jack: SMEW
Jill: `WREN
Jack: NIGHTJAR
Jill: ROC

The result is a resounding victory for Jill with 131.6 to Jack's 153.4.

Had either failed to reply, a penalty of 100 points would have been added. Best of all, one can even play a crossword-type game which rewards the skilled use of the lowest-value letters, once again trying to make the lower of the two scores.

Draw a grid of any reasonable size – say, 15 × 15 – and insert the pinword in the centre. You now build from this with any word you choose.

Each player (on a grid of this size) has a limit of any 50 letters and the game ends as soon as one player has exhausted his or her stock. The unused letters of the opponent are now valued 7 points each and the resultant computation added to that player's score.

In a Jack-vs-Jill contest the pinword (the nearest 3-letter word found by sticking a pin in a book) is TWO and Jack is to go first. He plays the word DIZZY in this fashion:

D I Z Z Y
T W O

and records the fact of having *added* five letters to the grid. He scores 13.5 points for DIZZY and 12 points for DO. His opening total is 25.5.

By playing QUIZZICAL (35 points) through either Z of DIZZY, Jill has *added* eight letters to the grid and has only 42 letters remaining to Jack's 45. As Jack went first and it is only fair that Jill should have an equal number of turns so, should Jack be the first to finish, he must still allow Jill one last turn. Jack may have the lower score but Jill has the advantage in letters used. Whilst neither player is likely to convert QUIZZICAL to QUIZZICALLY at this stage of play, one or the other may be forced to do so at the end of the game in a desperate attempt to shed his or her last remaining letters.

No word may be repeated. Penalize on a basis of 7 points per *added* letter for an invalid word if you do not wish to make a mess of the grid, otherwise the offending word is removed and the turn is forfeited.

(o) *Subjective discoveries*   A word is selected. The object of the game is the production of related words using only the letters of that original word.

For example, the word HAMLET. As a description of a geographical location its potential is zero, but, as a personal forename, it can be transposed immediately into the anagram, THELMA. Personal forenames (christian names, biblical names, classical deities, acceptable short forms e.g.

HAL for HENRY, etc.) is an especially fertile field, so the game will be illustrated with personal forenames as the subject.

HAMLET/THELMA is arranged in its alphabetical order as AEHLMT and this is termed the basic unit. Each time a basic unit is employed in full this will score a point so that HAMLET and THELMA have produced a score of 2 points. The biblical HAM together with TEL (can be a short form of Telemachos, and in the UK is a short form of Terence) also utilizes a basic unit and the score is now 3 points. For convenience, consider HAMLET and THELMA as 'individuals', the combination of HAM/TEL as 'twins' and now we have the third category, the 'family', which is where the fun really begins.

ALMA could be produced from two basic units by the deletion of A, L, M from the first unit and A from the second unit. Thus we are left with the units EAT and EHLMT. No points are added. MEL (short for Melanie or Melvyn) is taken into the family and our units are now HT and EHMT. To delete EHMT as 'THEM' is invalid – it is beyond the limits of the subject – and it may be that in order to delete the HT of the first unit we choose ALTHEA.

The units are now as follows:

First unit, exhausted. Second unit, HMT. Third unit, EHMT. Fourth unit, EHLMT. A point is now available (for that first unit) only if we can use *all* of the remaining letters of *all* the remaining units. We must now score not one point by beginning a family with ALMA but at least four points with a family which has ALMA, MEL and ALTHEA.

Finally, the most frustrating rule of all – no word may be repeated.

To illustrate the utter frustration of Subjective Discoveries the example of a base unit AADLNOR in the category of personal forenames is given below:

Individual (male): ARNOLD (1 point)
Individuals (female): ARNOLDA, ORLANDA, ROLANDA, RONALDA (4 points)
Twins: ROD, ALAN; RON, ALDA (2 points)
Married couples: DON, LARA; DAN, LORA; ROD, LANA; DAR, NOLA (4 points)
First family: AARON, DANA, DOLL, ALAN, DORA, DONNA, DARRAL, ROALD, LORNA (6 points)
Second family: ARNALD, ARNOLD, RONA, ALDA, DONAL, ROLAND, RANDAL, RONALD, OONA, RA, ADA, NORA, ALLARD, ORLANDO, DONALD, AARON, LARA (12 points)

29 points, except that some of the names have been repeated so one has to edit accordingly.

ROD is both a twin and husband.
ALAN is both a twin and a member of the first family.
ALDA is both a twin and a member of the second family.
LARA is both a wife and a member of the second family.
AARON is in both families.

The twins can be deleted. DON and LARA can be divorced, but AARON is the blighter and, in the interests of greater points, the first family has to be torn asunder.

The score now stands at 20 points and one has: DON, RON, DANA, DOLL, ALAN, DORA, DONNA, DARRAL, ROALD and LORNA not to mention ANN, ANNA, ALAN, AL, ALARD, AANNA and goodness knows who else desiring to belong to a family so increasing the score.

Can you do it?

Alternatively, suppose you break up the second family and have all their names available in a complete arrangement of everyone. Would another divorce help? Only the five individuals are sacrosanct in any attempt to exceed this current score of 20 points.

Subjective Discoveries is frustration at its most sublime.

(Note: All of the curious names quoted have appeared in print. Some are early forms whilst the others may well be personal or parental affectations possibly limited to a single individual. I know of DAR only from the late Dar Robinson, the famed stuntman who performed the classic fall in the film Highpoint, *whilst AANNA came to my attention after completing the above example. She was interviewed for the 13 November 1988 issue of* You *magazine, and, as A was one of the 'problem' letters in the construction of the two families noted above it may well be that AANNA is a particularly useful female in the absorption of the problematic A.)*

(p) *Antigrams*   The best anagrams are those which are the most apt, the most ironic or the exact opposite in meaning. An antigram is the one which is the exact opposite, though this can sometimes depend upon your point of view. The following are all anagrams. Some are obvious antigrams, some are clever ironies and only become antigrams in personal opinion.

circumstantial evidence	can ruin a selected victim
considerate	desecration
diplomacy	mad policy
enormity	more tiny
evangelists	evil's agents
funeral	real fun
infection	fine tonic
legislation	is it legal? no
marriage	a grim era
misfortune	its more fun
mother-in-law	woman Hitler
protectionism	nice to imports
united	untied
violence	nice love

(q) *Anagram Curiosities*   Many words which are basically mutually related remain anagrams no matter how they are reconsidered in the light of addition of prefixes and suffixes. CORK and ROCK, for example, are still anagrams when they become CORKS/ROCKS; CORKING/ROCKING; CORKLIKE/ROCKLIKE and UNCORKED/UNROCKED.

This is not true of all such pairs, however. ACT and CAT cease to be anagrams as present participles – ACTING/CATTING introduces an extra T. By contrast, previously unrelated pairs become anagrams only with the addition of suffixes and prefixes and the letter E features in a considerable number of these.

CASH and CHASE only transpose as verbal inflections: CASHED/CHASED; CASHES/CHASES; CASHING/CHASING – but consider how this letter can take CART to TRACE to CREATE: CARTED/TRACED; TRACEABLE/CREATABLE

Can you produce a similar or better chain of E factor anagrams or, indeed, bring any other aspect to bear in the study of these curious aspects of the language?

(r) *Lipograms*   Since classical Greek times a few writers have produced compositions which deliberately exclude a particular letter of the alphabet. For example, the great sixteenth-century Spanish dramatist, Lope de Vega, wrote five novels, each of which suppressed a different vowel in turn. However, the most famous lipogram is Ernest Vincent Wright's 50,000-word novel, *Gadsby*, which was written, according to his introduction, 'with the e type-bar of the typewriter tied down'. It is one of the world's rare books and a copy complete with dust-jacket was once sold for $1,000. What is so poignant about this is that Wright never received a penny for his efforts. He paid for the book to be produced and died on publication day, 6 October 1939.

It is fitting to record that one of the few people known to possess a copy is the editor of *Word Ways*, A. Ross Eckler, whose lipogram versions of 'Mary Had a Little Lamb' are the most oft quoted examples of this art. Here are just two of them. The first omits the letter S and the second is minus the T.

> Mary had a little lamb
> With fleece a pale white hue
> And everywhere that Mary went
> The lamb kept her in view;
> To academe he went with her,
> Illegal, and quite rare;

It made the children laugh and play
To view a lamb in there.

Mary had a pygmy lamb,
His fleece was pale as snow,
And every place where Mary walked
Her lamb did also go;
He came inside her classroom once,
Which broke a rigid rule;
How children all did laugh and play
On seeing a lamb in school.

(See also Qwaints (page 241) for a particularly apt lipogram.)

(s) *Palindromes* A word, such as DEIFIED, is called a palindrome as it reads the same backwards as forwards; so too is a phrase or statement such as these:

  Madam, I'm Adam
  Never odd or even
  Dennis and Edna sinned
  Satan, oscillate my metallic sonatas
  Able was I ere I saw Elba (attributed to Napoleon)
  Egad! A base tone denoted a bad age (attributed to Henry
    Purcell)

(Other examples may be found on page 234.)

One of my own contributions to this genre is unique. It is

based upon the English word XI. XI describes the fourteenth letter of the Greek alphabet. In upper case XI is written in Greek as Ξ and half a dozen of these appear as:

Described in English, aptly using capital letters, this becomes:

SIX XIS

and so, both in English and in Greek, the palindrome not only reads the same forwards and backwards but also upside-down!

(t) *Pangrams*   A sentence that contains each letter of the alphabet is a pangram. Examples:

The quick brown fox jumps over the lazy dog (complete alphabet + 6 letters)

Pack my box with five dozen liquor jugs (Complete alphabet + 6 letters)

Waltz, bad nymph, for quick jigs vex (Complete alphabet + 2 letters)

The ideal pangram not only contains each letter only once but is also easily understood. Unfortunately the best minimal pangrams published to date have not only needed the majority of their words defining but the resultant statement still needs an explanation even when the meanings have been given. These are three of the very best:

Cwm fjord-bank glyphs vext quiz (Carved figures – GLYPHS – on the bank of a fjord in a rounded valley – CWM – vexed – VEXT is a seventeenth-century form – an eccentric person – QUIZ.)

Cwm kvutza qoph fled brigs (The wryneck bird – JYNX – from the communal farming unit – KVUTZA – designated by the nineteenth letter of the Hebrew alphabet – QOPH – and situated in a rounded valley – CWM – fled from the prisons on a ship – BRIGS.)

Vext cwm fly zing jabs Kurd qoph (A vexed – VEXT – fly in a rounded valley – CWM – humming in a shrill fashion – ZING – jabs at the nineteenth letter of the Hebrew alphabet – QOPH – drawn by one of a Moslem people dwelling mainly in a region situated in NW Iran, NE Iraq and SW Turkey – KURD.)

The difference between these three minimal pangrams and the 'Waltz bad nymph' construction is immense. Not only does the latter require no words to be defined but its statement stands complete. Is the ideal pangram possible? No words should be defined and no explanation offered.

The use of the obsolete VEXT provides the key. A reasonable person can both understand it and assume it to be an old spelling of a word in current usage. Given that convention for this particular form of word play do you understand this following attempt of mine to achieve the first 'perfect' pangram? If you do not, then I have failed and it is no better than any of the others.

Qwyk bitch vox jumps glaz'd fern

However, the truly fascinating aspect of these six words is that they can be rearranged into a parody of the famous 'Quick brown fox' pangram known to most typists. A detailed explanation is required – though Devonians who still retain VOX in the adjective VOXY, where others have FOXY, will be a step ahead of most. GLAZ'D (this abbreviated form of GLAZED can be found in the *OED*) is no longer considered in the above sense of 'covered with frost' but, believe it or not, as a synonym for BROWN! Amazingly, both GLAZED and BROWN once held identical meanings as 'shining'. FERN is no longer the plant of the above but its former adjectival sense of 'ancient' is revived for the parody. True, ancient and lazy are hardly the same thing but an ancient canine would certainly behave in a similar sluggish manner to that of the famed lazy dog. Typists of the English-speaking world, here is your revised fingering test. I hope you like it.

Qwyk glaz'd vox jumps fern bitch

(All of the above words including QWYK can be found in the *OED*.)

(u) *A Basset of Beasts* Someone defined a camel as 'a horse designed by a committee' and this definition has enjoyed so much success that it is now part of the 'public domain' of wordsmithery discussed earlier. But do any other creatures exhibit similar traits of collective construction? This thought gripped me one bored evening and I came up with the following:

ALLIGATOR: a pussy cat designed by the Ku Klux Klan.

RHINO: an antelope designed by the Pentagon.

OSTRICH: a domestic fowl designed by a Kentucky Fried Chicken conglomerate.

VAMPIRE BAT: a butterfly designed by Transylvanian nobility.

ROC: a carrier pigeon designed by Arab terrorists.

SHARK: a goldfish designed by the Mafia.

KANGAROO: a frog designed by writers of Australian fairy stories.

SNAIL: a worm designed by a mobile homes association.

Can you bring into 'outward manifestation' any others? That is a convoluted reference to the afterberner title as the *OED* defines a BASSET as 'an outcrop' and OUTCROP also has a figurative meaning as 'a coming into outward manifestation'.

(v) *Amalgams* is another of Susan Thorpe's ingenious neologisms; this word she coined to describe the resultant anagram of combining two names as HIS + HERS can be shuffled together to create SHERISH, an obsolete spelling of CHERISH. We play this as a form of postal amusement, giving each other vaguely logical pairings and seeing what the other can produce from them. Some of the results can be highly entertaining as Susan's brilliant amalgam of SAINT + DEVIL as INVALID SET! Another which appeals to me is SLEEPING BEAUTY + RIP VAN WINKLE with the resultant 'honeymoon saga' of WE BEGIN NUPTIALS. REVEL? NAY . . . KIP! A particularly clever Thorpian amalgam is NUREYEV + SALOME as SOME ENVY ALURE. Sometimes we resort to the odd bit of cheating in order to achieve an apt amalgam. MISS PIGGY plus *Animal Farm*'s NAPOLEON has a Merry Melodies flavour with the aid of a qwaint, 'SLOP' N'NOISY PIG GAME, the stammering porcine character influencing this construction. However, for *real* Cheater's Amalgams these two take a little beating:

NOAH WEBSTER/MARY PICKFORD FAIRBANKS: 'FRABBPORKFRASH' MAKES NEW DICTIONARY.

DAME JULIANA BERNERS/COLLECTIVE FARMER: A JUMBLE OF CARRETINE (CLEVER RED ANIMALS).

CARRETINE now joins SAMORAEL BATS in the wordsmith's bestiary of cheater's creatures (the bats having surfaced in a Cheater's palindrome). If this concept appeals, try it as a solitaire amusement before involving a chum in this particular devilish creativity.

THE
CODEBREAKING
SERIES

The Codebreaking Series

Two serious and two 'fun' codes form the basis of this series strictly for wordsmiths. The serious codes are games numbered 1 and 3. The 'fun' codes are ideal for postal challenges of a lighthearted nature. But any reader who wishes to communicate such as an adulterous message via either of the 'serious' systems should note the ease with which either could be 'cracked' by a literate cuckold or a lexically-adept wronged wife!

1 Company Policy

The organizer of an assembly of wordsmiths creates a code (technically, a cipher) by assigning random letters to the alphabet. Nothing so childish as Caesar's A = F, B = G, C = H, etc. but a thorough random mixture such as A = Q, B = G, C = P, etc. The organizer then writes – or types – a message written in this cipher with sufficient copies for each contestant in a race to see who is the first to decipher the complete message. For the convenience of the 'codebreakers', produce at least a full paragraph of conventional prose; but, do *not* utilize a famous statement – such as the Gettysburg Address – in which once the first few words have been deciphered then everything else follows automatically. By all means *begin* your paragraph with a famous phrase which might suggest that this is what you have done, but avoid trying to be too clever – it is not you versus the company but a competition amongst those assembled. Mirror, as I have done below, the accurate spacing of words which, for simplicity's sake, also includes all punctuation. Leave sufficient space beneath the coded message for the competitors to write their solutions and, at the side of the page, provide a complete alphabet for them to record their findings beside each letter. Any reader who is also a member of the American Cryptogram Association should note that this 'coded message' does not conform to the Association's standard practice of basing a random code around a heterogram-style keyword to which a cryptic clue has been given. *The cipher is, as advised above, a purely random mix.*

Z CFSGPA ANDA JSQSFDX

OBDFAZVCW BVMXG GSWSDA ANG

GSYVRFDA'O RXPQAVQ PQ D CFSOPGSQAPDX

RVQASOA

In order to 'crack' this code look for the obvious 'give-aways' first. One of the easiest is the apostrophe-O; this O has to be either an S for the possessive case or else a T for an abbreviated phrase. To determine which it is now look for a possible **the**. Is ANG **the**? If it is, then what can ANDA be

other than **that**? If A = T, then apostrophe-O *must* make O an
S! Alternatively, consider the single-letter words, Z and D.
One of these is almost certainly going to be an A whilst the
other is most probably an I. Can you discover elsewhere in
the text a word-shape which would make sense of either of
these two vowels? If you wish to 'solve' this puzzle note
that one of the 'words', OBDFAZCW, is a heterogram (a word
comprising completely different letters with no repeats)
but, even so, you should still manage to 'crack' it!

Computer buffs – for whom the ACA's standard practice
is ideally suited – may be interested in reading the
Codebreaking Postscript which follows the games, and
base a challenge to fellow mechanical wordsmiths on this
technique.

2 Plooman's Lunch

A postal game for a literate friend. It is based on the techniques mentioned under the game of Ploo (page 64). To
'solve' it consider the smaller words and determine how
many letters were 'looped' to form the consequent polygram then make a similar number of 'loops' with the larger
'words' and see if a logical – albeit ludicrous or unbeliev-
able – statement emerges.

I CTPREDI ATTH HET PEPO LLWI ZERECOGNI

HET ICHERO TYSANCTI FO USVARIO

TSPROTYESTAN CHSU AS NGNUMBERI

CEFLOREN LENIGHTINGA NGAMO HET

TSSAIN

3 Face 2 Face

This is a reasonable code for Valentine's cards and similar romantic missives but, like the others, can be 'cracked' very easily, especially with the aid of a computer. The idea is that those 'in the know' share a keyword in the form of a fairly lengthy heterogram which they resolve to keep secret. That keyword is used both for the creation of the message and, by reversing the procedure, deciphering it. For the sake of illustration I will use the heterogram GERA-NIUMS as a keyword. Beneath this I will write a personal message to the beautiful MHW who shares the knowledge of our keyword. When constructing such a message, merely write the keyword on a piece of 'rough working' then, beneath it, write out the message very clearly ensuring that each individual letter directly corresponds vertically with a letter of the keyword. Normal word spacing is ignored. Thus:

G E R A N I U M S
T H E A U T H O R
S E N D S H I S L
O V E T O M H W

Now, the column headed by the lowest letter in alphabetical order (**adt** under the A) is extracted as the first trigram of the message. This, in turn, is followed by the next column in keyword alphabetical order. And so on until the whole message has been written. It will then look something like this: **adt hev thm tso osw ene rl hih**.

To 'crack' the code merely look for 'real words' occupying similar positions in each trigram (or polygram, if longer columns have been created). Ambiguity is always a snag but, by a process of trial and error, one should without knowing the keyword be able to reassemble the columns and so read off the message.

As a game, two wordsmiths face each other and send 'secret messages' of this type to see who is the better codebreaker. To give you an idea of the difficulty or otherwise of this game I conclude with a third coded message based upon a heterogram which you might well guess, as guessing your opponent's choice of keyword is a legitimate factor of this game: **dnnfralnie pwcsprperp aicrmrose rhesarumai terletani tpieihnal hrnsremul itdwtgita itneeaevtx eeaoiibelr chpaheciw**.

As will be seen from the GERANIUMS message, the smaller polygrams occupy terminal positions as columns, which provides you with your first clue.

4 Neat Codes

The name is an anagram of ANECDOTES and that is the essence of this pure fun challenge. An anecdote is rewritten with all words transposed for either postal or face-to-face amusement. Much of the fun arising from the mixing of deciphered words with those of the scrambled text especially if slightly inebriated and displaying one's lexical skills to another.

A EX-HARPER-LOGIC VERSING NI HET VANY IN-DRUG HET CONDES DROWL RAW SAW I-VERSING ERNIEST GNOMIC-C-MEN. WHIT HET RETTLE S HEWN, DENSLY-DUE, SHI OBAT SAW DEED-PO-ROT. SA EH MAWS ROF FEASTY DRAW-SOT A FILE-O-BAT EH MACE PU WHIT HET I-FIND-NO-TIE CHHIW DAH LU-DEED MHI. 'NIS, SO-RACE MHIW'

Codebreaking Postcript

For its coded puzzles named cryptograms, the ACA provides additional 'evidence' to enable the (computerized) codebreaker to arrive at a solution by means other than the application of logic outlined in the game called Company Policy. A cryptically apt title is given to the puzzle which both suggests the context and the heterogram on which the scrambled alphabet is based. Suppose that I had followed their lead and decided that NOSTRADAMUS would be my basis of 'scramble' then I would first have to delete all duplicated letters in order to create a heterogram – NOS-TRADMU. This would then be placed beneath a complete alphabet at some random point ensuring that it coincided in position with letters in the plaintext alphabet above. Thereafter, I would write out an alphabet which 'looped' back to the beginning but *excluded any letters in the heterogram.*

A B C D E F G H I J K L M N O P Q R S T U V W X Y Z
Q V W X Y Z N O S T R A D M U B C E F G H I J K L P

Whilst this is more in keeping with secret codes as used by the intelligence services prior to the introduction of sophisticated computer-generated systems it is, to my way of thinking, less of a cerebral challenge than the scheme outlined in game 1, Company Policy, as all one needs to do is make an educated guess at the heterogram and merely slide it back and forth beneath a plaintext alphabet – a task better undertaken by the famed monkeys and typewriters or a committed computerist. Not all of their challenges are for the generation which suffered atrophy in the fields of Flanders, some are truly mind-boggling especially those set by a lady who, in private life, is a very old nun. But, if you wish to employ a secret code of your own then you cannot do better than follow the precepts of a Greek who expired in classical times. Named Polybius, he devised it for use by hilltop messengers holding torches rather like modern semaphore flags or batons. Nowadays, his system is the basis of a truly sophisticated cipher described below.

The Polybius Square   Essentially, this is a simple mathematical cipher converted into a code by means of a keyword. The only secrecy required for a high degree of security is the restriction of the keyword – which can be changed at will – to those who 'need to know'.

To create the cipher draw a 5 × 5 grid as illustrated below, writing the alphabet, letter by letter, in each of its small squares and doubling up the I and the J as one is hardly likely to confuse them in subsequent use. Map-style grid references replace letters with two-figure numbers so that A is represented by 11 and Z by 55.

	1	2	3	4	5
1	A	B	C	D	E
2	F	G	H	I	K
3	L	M	N	O	P
4	Q	R	S	T	U
5	V	W	X	Y	Z

Naturally, you need to agree which numeral comes first – the horizontal or the vertical – but, for the sake of illustration, I will use the vertical numeral as the 'tens' and the horizontal numeral as the units – so spelling MAGGIE as 32.11.22.22.24.15.

A message written in simple mathematical symbols such as this could be as easy to 'crack' as that of the scrambled alphabet described under game 1; every 11, for example, being an A. But this is where the 'clever stuff' comes in. By adding the mathematical value of the keyword to the original 'ciphertext' (the text written in basic mathematics) then one makes such dramatic differences to the whole thing that codebreaking becomes next to impossible for the amateur. Now, using my codeword of GERANIUMS and sending MHW the identical message to that in game 2 you will see that none of the skills required for success in game 1 can be employed by a 'third party'.

My next step is to discover the mathematical expression for GERANIUMS. This is 22. 15. 42. 11. 33. 24. 45. 32. 43. This keyword is added to the message on a continuous basis such that once I have reached the s (43) I now return to the G (22) and go through it yet again. If that annoying 'third party' has tumbled to our secret then we could always send each other DAFFODILS (12. 11. 21. 21. 34. 14. 24. 31. 43) instead! Now the message, scented with geraniums:

Plaintext	T	H	E	A	U	T	H	O	R	S	E	N	D	S	H	I	S	L	O	V	E	T	O	M	H	W			

Ciphertext 44 23 15 11 45 44 23 34 42 43 15 33 14 43 23 24 31 34 51 15 44 34 32 23 23 52

Keyword 22 15 42 11 33 24 45 32 43 22 15 42 11 33 24 45 32 43 22 15 42 11 33 24 45 32

Codetext 66 38 57 22 78 68 68 66 85 65 30 75 25 76 47 69 63 77 73 30 86 45 65 47 68 84

BRINGING
TO BOKE

Bringing to Boke

A challenge for a word game party

If you desire to pair comparative strangers for various planned lexical activities then you might consider utilizing collective nouns as a basis for a fair and random selective system. The idea being that a simple lottery has, say, the men drawing 'nouns', with, say, the women drawing 'collective nouns'. Freely available is an 'answer sheet' so that Wicked Uncle Don Juan (who drew SHEEP) who has an eye for Goldilocks (who drew SWARM) cannot get away with 'a swarm of sheep' but must find his 'true' partner. Like Rail with Lady Ann Beeswax, this makes a good 'icebreaker' for further activities. To assist, I append a short selection of nouns of beastly assemblage:

ANTELOPES herd; ASSES pace; BADGERS cete; BEARS sloth; BEES swarm (*or* grist); BITTERNS sedge (*or* siege); BOARS sounder; BUCKS brace (*or* leash); CATS clowder; CATTLE drove (*or* herd); CHICKENS brood; CHOUGHS chattering; COOTS covert; CROWS murder; CUBS litter; DUCKS badelyng; ELK gang; FERRETS fesnyng; FLIES swarm; FOXES skulk; GEESE (in flight) skein, (on ground) gaggle; GOATS tribe; GOLDFINCHES charm; GROUSE covey; HARES down (*or* husk);

HAWKS cast; HOUNDS mute; KANGAROOS troop; KITTENS kindle; LARKS exaltation; LEOPARDS leap; LIONS pride; MARES stud; MALLARDS suit; MONKEYS troop; NIGHTINGALES watch; OWLS parliament; OXEN yoke (*or* drove, team *or* herd); PARTRIDGES covey; PHEASANTS nye; PLOVERS wing (*or* congregation); PORPOISES school; QUAILS bevy; RAVENS unkindness; ROOKS building (*or* clamour); SEALS pod (*or* herd); SHEEP flock; SWALLOWS flight (*or* conglobulation); SWINE drift; TEALS spring; WHALES gam (*or* pod); WOLVES rout (*or* pack); WOODCOCK fall.

To supplement these you may care to consider some of the Afterberners discussed in WORDSMITHERY.

Note

Whilst FESNYNG (of ferrets) *looks* like the Middle English of Dame Juliana it is, in fact, an erroneous form which has become established as a standard collective noun. **The Boke of St. Albans** actually has a BUSINESS (of ferrets) using the word in its then alternative meaning of 'busyness'. What is likely to have happened is that some other writer probably had 'busying' in a Middle English spelling which was either misprinted as FESNYNG or else was amended to that by a later writer in an attempt to create onomatopoeia with the 'traditional' Middle English appearance. Thus, both 'a business of ferrets' and 'a fesnyng of ferrets' are equally correct today.

By contrast, the error of 'a conglobulation of swallows' arose quite differently. In Dr Johnson's day it was believed that swallows hibernated by spending winter asleep at the bottom of ponds so that the great lexicographer recorded the verb CONGLOBULATE as, of swallows, to assemble all of a mass prior to plunging into water.

THE
HOUSEHOLD WORD
SERIES

The Household Word Series

Nine games, Numbers 1, 2, 4, 5 and 7 are ideal for children. Number 6 is more for adults in party spirits. Only numbers 8 and 9 are tests of skill.

1 I Spy

A traditional family favourite and one which Granny uses to keep a child amused by posing such simple questions as: 'I spy with my little eye something beginning with T.'

The letter T will be the initial letter of an obvious domestic item such as a table. The child now guesses and Granny may or may not give additional clues if she sees that frustration has set in after, say, both television set and telephone have been rejected as being incorrect. The usual rule is that one takes turns posing questions of this type.

2 I Can See

'I can see one of these in the room,' says Granny, 'and it's made of wood.'

That is her first clue in a series which, for younger children, will reveal an obvious object such as a table. The clues she gives are the sort which children can reproduce for themselves quite easily. These will be such as where it is or is not situated; its colour or a colour which it is not; its size, and so on. The older the children, the more obscure the object.

She has a flexible attitude to the game, varying it according to numbers present, their ages and how soon she wishes to take her afternoon nap. On a one-to-one basis she and a grandchild take turns to challenge each other. They have a maximum of, say, three guesses. These guesses begin as soon as the one setting the challenge has given a reasonable cryptic definition. Granny's full opening statement might well be, 'I can see one of these in the room. It is made of wood. It is square, but it's not near the window. What is it?'

If the child guesses incorrectly or is baffled, Granny awards herself a point and gives another clue. 'It is very large' is one for a slightly older child or, if coping with the limits of a younger child's attention span, 'It's got the teapot on it.'

Somehow the child always just manages to score that one point more than Granny in this game and never seems to notice (as other games will show) how she not only improves with age but has a nasty habit of winning them! When there are more children participating, Granny brings a little drama into the game and, this time, rewards those who guess correctly.

She will say something along the lines of: 'I can see one of these in the room and it's made of wood. Now, who would like to guess what it is? If you are wrong you are *out* and may not have another guess. But, if you are right, you will win a button.'

She pauses and surveys the scene.

'It's my red pencil,' could be an immediate response.

'Now, wait a minute,' says Granny, 'before you guess don't forget that if you are wrong you won't win a button. I shall give you more clues in a moment.'

A touch of caution affects the young company.

By the time she has revealed that this object is also square, not near the window and large, at least one child should be able to identify the table. The little lad with the red pencil has got the right answer and blurts it out.

Granny still preserves the drama. Her tin of buttons is open and tempting. The honour of being the first to have one of Grandpa's old shirt buttons is at stake. She does not confirm his answer – yet. She knows that the others will follow his lead. All, that is, save the lad's younger brother who will say, 'Chair', just to be different. Granny takes command of the vocal chaos.

She repeats her counsel about incorrect guessing but lays greater emphasis on the winning of one of Grandpa's coveted shirt buttons. When those who wish to say 'table' have clearly indicated their desire, she awards buttons. The stubborn younger brother has to wait for her next mystery object.

(For the adult version of this game see Dutch Auction, page 344)

3 Crambo

Pepys Diary for 20 May 1660 carries the following entry: 'From thence to the Hague again playing at Crambo in the waggon.'

Pepys is only one of the great literary figures who has enjoyed this classic spoken word game for two players.

It consists of one person speaking a line which the other answers with a rhyming line, but no word of the first line must occur in the second.

4 Dumb Crambo

A rhyme of a given word is mimed until guessed. Unlike Crambo any number can play.

5 Chinese Whispers

The players sit in a circle and a message is whispered round. Each player must pass on what he or she honestly believes he or she heard. Consequently, a message such as 'Great. Omit anemone' will eventually return to the first player in a form rather like, 'Grey tom ate an enemy.'

6 Wicked Whispers

The adult version of Chinese Whispers surreptitiously inserted into the basic game. One or two people seated in the circle are made the victims of scurrilous gossip whilst innocently expecting to pass on a normal silly message. The acid test is – will the original gossip return as given, or will tact or some other emotion render a change?

Similarly, messages of various sorts such as the whisper that one person has part of his clothing embarrassingly unfastened can be introduced into a seemingly innocent circle of adults playing a children's game.

7 Simple Addition

This game takes many basic forms but its object is to add so much additional detail to the original sentence that players become confused and have to drop out.

The first player says something along the lines of: 'I packed my bag and in it I put [whatever].'

Or: 'I went to market and there I obtained [whatever].'

Or even: 'I pulled back the covers of [somebody's] bed and there I discovered [whatever].'

The second player now has to repeat the original sentence but adding additional items which can be as ludicrous or as sensible as he or she wishes. Subsequent play follows the same pattern.

As more and more items are added it becomes increasingly difficult to remember everything. Eventually only the winner remains.

8 Ghost

A two-person game in which the object is *not* to say the last letter of a word containing five or more letters. Each player takes turn in giving a letter but can be challenged by the opponent if he or she cannot believe the letters are leading to a possible word. It is advisable to have a dictionary handy to settle disputes. For example:

Jack: D . . . (he has no particular word in mind).

Jill: DZ . . . (she has DZOBO or DZOMO in mind; she hopes he will challenge).

Jack: DZI . . . (he has DZIGGETAI in mind, which, even though it would still force him to say the last letter, hopes will be challenged on the grounds of impossibility).

If a player challenges the last given letter, the other must both spell it out correctly and prove its existence in the agreed reference work. Whoever wins that challenge, wins that particular round. Normally, however, players will stick to everyday words and the D of this example would be followed by, say, an E and the contest would progress to a word like DENSITY which Jill would win. DENSELY or DENSE-NESS are impossible as Jill would win on DENSE. (DZOBO, DZOMO and DZIGGETAI are all names of creatures defined in the larger dictionaries.)

9 Goal

A minimum of ten players are required to play this fast-moving version of verbal soccer. For convenience of illustration assume that we have a contest of men versus women, all seated at a long table. Jack and Jill are respective captains and stand down until the first goal is scored by either team. The eight people in play are seated thus:

	(Woman 4)	(Woman 3)	(Woman 2)	
	Striker	Midfielder	Defender	
(Man 1) Goalkeeper				(Woman 1) Goalkeeper
	Defender (Man 2)	Midfielder (Man 3)	Striker (Man 4)	

Spins of the coin have Jack acting as the linesman, Jill as the referee and the kick-off is by the women.

The woman midfielder, Woman 3, begins by stating vowel or consonant and Jack now consults the Bingo Letter-Frequency Table (see page 37) and selects any line of letters commencing with her choice. Assume that she has chosen a vowel and Jack chooses line number 2 which reads as follows:

I R Y N I S H A Z U J S E F O V E N G I G R Y T

He announces its first letter, I, and play is deemed to have passed to Woman 2. She has a mere two seconds (judged by the referee, Jill) in which to state a valid 2-letter word containing the letter I. She says IT.

As she is successful the 'ball' is passed upfield to Woman 3 who has a similar two seconds in which to get it to her team's striker. She does this by adding another letter to IT in order to produce a valid 3-letter word. She says SIT.

The ball is now at the feet of the woman striker, Woman 4. She has to add another letter within the time limit in order to shoot for a goal. However, let us say she overruns her time as she can only think of one word and is too embarrassed to say it.

Jill announces that the ball is loose by saying, 'Go". The woman striker and the man defender are both free to state a valid 4-letter word. Three possibilities arise:

(a) The striker recovers her equanimity and says, say, SPIT. The male goalkeeper must save the shot if he can. A successful save with, say, SPITS will be discussed below. Failure results in a goal for the women's team.

(b) The defender gains control of the ball with, say, SPIT. He passes to the midfielder who, by saying, say, SPITE now has the ball with his striker who, by saying, say, PRIEST, has fired a cannonball shot at the women's goalkeeper.

(c) Neither player can think of a suitable word within the time limit and Jill calls out 'Stop'.

In the event of the goalkeeper saving a shot, the linesman calls out the next letter of the Bingo line. In this example it is R. The goalkeeper must now turn this into a 2-letter word for passing forward to his defender. (Some simple letters will prove very tricky for anyone other than a wordsmith. Q is obviously very difficult but so too, surprisingly, is C. Abbreviations are not allowed and that rules out, unless you are a wordsmith, CO. An expert wordsmith, however, would not have the slightest problem with either Q or C. The extant words of CA, CE, CO, CU and QI are defined in the Miniglossary, as are the obsolete words CI and QU – both equally valid for play – and even such 'C words' as AC, CY, IC and OC are mentioned.

If the goalkeeper, having saved the shot from the female striker, turns R into such a valid word as OR, play follows its logical progression. But, should he fumble by exceeding the time limit Jill will call out, 'Go'. *Three* players now race for the ball – the woman striker and men's goalkeeper and defender. Whichever is first to say such as ER, OR or RE sends the ball in the logical direction.

Similarly, if the referee says 'Stop', the linesman will call out the next letter and the relevant players race for it.

The referee is the sole judge of all matters pertaining to play. Jill, for example, will not need to have a stopwatch for timing but will use her common sense. Similarly, if two players call out words almost simultaneously when going for a loose ball, it is she who decides who was the first. Alternatively, she may call upon the linesman for a fresh letter.

If Jill considers a word is likely to be invalid she is entitled to hold up the game whilst she investigates. For example, SITE might be followed by PISTE: once she is satisfied that the player has correctly used a word meaning a ski slope and that all understand how it is spelt, she waves play on. Sometimes the referee may wish to consult the dictionary in the event of a word about which he or she has doubts. This brings us to fouls and penalties.

A foul is committed by giving an invalid word. A goal-keeper's foul is treated as a penalty.

(a) In the event of a foul, the offending letter is removed and the player directly opposite now has possession of the basic word.

(b) In the event of a penalty, the offending letter is removed and the striker has a free shot with any additional letter at the goal.

Once a goal is scored, Jack and Jill are replaced as officials by other members of their teams. A woman now takes charge of the Bingo Letter-Frequency Table and a man is the referee. As with standard football, the team that had the goal scored against it kicks off.

The game lasts either for an agreed length of time or else ends when one side has scored a particular number of goals.

If, say, twelve people are involved this will produce a goalkeeper, a defender, two midfield players and a striker. The kick-off is always with the midfield player next to the defender.

Goal is an ideal game for competition between representatives of different taverns or schools. It is recommended that independent officials be used wherever possible.

Serious competitors should draw up their own rules concerning such matters as substitutes, but there is no objection to players, for tactical reasons, changing playing position (e.g. goalkeeper to striker). All changes of this nature may be made only after either team has scored a goal. If a team is a player short and wishes one of its number to fulfil more than one role (e.g. be both a mid-fielder and the striker) this can be permitted only if both the opposing team and the referee agree and if the constitution of the competition permits this.

On the question of time for a move, two seconds is ample for wordsmiths but non-wordsmith adults or children may require more time. Time limits are deemed to be two seconds unless otherwise agreed by all. As an alternative to a stopwatch for a serious contest, chess clocks may be used. The organizers must agree suitable penalties for the team which runs out of time first, and these penalties should relate to the amount of time by which the team is out of time. They can take the form of goals disallowed or else additional free kicks by the team having unused time. Such penalties are left to the discretion of the players.

THE
CHARADE
SERIES

The Charade Series

Fourteen games to delight the show-off. The children's game is the first version of number 3. The second and third versions are for slightly inebriated adults, as are numbers 10, 11 and 12.

1 Charades

The all-time classic mentioned in the works of such writers as Sheridan, Thackeray and George Eliot, and also known to British television viewers as a celebrity panel-game series called *Give Us a Clue*.

At its simplest, a multisyllable word is chosen. Say, CATATONIC. A player breaks the word down into sections, not necessarily syllables, and mimes to the company each section separately. For CATATONIC a player might mime:

  (a) CAT followed by A followed by TONIC
  (b) CAT followed by (H)AT followed by TONIC
  (c) CAT followed by (H)AT followed by O followed by NIC(K)

or any other combination which readily suggests itself. The company now has to guess the word.

Although most readers will know how to play this game, team captains should remind their players of the following basic rules:

1   Give *clear* signals as to which word or syllable you are miming.
2   Listen *carefully* to what your team-mates say. Often the correct word or syllable is stated but missed by an over-anxious performer.
3   If your team-mates are completely baffled by what you are attempting, then stop and reconsider the situation. Could you tell them the same information in a different way, or would it be better to attempt a totally different word?

One of the failures in *Give Us a Clue* was when a particular celebrity was given a certain film title. How could *The Lone Ranger and the Lost City of Gold* be mimed? He mimed somebody riding a horse, with the predictable result that his team-mates guessed at a first word of RIDER or JOCKEY.

How could it be done better? First of all, give the conventional sign for a film title: which is to mime the action of a silent-film cameraman using an old hand-wound movie camera.

Secondly, hold up nine fingers to represent the nine words of the title.

Thirdly, if you wish to portray *The Lone Ranger* as one item clearly indicate that you are miming the first three words. This is achieved by:

(a) Tapping the top of your head to indicate a name.

(b) Holding up first one finger, then two fingers, then three fingers, to indicate three words.

(c) Pause to see if the point has got across. If it has, continue.

(d) Mime *not* a man on horseback, but a masked cowboy.

(e) If this fails to get across, stop and take the whole thing word by word. Ensuring that you clearly indicate with your fingers which word is being attempted.

THE   The conventional sign for this is the shape of the letter T formed by your index fingers.

LONE   If you cannot see a clear way of conveying this word, hold your ear to indicate that what you are about to do 'sounds like' this word. Now choose from BONE, CLONE, CONE, HONE, JOAN, MOAN, PHONE or TONE. Mime one of these.

RANGER   You will have to have particularly stupid teammates if you have to mime this word. As they have already been told that this is the third word of a name and they now know that the first two words are THE LONE, they should have already said RANGER. Have they? Did you fail to hear it? Listen carefully. If someone says it, touch your nose and point directly at that person and force him or her to say it again so that everyone gets the message.

But, assuming that no one says it, try the masked cowboy routine again. Still failure. Would 'sounds like' DANGER, MANGER or STRANGER get across? Probably not.

So split the word into syllables. RANG-ER. The conventional sign for this is to place two fingers against the arm. Now place one finger against the arm for the first syllable.

RANGE   Mime a cooking range. Alternatively it 'sounds like' CHANGE (money in the pocket). Once someone says RANGE now try and force him to extend the word. You signify this by holding your hands in the praying position and extending them outwards. Surely someone is going to turn 'The Lone Range' into 'The Lone Ranger'? No?

ER   Signify the second syllable by placing two fingers against the arm. Now hold your thumb and index finger close together to indicate a little word or syllable. It 'sounds like' BURR, CUR, FUR, HER, MYRRH, PURR, SIR or WHIRR. Choose and mime. Or point to FUR, point to HER, point to SIR.

AND   The conventional sign is to display a wrist with a drooping hand and to move the other hand over the top of it. (H)AND.

THE   As before.

LOST   Mime LOST or 'sounds like' ACCOST, BOSSED, COST, DOSSED, MOSSED or TOSSED.

CITY   'Sounds like' BITTY, DITTY, GRITTY, NITTY, PITY, TITTY, or WITTY.

OF   Signify small word.

GOLD   Point to some gold in the room. Failing that choose any suitable 'sounds like'.

To play, divide the company into teams – say, men versus women. Now separate into different rooms and devise an agreed number of titles of books, plays, films, television shows and songs. The bookshelf, the show-page section of a newspaper will provide plenty of inspiration. Write these titles down on small pieces of paper, which are then folded and put into a hat.

Return to the games room and play. The men have to mime those chosen by the women and vice-versa. Impose a time limit and award a single point if a team guesses it correctly. The point is not transferable in event of failure.

Do not be afraid of making a fool of yourself but do not invite Simple Simon to participate! This, one of the all-time great party games, should be played by folk who share a similar disposition and sense of humour.

If neither you nor your company has ever played it before try a session with easy titles to begin with. Something along the lines of *The King and I*. You will soon wish to progress to the real 'stinkers' that the producers of *Give Us a Clue* reserve for team captains. Charades is one of the all-time great party games.

2 Adverbs

Divide the company into two teams – say, men versus women. They separate to plan their strategy.

The men write down an agreed number of adverbs (words such as PROUDLY, ANXIOUSLY, STUPIDLY, EMOTION-ALLY, RUDELY, ARROGANTLY), all of which are very well known. These are written on separate pieces of paper which are folded and put into a hat. At the same time they write an equal number of activities such as BUYING A LOAF OF BREAD, TAKING THE DOG FOR A WALK, CHATTING UP YOUR FAVOURITE FILM STAR or whatever. These are also put on separate pieces of paper which are folded, and put into a *different* hat. The women's team are preparing similar adverbs and activities for their hats. When the teams are ready the hats prepared by the men are put side-by-side at one end of the room and the women's hats are similarly placed at the other end of the room, or wherever else where they will not be confused. A toss of the coin decides who goes first.

Jill is first. She draws out of the men's 'activity hat' the statement HANGING OUT THE WASHING. This she reads aloud. Next she draws out of the men's 'adverb hat' the word FOOLISHLY. This she does *not* announce but now has to enact the scenario of 'hanging out the washing, foolishly' to her team-mates. She is allowed to speak but must not under any circumstances utter the significant adverb.

The women are permitted a total of five guesses as to the adverb. If they guess it correctly first time they are awarded 5 points, second time 4 points, and so on until they have exhausted their guesses. As players will tend to shout all at the same time and disputes could easily arise as to who said what in which sequence, one of the men acts as umpire. Jill gives him her adverb in advance of enactment and his judgement has to be accepted. Similarly, a woman acts as umpire for the men.

The contest is played with teams taking turns to perform and the winners are the team with the greater total at the end of the session.

3 Who's Zoo

(a) *Animal Farm* (*the children's version*) The organizer writes down a number of suitable names of animals – CAT, DOG, HORSE, COW and the like. These are written on separate pieces of paper, folded and put into a hat.

The company is divided into teams – say, boys versus girls.

Suppose that a girl has drawn CAT. She now has to mime the action of a cat to her team. She may not speak or make any sound such as *miaow*.

Her team has a maximum of five guesses and, as they may well all shout at the same time, the organizer must be in command of the situation until sensible self-discipline prevails after one or two children have had a turn.

This is done by stressing the points which can be won on any scale you consider suitable. For example, 5 points on a first correct guess, 4 points on a second guess, and so on. You now ask her team who is going to have that first guess. The ones who said such as CAMEL, GIRAFFE, SPIDER or WHALE are likely to calm down and listen to the more sensible suggestions such as CAT, LION or TIGER. The little girl, meanwhile, must remain as a cat.

You now say, 'Who is going to risk *losing* 5 points for the team by making a wrong guess?'

They will soon sort themselves out and appoint their own 'spokesgirl' for that initial guess. Whatever points they win will spur the boys to perform better.

Soon your role will be merely that of a scorekeeper and perhaps not even that. They will soon take the game in their stride and be fully aware of the cumulative totals.

(b) *Acting the Goat* (*the slightly inebriated adult version*)
The company divides into teams – say, men versus women,
and each team is armed with pencil and paper.

A woman writes down, say, GOLDFISH on her team's
paper and her colleagues agree. Two men are invited to
leave their team-mates, one of them will take the floor and
the other will join the women, he is made privy to the
secret. The victim on the floor is not.

The victim must now mime a goldfish as directed by his
former friend. The director's instructions might well be:

1 Lie on your stomach.
2 Have your arms by your side and your feet together.
3 Flap your hands and wriggle your feet.
4 Open and close your mouth.
5 Now go round in circles.

The men have to guess what it is. They are permitted five
guesses on a decreasing points scale and the women see
that play is fair. They decide which guesses are to be taken
seriously!

(c) *Supergoat* (*A second slightly inebriated adult version*)
This time, instead of one victim there are two, and the
director has to get the message across within 60 seconds
(if played seriously and stone-cold sober) or from two
minutes upwards (according to the state of the
participants). There are no limits to guesses and only a
single point is at stake.

The women have now selected two very different creatures and the director's instructions to Bill and Ben might take this form:

To Bill: 1 Stand at a position of attention.

2 Keeping your upper arms still with elbows pressed against your sides, stick your lower arms out as far as you can.

3 Now flap them madly and keep them flapping until I tell you to stop.

4 On the word 'Go' take a very quick step backwards then run around the room.

To Ben: 1 Get down on all fours.

To Bill: 1 Go!

To Ben: 1 Keep perfectly still.

2 Don't laugh or make any other sound.

To Bill: 1 When I say 'Stop' I want you to stay where you are with your left arm and left legs perfectly still but still keeping your right arm flapping.

2 Stop!

3 Wriggle your right leg and still keep that arm flapping.

To Ben: 1 Still in a position of all fours, raise yourself to tiptoes.

To Bill: 1 Slow your movements down.

2 Put your leg down.

3 Stand still.

To Ben: 1 Rush across and eat him.

Can the men identify a spider and a fly within one minute?

Base your timings on a first performance, making suitable allowances for the skill of the director. If the first director was particularly good, that will set a high standard for the others to follow. But, if he was incompetent, and had no idea how to cope with, say, a snake and a mongoose or an elephant and a mouse or whatever, then assume that others will do better and make a reasoned judgement as to what time to allow for all other competitors. Avoid, if possible, having a fool as the first director.

In this version, players take turns to be the director and they assemble their own cast of victims.

For Acting the Goat or Supergoat it is entirely up to you how specific you wish to be. For example, if you see a way of distinguishing between, say, breeds of dogs – Bill *looks* like a bulldog and Ben *looks* like a corgi and you permit one of the women's team to take the floor and stand there looking regal for Ben to play to – that is fair. Otherwise it is better to stick to having Bill as a dog and Ben as, say, a cat. Equally, the ai. This is the three-toed sloth. For a sloth, pure and simple, Bill would have to look like something large and cumbersome hanging upside down from a tree. For the ai, Bill would have to, say, remove his shoes and socks then cover two toes on each foot with a sock and hang upside-down from his tree only his thumbs and index fingers visible together with his strangely covered feet.

The two captains should agree ground rules in advance based upon the composition of the company. It would be wise in these circumstances to have at least one of the captains female (however the teams may be divided) so that she can impose limits based upon certain practicalities such as dress.

4 Call My (Domestic) Bluff

Devised by one of the leading American panel game inventors, *Call My Bluff* failed to get taken up by any US television network but the BBC bought it for Britain where it was such a hit that they even had enquiries for the American rights from a Stateside network! Now, Brits play it at home just like any other parlour game except that they copy the television format. This necessitates advanced planning but the wordsmith element of the family can, with forethought, make a valuable contribution to a pleasant evening's entertainment.

Decide, in advance of the intended session, the composition of the competing teams and who will occupy the 'chair'. Ideally, you will require at least one wordsmith per team who is prepared to provide the 'scripts' whilst the remainder should possess lively wits and a sense of humour. The standard team is a wordsmith-captain and two others who can be, if necessary, pi-men, but most definitely not Simple Simons! The chairman is the host or hostess whose main duty, apart from keeping the scores, is to maintain a happy atmosphere. Not that a chairman is necessary but, at least, it provides a billet for a witty companion who would otherwise be left out in the cold. The game consists of three different definitions – each spoken by a different player – being offered for a single *unusual* word and it is up to the opposing team to identify the correct one. This is where the wordsmiths come into their element as it is their responsibility to provide one true and two false *but plausible* definitions and then, as captains, ensure that the person best suited for making which statement is given which definition. For example, if you had provided the following three definitions of HYRAX, which – irrespective of the truth – would you assign to each of two chums and which would you prefer to deliver yourself. Each definition is written on a postcard used as an *aide-mémoire* rather than a 'script'.

(a) A rabbit-sized relative of the elephant which lives in a burrow. The species known as a rock hyrax uses a communal latrine which facilitates the gathering of its excrement which contains an ingredient used in the manufacture of perfumes.

(b) A mythical creature having the body and forelegs of a lion; the rear of a serpent and the head of a beautiful woman. The hyrax featured in the legend of the Trojan hero Brutus when he settled with his followers in what is now Brittany in northern France. Brutus overcame the creature by romancing the 'head' whilst some of his warriors threw spears at the beastly parts. Subsequently, Brutus led his followers across the sea to the Isles of Albion where they overthrew a race of giants to establish themselves as the first Britons.

(c) A type of girdle worn by a virgin in classical Greece to demonstrate her status. The wedding ceremony had her discarding this in favour of a married woman's girdle.

The true answer is (a) but, irrespective of the truth, can you visualize which 'definition' would be best delivered by which team-mate? If your team-mates can come up with better 'false' meanings than yours then you could always have a pre-contest strategy session. But, however you organize the event, it is better to have the teams organized in advance of the game.

As players have to ad-lib their own definitions – unlike the television professionals – so it is wise to place limitations on the amount of waffle permitted with the 'false' meanings otherwise that could give the game away, though the same limitation is equally vital when one is delivering a true definition which has a plenitude of facts. For example, OPERCULUM might be defined in the following terms:

'A secretion of hardened mucus, sometimes strengthened with carbonate of lime, with which a snail seals the aperture of its shell during hibernation. It contains minute perforations directly opposite the respiratory orifice.'

Unless you would normally speak like that, don't! Instead, paraphrase. An average person might say something on these lines:

'A sort of gunge that a snail produces to seal the aperture of its shell when it hibernates. Sometimes it strengthens this yukky stuff with carbonate of lime but leaves little holes opposite its nose or whatever snails breathe through. In short, snail snoozing gunge.'

Naturally, the wordsmith-captain cannot write an individual's vernacular rendering of a technical definition but allowing freedom to paraphrase while not straying from the facts it is well within the spirit of the game. However, let us suppose that the word FEAK has been selected and, for incomprehensible reasons Simple Simon has been drafted in as a last-minute substitute for an injured player. He faces the captain's 'script' which reads:

'FEAK – "when she hath fed she feaketh her beak not wipeth it" so a seventeenth-century grammarian instructed. "She" is a hawk and the verb "to feak" is still used to describe the action of a hawk after feeding.'

Spoken word-for-word by a dullard this could sound as boring as a railway timetable but what else can one do with it? A wit, repeating it word-for-word would lay great stress on the words **feaketh** and **wipeth**. Feaketh is a command; wipeth is beneath contempt. Quoted in that mock-serious fashion it suddenly becomes very funny. Equally significant is the use of a judicious pause. The wit would stop after delivering the first sentence, giving the audience time to digest his curious uttering, which they do not understand in the slightest. Only then, would he deliver the *dénouement* of the second sentence. The art of humour, as the late Kenneth Williams instructed a fellow thespian, lies in emphasizing the significant word or words.

Now, the 'false'. How do you set about writing the fiction?

If you doubt your ability to produce convincing 'false' descriptions then limit your selection to those words which contain a recognizable element. For example, the word BACKSTRESS.

If this appears to you as BACK-STRESS, then describe the word as meaning some form of pain in, say, the lower back. To surmount the difficulty of medical terminology have as the sufferers of BACK-STRESS the sort of people who use normal English – miners, sailors or all-in wrestlers. It can then be an occupational hazard of one of these, such as Cornish tin miners, Pennsylvanian coalminers or whatever. Thus, even if the opposing team are all doctors even they cannot say for certain that your description is false. Alternatively it appears to you as BACK'S-TRESS. A tress is a lock of hair – it is for the back. So, it could be a false hairpiece worn down the back as a fifteenth-century vanity of the fashionable women attached to some European court or city. How many of your friends could possibly know how the 'smart set' of Budapest arranged their hair in 1486?

It might even appear as BACKSTR-ESS, a female BACKSTR. If you can define a suitable BACKSTR then she is one of those, only in a frock. And that, believe it or not, is the true definition although, technically, the word is a double feminine form.

The scoring and the time allotted for each individual definition is a matter for your own judgement – or that of the chairman – but it is great fun, I assure you, so long as you keep the dullards busy replenishing the glasses and not active participants.

5 Newby's Bluff

A game rather like Call My (Domestic) Bluff but with a subtle difference – all the statements can be true, or false or a mixture of both!

Few will know that the word **correspondence** had a sixteenth-century meaning of sexual intercourse, or that the word **share** once meant the pubic region. Not that this is a game of dirty words, just that many words we take for granted have or once had other meanings. These meanings are easily found in any large dictionary – simply skim through the pages and stop at an extended entry for any well-known word. For example, the word SET has more meanings than any other word in the English language.

An ideal game for two teams of three adults, it makes a perfect foil for the British quiz addicts who organize leagues and knockout tournaments between representatives of public houses.

The teams agree upon a good dictionary. They are told in advance which letter of the alphabet they may make their selection from but they do not know which letter will be the province of their opponents – merely that it is different. Each side researches its own words. They select, say, a dozen each. They now write down three simple definitions for each word. It is entirely up to the team how many of the meanings are true, the only stipulation is that the word must be well known. For example, in a contest between the Nag's Head and the Royal Oak the 'Nag's Headers' chose the word SET. How many, if any, of these meanings are true?

Tom: A noun. A square in the pattern of a tartan.
Dick: A noun. A frame supporting the roof of a mine.
Harriet: A verb. Of a rabbit, to be resting.

If you have a pocket dictionary, none of them. If you have a good family dictionary, only one, Tom's definition. If you have an excellent dictionary, the lot.

To play, it is best to have an independent third party who acts as umpire, scorer, takes the chair for the contest and has notified each team in advance which letter they will be using. This third party possesses a copy of the agreed dictionary and he or she takes the ultimate responsibility for deciding whether or not a particular definition is true or false. For example:

Harriet: A verb. Of a buck, to be resting.

The male of the rabbit is the buck, but a buck is also a male deer. The verb does not apply to deer. Is this definition true or false? The umpire, upon the evidence on hand, alone decides. Whatever subtleties may have been in Harriet's mind when she phrased it in this form are of no consequence, the umpire has the last word.

If no third party is available, the team agrees in advance that one will select a letter from the first half of the alphabet and the other from the second half. They agree any arbitration procedure amongst themselves.

The game is played for points, three points being at stake for each round of three definitions of a single word. If those guessing are right, they score a point. If they are wrong, the point goes to the team making the definitions.

6 Just a Minute

An off-the-cuff public speaking contest which, by being played by teams of two people, is not as daunting as it sounds and far more fun.

The company divides into two-person teams and the whole proceedings are directed by a non-playing organizer. The rules will vary according to the number of participants but as few as six people (three teams) can compete. As the competition requires various officials, so at least one team will be needed to provide these neutral functionaries each round.

The organizer prepares in advance a number of basic subjects for which any reasonable person can readily bring to mind a multitude of examples. These examples are significant as each one mentioned will score a point, but only until the others discover that basic subject. Any subject will do – Boys' names, Girls' names, Colours, Numbers, Countries, Animals, Household Objects are typical examples – and these have been put in a hat without anyone knowing any of the subjects.

It is a contest of both skill and bluff and the officials will be just as involved in the contest as anyone else. The organizer calls upon two teams. One will compete, the other will provide the officials. A competitor will draw a subject from the hat and all five people (the organizer, the players and the officials) will see what it is. All other teams will be the audience and will try to find out what the subject is. A points scoring system will be applied on the following basis:

(a) 1 point for each example mentioned by the players.

(b) A deduction of 2 points from the actual or future score of the team to which any member of the audience belongs who makes a wrong guess at the subject. A correct guess being made at any time during play ending the round.

(c) A deduction of 5 points is made against the players and the round immediately stopped if, in the opinion of the organizer, the players are being wilfully misleading. This being a matter of fine judgement so the organizer should be a natural leader who commands respect. The circumstances in which players are guilty of being wilfully misleading will become clear once an example, given below, is explored.

First, however, an explanation of the title. In the first minute of public speaking a minimum of four examples must be given. The whole of the time allotted to public speaking is a medieval minute (6 minutes in modern reckoning) and, if the speakers are not giving examples at least equal to the same ratio in the remainder of their allotted time, the organizer may call a halt to their activities. This is not necessarily foul play on their part so no points deductions are made. The audience, knowing that the organizer is being fair to all concerned, can concentrate upon isolating the examples. The players are being kept on their toes. A stopwatch is not necessary but a sensible attitude to time is required.

The two officials will act as positive and negative scorers, ideally seated either side of the organizer at a table. Each has a pencil and paper. The negative scorer records the deductions. Each time a member of the audience makes a wrong guess the minus-2 points is noted against his or her team. The negative scorer is *obvious* in his or her actions. By contrast, the positive scorer is very *discreet*. This is essential as the audience must not be made instantly aware of when an example has been given. The positive scorer and the organizer work more closely together to ensure that all examples (and some may be obscure) are correctly recorded.

Let us assume that the subject is Colours. The players take centre stage and hold a conversation. Wittily, they mention colours such as ORANGE, LIME, LEMON, ALMOND and PEACH, so keeping the negative scorer busy with such audience responses as 'Fruit', 'Trees', 'Flowers', 'Food'. This is excellent gamesmanship.

By contrast, suppose that the players had prefaced each colour with a masculine name, 'William of Orange', 'Harry Lime', 'Fred Lemon', so misleading the audience into thinking that the subject was Names. This is still fair but if the percentage of names heavily exceeds those of colours, then the organizer may construe this as being wilful and stop the round immediately.

If Just a Minute is being played with a great number of teams, the organizer should consider having non-playing scorers and limiting the number of responses from the audience. The easiest way of doing this is to stop play every minute and, on a 'hands up' basis, see how many agree that the subject is (still with this example) fruit or trees or whatever. This way each team has a minimum of a minute in which to record some points. Only the best, or the luckiest, will have the full medieval minute.

7 Flexiloquency

Flexiloquent is an old adjective meaning speaking words of double meaning, and that is the task facing you.

Each member of the company is challenged to produce an amusing extemporaneous tale without the audience being aware of the punchline. At the simplest level a prefix such as **cat-** or a suffix such as **-ant** is chosen and the speaker has to contrive a situation in which the prefix or suffix becomes part of the final comment. For example: 'My cat was feeling jaded so I gave the CATATONIC.' Or: 'The ants went on a supersonic jet flight. They became known as CONCORDANCE.'

At the highest level a well-known proverb or saying is the subject material and some of these pass into common usage as classic shaggy-dog stories. For example:

The native king collected thrones which he stowed in his grass hut. One day they all fell on top of him. The moral of the story is – PEOPLE IN GRASSHOUSES SHOULDN'T STOW THRONES.

Hiawatha had three wives. One slept on a bed of buffalo skin, one slept on a bed of moose skin, whilst his favourite slept on a bed of hippopotamus skin. All gave birth to sons at the same time. The ones on the buffalo and moose hides each had one son but the one on the hippopotamus hide had twins. Which proves the old saying that THE SONS OF THE SQUAW ON THE HIPPOPOTAMUS HIDE IS EQUAL TO THE SONS OF THE SQUAWS ON THE OTHER TWO HIDES.

As 'fabled phrases' some of my own efforts have been published, this last example leads to a proverbial punchline:

The era of Queen Anne, the last Stuart monarch of Great Britain, was one in which many of our best-loved proverbs arose. Typical of which was the one recounted to her by a favourite courtier. He told the queen of an unfortunate Siamese fellow who fell foul of a malevolent dwarf who, in the best fairy tale tradition, gave him a choice of three tasks to perform in order to gain his freedom. All three tasks concerned the little man's obsession with angling. The prisoner made his choice and, as the courtier informed his monarch, 'THAI MAN TIED WEIGHTS FOR GNOME, ANNE'.

Even British newspapers are not immune to this activity. An issue of the *Daily Mail* in June 1988, discussing the testing by potential purchasers of perfumes, carried the headline, SOME THINGS ARE TRIED TO SCENT US. Devotees of the *Daily Telegraph*'s simple crossword have cherished the answers to questions 1 and 2 across for many years. For example, 1 across STORIES, 2 across CHEETAH. To get the point, say these two answers together – STORIES CHEETAH! Shakespeare is renowned for his puns but, unfortunately, his best are too bawdy to record in this family volume.

To play, divide the company into two teams. The teams now agree to a basic small word. Examples of ANT and CAT have already been given but such as BE (which can become BEE for punchlines of BEFALL, BEHOLD etc.) SHIP, (CENSORSHIP, MEMBERSHIP, etc.), NATION (INCARNATION, POLLINATION, etc.) and OUT are just some of the suitable choices.

Suppose that ANT is chosen. A player must now construct a tale in which ANT features in the punchline. If he or she succeeds in creating a punchline *which comes as a total surprise* a maximum of three points is awarded by the opposing team. However, the really witty can ask for any multisyllable word or short phrase (CONSTANTINOPLE or TIME FLIES are typical examples) and play for a maximum of five points, the word or phrase being chosen by the opponents. If he or she cannot see any virtue in the particular choice, the option of returning to ANT is still available. Finally, the supreme wit can ask for a proverb and attempt to score a maximum 10 points, with the ANT option still open.

There is just as much fun in the judgements as in the storytelling, the opponents behaving like a panel of experts and making and giving advice along the lines of 'I wouldn't give up your day job yet, dearie' or 'Don't call us, we'll call you'. Then, mock-seriously, discussing what points to award.

If you are scared of going first remember that soon you, too, will be a judge – and revenge can be very sweet.

8 Blind Gue

All that is known about Blind Gue, apart from the fact that it is a version of Blindman's Buff, is that in 1604 a charge of sixpence was levied for participation in a session of the game. It would be reasonable to assume, however, that the company was adult, mixed and, in all probability, rather merry.

As a modern word game for a similarly extravagant company consider a gue (an old word for a scoundrel) blindfolded and attempting to find a word or phrase by touching various people and/or objects.

A player pays an agreed fee into a charity tin and leaves the room. The company suggest a word based upon (among other things) their consideration for the feelings of the gue and who amongst them is willing to be touched as an aspect of guessing. Once agreement has been reached, the gue is asked to return, then, blindfolded, given the requisite information and led to the person or object providing the first word or syllable. For example:

A male blind gue is told that he is trying to discover the identity of a famous historical personage. He is led to person A, who is male. Person A, on being touched, behaves in a camp fashion. The gue is told that he has touched the first word. He is now led to person B, who is female and her name is Anne. The answer, of course, is Queen Anne – or Victoria or Mary or whoever supplies a suitable name.

A female blind gue might find herself having to decipher a Shakespearian play by touching Henry four times (he keeps moving around the room) then parting two objects for *Henry IV Part 2*.

If a word like APPLEJOHN is chosen and no John is present, the gue can always be led to an object conveniently sited in the bathroom. Parts of the anatomy can supply aspects of such words as FOOTBALL or THUMBSCREW. Anne could find herself as the first syllable of such as ANTIQUE and Bill, followed by an eye, followed by touching everyone could be BILIOUS.

So long as a forename, nickname or surname or else a specific portion of the anatomy is an aspect of the word or phrase the gue has a reasonable chance of guessing correctly. You can always have a person identify himself or herself by touching a window BLIND then plunging his or her hands into a bowl of particularly nasty GOO! The game is as funny as you care to make it.

Alternatively, you may prefer to play an equally genuine old game adapted for a modern assembly of word players. Perhaps combining the two games into one session – according to your regard for the current gue. If so, call the portmanteau version 'Blind Cockles' and insert the occasional joker of the following game, Hot Cockles.

To gain the maximum fun from this joker, leave it until volunteers are literally queuing up to be the gue and the ideal mug has just left the room.

9 Hot Cockles

A very old rustic game, first recorded in a literary work of 1580. Essentially it is Blind Gue played by sadists. This time the hooded person has to kneel down and guess who has hit him.

As a word game it can be adapted, less painfully, as follows:

A volunteer leaves the room. The remainder of the company agree upon a word or phrase, say, FISHING SMACK.

The volunteer returns, is blindfolded and asked to kneel down. He is told to perform the action of fishing. His task is to identify the two-word description of a mode of transport. He continues to mime the part of a fisherman – then somebody smacks him!

Words such as HIT, KICK, BLOW, BUFFET, STRIKE, BOOT, PUNCH, WHIP and the like can be readily adapted for slightly inebriated word fun by hot cocklers.

10 Cold Cockles

The UK social set known as 'Sloanes' are rich and upper-class and known for such heights of mental agility as throwing bread rolls at each other. Avid Sloane-watchers have yet to record an example of their involvement in word play, so to fill a gap in their entertainment, Cold Cockles has been devised.

A volunteer has to guess a well-known phrase. He is dispatched from the company, whilst they agree the phrase amongst themselves.

On his return to the dining-room, everyone throws bread at him. Obviously the answer is, 'He is well-bred'!

Another example could have him leaving the room in the company of a sweet young thing. They return and he is told to make sense of a well-known phrase concerning his female partner. The company now smother him in trifle. The sweet young thing is left untouched. Obviously, 'she is not to be trifled with'!

(Cold Cockles was suggested by Joan Smith as an up-market version of Hot Cockles.)

11 Rail with Lady Ann Beeswax

One of the meanings of RAIL is 'to jest' and RAIL, LADY ANN BEESWAX is an anagram of my daughter, ALEXANDRA LISA NEWBY. One of her favourite word games is the construction of 'alter egos' by anagramming the names of guests to her parties. Jestingly, her guests now assume the 'persona' Alex provides for them and so her father – alias BEN PEWTERY – might well find himself discussing the 'lifestyle' of W. O. ANGIE TAR-RUB G.M. (alias Maggie Warburton) whilst JANIS MOTH (Joan Smith of Cold Cockles fame) is telling NURSE PATHOS (Susan Thorpe) her troubles. The game is a great icebreaker at the word game parties my daughter loves hosting as one can also have fun attempting to unravel the real name of the person one is addressing.

THE
QUESTION AND ANSWER
SERIES

The Question and Answer Series

Twenty-seven games including the six variations listed under number 15. The children's games are numbers 11, 12, 13 and 15.

Only Number 14 is appearing in print for the first time. It, too, can be played by children.

1 Twenty Questions

Animal, Vegetable or Mineral is the alternative title of this perennial favourite.

A player thinks of any object. It can be as simple as Africa, or as bizarre as Robert the Bruce's spider. The player now announces whether the object is animal, mineral or vegetable or any combination of all three. Everyone else is allowed a maximum of twenty questions between them in order to discover this mystery object. The art of the questioner lies in clever elimination by category rather than by asking specific questions. For example, if the object is France and it has been established that one is seeking a geographical location, silly players waste questions by making wild guesses such as 'Is it

Scunthorpe?' rather than beginning an elimination of the globe either by hemisphere or continent.

All the questions must be capable of being answered by a simple yes or no and no clues are given.

2 Twenty-one Questions

A test of wit between a player and the rest of the company.

The player thinks of any object. Let us suppose Jack chooses a blackbird. He writes **blackbird** on a piece of paper and conceals this from the rest of the company. They are going to ask him any general knowledge questions they wish, each of which must be capable of a single descriptive word answer. At some point he must answer BLACKBIRD to one of these questions. His task if to get away with it. Their task is to catch him out.

This is not a general knowledge quiz, nor a silly question-and-answer session but a test which is finely balanced between these extremes. As Jack is unlikely to be asked a question to which the absolutely correct answer is BLACKBIRD he must grab any opportunity which comes his way to use it. Obviously if he has answered all previous questions correctly, then his BLACKBIRD is going to stick out like a sore thumb. Therefore, he must answer all questions incorrectly but within a degree of tolerability. What is tolerable? For the question 'What is the capital of England?' intolerable answers would be BLACKBIRD or ARMPIT. But, BIRMINGHAM, EDINBURGH, SCUNTHORPE or even, at a pinch, MOSCOW could be tolerated.

The company collectively are the judges of what is tolerable. They cannot be too pedantic as each will, in turn, be facing the same test. Certainly they should insist upon a better answer than ARMPIT for England's capital, but it is up to them if they are prepared to accept MOSCOW. If collectively they reject MOSCOW, Jack has to give a more sensible but equally incorrect answer.

There is neither need nor purpose in the company taking strict turns to ask a question. Some people will freeze when it is their turn to think of something to ask even when they could ask anything in the world they wished. Let those who have questions ask them. But *never* ask a question which can be answered by anything other than a name of a physical object, be it animal, vegetable or mineral or any combination of all three. Never accept anything other than a single-word answer. Otherwise Jack could have written the word, YES, and be bound to get away with it at some point, or else slip his secret word into a sentence or even a paragraph given in reply to a question.

Jack is facing a maximum of twenty-one questions. He must say his word at some stage. The company, collectively, is allowed to denounce him only once. Once he has got away with it, he has won. The quicker he gets away with it, the more points he will score. 21 points on the first question, 20 points on the second with progressively fewer until a minimum of 5 points can still be won. Only he may win these points, it is up to the company to stop him.

The twenty-first question is unique. He is forced to say his word, no matter what question he is asked. However, if his answer is tolerable (based upon past judgements) then he cannot be denounced. He scores 5 points. If his answer is intolerable, every member of the company receives a bonus of 5 points. It is up to the company to be fair, as they are also going to be in the same situation.

However, the company are not the masters of everything. Suppose they denounce Jack at a stage prior to the twenty-first question. True, if they are right Jack will fail to score, but, if they are wrong, Jack will not only gain the points relevant to the stage at which he is denounced but they deny themselves a possible bonus on the twenty-first question. Dare they denounce?

3 Proverbs

A great family favourite and fun to play as a team game, though the concept is easier to explain in terms of a one-to-one contest between Jack and Jill.

Jack has thought of the proverb, TOO MANY COOKS SPOIL THE BROTH, and Jill has the task of discovering it. Jack tells her that there are six words in his proverb but, beyond that, he gives no information. Jill will now ask him six questions and Jack will include each word of his proverb in turn in each answer. For example:

Jill: Have you ever worn purple braces?

Jack: Only TOO often, I'm afraid, but I prefer blue ones.

Jill: Why are you so offensive to Mother?

Jack: I've told you MANY times that she annoys me by putting mothballs in my coffee.

Jill: Will you give me a sensible answer next time?

Jack: Sweetheart, your mother COOKS up the wildest tales about me and you believe her. But, yes, I will give you a sensible answer next time.

Jill: What is six times seven?

Jack: Forty-two, I think. But I won't SPOIL things by saying anything silly.

Jill: Do you like Felicity's new hair-do?

Jack: Not as much as THE old one.

Jill: Do you like my new hair-do?

Jack: I don't think that you'd consider me a fine BROTH of a boy if I didn't tell you . . .

Jill: Too many cooks spoil the broth!

As will be seen from the above exchanges, some words are much easier to disguise than others and this is where both tact and tactics come into play when the game is played in its traditional form as a contest between teams.

Jill is a great player of word games but Felicity is not and Mother is about average. In a team contest with the men versus the women Jill is the natural leader of her side and so she contrives to give Felicity the easiest words to answer, Mother the average words, whilst she tackles the most difficult words herself. This is not always possible as one usually arranges for each person to answer in turn and normally goes around the team in a natural clockwise sequence. Suppose that the women select the proverb PEOPLE IN GLASSHOUSES SHOULDN'T THROW STONES, and the three of them are seated Mother, Jill, Felicity. Felicity is the problem and a word like GLASSHOUSES would give her the vapours. Unfortunately, both she and GLASSHOUSES fall into the third position, and to compound the problem she would also have to cope with the last word, STONES, when each of the women face a second question.

If Felicity is honest about her shortcomings the women could always change places but, apart from anything else, the men would know immediately that Felicity has all the easy words such as AND or THE and so concentrate more upon the answers of Mother and, especially, Jill. The best tactics and the most tactful way (Felicity may not think that she is stupid) is for Jill to take the first question from the men and so have

Jill:	PEOPLE
Felicity:	IN
Mother:	GLASSHOUSES
Jill:	SHOULDN'T
Felicity:	THROW
Mother:	STONES

When it is the women's turn to ask the questions Jill is very likely to be faced with the problem that Felicity will not know what to say. With every question in the world possible, people still freeze up in this situation. Again, players take turns in asking the questions so how does Jill cope?

Before the questioning begins, Jill confides to both Mother and Felicity a 'ploy'. 'One of the cleverest questions one can ask', says Jill, 'is the same question that someone else has just asked. That always baffles them.' What Jill is *really* saying is, 'Felicity dear, if you can't think of what to ask, just say the same as me.'

The teams may either take turns to choose a proverb or

else the winning side continues to choose proverbs until defeated.

As there are both well-known and obscure proverbs available so it is up to the teams to choose as they wish. Do not, however, be pedantic and insist that those guessing must render a word-for-word accuracy. If they can produce the general sense including the significant words, that is fair enough. In any event, who is to say that the proverb beginning, PEOPLE WHO LIVE IN GLASSHOUSES, etc. should not be THOSE WHO DWELL IN GLASSHOUSES, etc. or any other, similar, phrasing which this proverb can and does take. The same is true for many of the others.

4 Botticelli

A player chooses a famous person, living or dead, fact or fiction, and gives the initial letter of the subject's surname. Let us suppose that Granny selects William Shakespeare.

Having only an s on which to base their strategy, everyone else now asks indirect questions:

Jack: Are you a famous composer?
Granny: No, I am not Schubert.
Jill: Are you a famous actress?
Granny: No, I am not Sarah Siddons.
Mother: Are you a famous writer?
Granny: Yes, but I am not Shaw.

Jack, Jill and Mother could continue this elimination process even further by asking if the person is a poet or a playwright but, as yet, may not ask such direct questions as 'Are you a man?' or 'Are you still alive?' One of these may only be asked once Granny fails to produce a suitable name in any particular category. Hence:

Jill:	Are you a famous pop star?
Granny:	(says nothing)
Jill:	Are you still living?
Granny:	No.
Jack:	Are you a famous footballer?
Granny:	(says nothing)
Jack:	Did you once live in Stratford-upon-Avon?

And now the game is won. But Granny got her revenge later.

Again she chose an s and it was ages before anyone discovered that it was an English king. Even then they had to give up as she was the only person who knew that Edward VII had the surname Saxe-Coburg-Gotha!

5 Good and Bad

Jack has selected a letter of the alphabet. Mother, Father, Jill and Felicity are attempting to find which letter it is. Jack now asks each person a question in turn, replying to the answer with the word 'good' if it contains his letter and 'bad' if it does not. It is a contest amongst the four being questioned to see who first discovers the significant letter. They either answer a question sensibly with a single word or else state what they think the letter is – however, if they guess incorrectly they are eliminated. A sample game with

R as Jack's choice could proceed as follows:

Jack:	What did Granny give you for Christmas?
Jill:	Perfume.
Jack:	Good.

Jack:	What did you have for breakfast?
Felicity:	Muesli.
Jack:	Bad.

Jack:	Give me a word which describes Jill.
Father:	Precocious.
Jack:	Brilliant . . . er, I mean good.

Jack:	Who is your favourite Shakespearian character?
Jill:	Portia.
Jack:	Good.

Jack:	Where would you like to go on holiday this year?
Jill:	Portugal . . . and you're paying!
Jack:	My share, sweetheart, my share . . . but good.
Jack:	How old are you?
Felicity:	The letter P.

Felicity drops out. Both Jill and Mother now know the answer, but will Father get it first?

6 Questions and Commands

This game is probably as old as Crambo and is recorded in literary works dating back to 1673. Very little is known about it other than that it seemed already then to have enjoyed a life of over a hundred years; that one person was the 'king' of a session of the game; that kissing came into it in some form; and it appeared to consist of one person addressing ludicrous questions and commands to each member of the company.

A modern equivalent might be a combination of the Yes/No challenge which the Canadian Michael Miles introduced to British television back in the 1950s and the imposition of forfeits on those people who fail to stand up to the 'king' for 60 seconds of this activity.

The Yes/No challenge only works well when one member of the group of games players is outstandingly dominant in mental agility and verbal dexterity and is, in effect, the 'king'. If you have such a 'king' then this is the game.

Each person in turn has to face a barrage of quickfire questions to which he or she may *not* answer 'Yes' or 'No', or nod or shake his or her head, and must reply immediately. Any breach of these rules during the 60 seconds of interrogation by the 'king' results in the paying of a forfeit. In addition to the 'king', a timekeeper and a referee are needed. For the sake of illustration let us assume the referee has a gong which he bangs once a player falls victim to the 'king'.

King:	What is your name?
Contestant:	Felicity.
King:	Felicity?

Contestant:	Yes.
	BONG!

King:	What is your name?
Contestant:	Jill.
King:	Jill?
Contestant:	It is.
King:	I like your dress.
Contestant:	Thank you.
King:	Did you buy it at Top Shop?
Contestant:	I did not.
King:	You nodded your head then.
Contestant:	I doubt it.
King:	Not Top Shop?
Contestant:	Correct.
King:	Where?
Contestant:	I made it myself.
King:	You did?
Contestant:	I did.
	etc.

The successful merely bask in their own glory but the victims have to pay their forfeits and the following are, despite appearances to the contrary, not only socially acceptable but also exceedingly simple. The first one is a very old test of nerve – could it be as old as the original Questions and Commands?

1 Kiss four bare legs and one bare bottom.
2 Kiss the ugliest person in the room.
3 Bite an inch off the end of that teddy bear's nose.
4 Jump higher than the table.

5   Recite a nursery rhyme whilst standing on your head.

6   Throw this brick through the window.

7   Knock back half a bottle of whisky in one go.

8   Put a match to Mother's new curtains.

9   Display unbridled lust.

10 Remove all of your clothes.

11 Spit on the carpet.

12 Wash the pots.

How are these done?

1   Kiss the legs and the bottom of a chair.

2   Tactfully, kiss the back of your own hand.

3   Make a biting motion an inch *away* from the end of the teddy bear's nose.

4   Merely jump – the table cannot.

5   Simply say, 'A nursery rhyme whilst standing on your head.'

6   Open the window first!

7   Tap the bottle so that it moves backwards.

8   Merely put a matchstick against the curtains – you don't have to light it.

9   Open the book at this page and display the following words – UNBRIDLED LUST.

10 Walk out of the room – you take your clothes with you!

11 A spit is a sword, it is also a type of cooking implement and the same word also once described a straight horizontal mark used as a sign in a book. If you can obtain any of these simply put one of them on the carpet.

12 A *real* forfeit – wash the pots!

7 Stoppard's Questions

The first professional performance of Tom Stoppard's *Rosencrantz and Guildenstern Are Dead* was given at the Old Vic Theatre, London, by the National Theatre Company on 11 April 1967, and the work contains a classic sequence of word play. This word play is similar to the Yes/No aspect of Questions and Commands discussed above except that instead of one person trying to trick another, both are trying to trick each other.

The game is simply to answer a question with a question, and failure to do this results in a point being given away, the first to get three points wins.

The rules, as revealed in this sequence of witty dialogue, are

(a) No repetitions.

(b) No grunts such as a questioning exclamation like 'Heh?'

(c) No synonyms. The question in reply must not be the equivalent of a repetition.

(d) No rhetoric.

(e) No non sequiturs.

However, played as a game, the rules are essentially what you make them.

8 Spellbound

Spelling competitions were once quite popular, especially in Victorian times when Spelling Bees (as these contests are called) were a common public diversion.

If a simple spelling test does not appeal to you and, let's face it, they are a bit boring, try a similar challenge – spelling ordinary everyday words *backwards*.

Providing that you allow no hesitation or corrections of spelling, and insist upon a reply the moment the word has been given, even the family's acknowledged expert on spelling can fail with the simplest of words.

Play it as a team game on an elimination basis, with teams taking turns to test each other. The final player left unbeaten wins on behalf of the team. There are two different fun ways of organizing the contest, both of which are fair and involve no tedious delays.

(a) Open up any book or newspaper and whoever is testing each member of the opposing team merely states words in the order of occurrence on the page. Some will get easy words, some will get difficult words but, most importantly, an instant spelling check is to hand. Obviously, the 1-letter, 2-letter and 3-letter words are ignored.

(b) Begin with 4-letter words and ignore all others for that round. The next round is 5-letter words. All subsequent rounds are more than five. To try and find 6-letter and 7-letter words etc. in sequence is both time-consuming and boring. The categories of 4-letter, 5-letter and more than 5 are easy to recognize.

If the game is to be played as a formal competition rather like a Victorian Spelling Bee then the organizer should acquire one of the various crossword-solving books which list words in alphabetical order by numbers of letters. Under these circumstances a completely fair 4-letter, 5-letter, 6-letter, 7-letter, etc. sequence of tests can be conducted with the minimum of difficulty.

9 Bee Team

A team spelling contest played for points. Long or tricky words such as PARALLELOGRAM or YACHT are selected. Any ordinary words will do, providing that they are likely to cause problems. In fact, a team can object to a word if they have never heard of it.

Each member of the team being challenged has to give a letter in turn. Thus, with a three person team and a word such as PARALLELOGRAM the first player says 'P', the second 'A', the third 'R', the first now has to give the fourth letter (A), the second has to give the fifth letter (L) and so on until the word is either correctly spelt for one point; or an error, a hesitation or a change of mind gives the point away to the opposing side. Select an umpire who has a dictionary handy.

10 Junior Bee Team

The same game as Bee Team except that a different physical action or a different number is substituted for each of the five vowels. Easy words are chosen and the children have to, in the case of numbers, say 'One' if the letter is an A, 'Two' for an E, 'Three' for an I, 'Four' for O, 'Five' for U. The fun lies in the confusion, especially if you have them performing silly actions for the vowels.

11 Horace's Cat

A children's game but fun for all. Everyone knows someone who owns a cat and that owner's name is chosen for the purpose of the action. For the sake of illustration assume that everyone knows Horace and knows that he has a cat. It is a team contest with each member of a team coming under the spotlight in turn.

One team fires questions at the youngster in the spotlight and he or she has a minute in which to survive the interrogation without making an error, hesitating or changing his or her mind. With success, a point is scored for his or her team, failure gives the point away.

Any questions are asked, without bothering to take turns, but only four answers are given:

1   If the answer to a question concerns any person or any creature the reply is *always* 'Horace's cat'. For example:
    'Who is the President of the USA?'

'Horace's cat.'

'Who did you kiss last night?'

'Horace's cat.'

2 If the answer is 'No', the reply is *always* 'Yes'.

3 If the answer is 'Yes', the reply is *always* 'No'.

4 The answer to *everything else* is 'Cucumbers'.

The faster the questions are asked, the more likely the youngster is to be caught out. And a team that wastes time arguing over a matter of opinion: – 'Are you stupid?' 'Are you pretty?' – the less chance they have of catching a player over a point of accepted fact – 'Is Washington the capital of the USA?' – as they only have one minute.

12 Horace's Kitten

The kiddywinkies' version of Horace's Cat. The answer to *every* question is 'cucumbers' or any other word that is liable to make them giggle. If the child in the one-minute spotlight laughs, giggles, smiles, or has anything but a completely straight face he or she loses. For extra fun have a gong handy for striking on failure.

13 Spell it Out

A word-recognition game ideal for any category of player according to the degree of difficulty employed. At the childish/Simple Simon level one uses 'easy' words, whereas a pair of wordsmiths can give each other all manner of horrors. Hence, two descriptions.

(a) The Good Fairy has prepared a list of longish 'ordinary' words and challenges two teams of players to defeat each other in a competition which has her using the blackboard or any similar large scale display. She has, say, the word PRINCESS in mind and announces the total number of letters in that word (8). She writes its *first* letter (P) on the blackboard. She now asks one of the team to state whether the *next* is one of the following three possibilities:

1   The same – in other words, could the word possibly begin with PP?
2   Lower – could the letter be an A or an E or, perhaps, an L, all of which precede P in alphabetical order?
3   Higher – is it such as an R or a U, coming *after* P in the alphabet.

Once one team has made its collective decision, she asks the same question of the other and, after she has written R after the P, awards a point to whichever team gave the correct answer. The Good Fairy can always appoint a 'spokeschild' for each team if she considers it desirable or else ask each kiddywinkie (or simple one) to take turns in answering. Good Fairies know how to organize things so that all enjoy the fray.

(b) In a face-to-face encounter between two wordsmiths ingenuity is the order of the day. Q-without-a-following-U words are an obvious category – CINQFOIL, QADISTU and QARAQALPAQ are typical examples. But, how about such as AARDVARK or even AEGILOPS?

AEGILOPS, which is the longest-known alphone, has a variety of meanings any one of which has a potential as a mnemonic; it is a species of oak tree, tallest of those native to Greece; an ulcer in the inner angle of the eye; and (now considered obsolete) the wild oat or other weed of a corn-field.

Other long alphomes are such as BEEFILY and BILLOWY but, just as likely to frustrate an opponent, are the 'reverse alphomes' such as TROLLIED and SPOONFED.

Players who wish to extent validity beyond the limits ascribed to the saintly Bishop Aldhelm have with POTOOOOOOOO (pronounced 'pot eight Os') the personal name of an eighteenth-century racehorse about which little else is known.

14 Cut it Out

A competition for a children's party – and variations on this theme for adults as well as children.

The organizer chooses a dozen newspaper advertisements for well-known brands. These are removed from the newspaper and the brand names cut out.

The advertisements are mounted on card and each is numbered, before they are placed around the room in a random order.

There are various options now available.

(a) A simple contest to see who can get the most brand names correct. Answers being written on paper.

(b) Two sets of the twelve brand names are written on stiff card. One is in the possession of, say, the hostess and the other of the host. The two are widely separated but adjacent to tables or other clear surfaces.

The children are divided into teams – say, boys versus girls. After they have had time to study the adverts, the competitors are called to their corners: the girls to the hostess, the boys to the host.

The task is to see which team gets all twelve names in the correct numerical sequence first.

(c) The, say, boys' team have to name all twelve in the correct order. They call the answers from the positions where the advertisements are sited. They are allowed a limited number of guesses according to the way you wish to play it.

You may, for example, split them into pairs and have pairs standing by each advertisement and permit them just one guess, recording the results without comment.

A second way of doing it is to have a relay: each boy in turn dashes from the starting position and finds his assigned number and is permitted up to three guesses (3 points for a correct reply on the first guess, 2 points for the second, 1 point for the third). Under this option, you have two further choices. Either a fresh set of advertisements for the girls or

else, say, boys have odd numbers and girls have even
numbers.

Essentially, the options are governed by circumstances.
Such as numbers participating and how suitable the location for children to run around. You could easily turn the
above into four different games, depending upon how
much advance planning you care to undertake. One subject
could be adverts. Another, photographs of pop stars taken
from a specialist fan magazine. A third might even be pictures of Rupert the Bear and the like. (This would be
perfect for adults if you decided to play one of these
options at a party for grown-ups!) Choose any subject
which you think will appeal and give each game a different
name such as 'Adverts', 'Pop Stars' or whatever.

For older children and/or adults option (b) can be converted into a true word game. This time picture number 4
has to be identified not as RUPERT THE BEAR but an anagram
such as PETER A. R. HUBERT which is written on a *separate*
answer-card.

The anagram version of Option (b) can be made even
more devilish, if you wish. Suppose that the subject is
adverts and PERSIL washing powder is one of the items to be
discerned. Apart from making its anagram (select from
LISPER, PERILS, PILERS, PLIERS or PRILES) available on a card
also have some red herrings, other powder names such as
MOO (Omo), DIET (Tide), or ADZ (Daz) shuffled amongst the
cards, and you will be able to slip away for a quiet cup of
coffee that has been very well earned. Six games for the
price of your time and ingenuity.

15 Dutch Auction

A quiz on the meanings of words but with a delightful difference – everybody knows the word but few, if any, know the meanings. For example: 'The word I have chosen has five letters and begins with the letter A. I'll award you 10 points if you can tell me what it is. It means a large size of drawing paper.'

Assuming no one volunteers an answer, a second clue is given. 'For 9 points, I can tell you that the same word also means the bone which supports the skull.'

Still no takers. '8 points. It is also an Eastern silk-satin.'

The company is still baffled. '7 points. This word is a verb which means to carry on one's shoulders.'

Perhaps someone now has a glimmer of an idea but is keeping quiet. '6 points. Its other meaning as a verb is to prop up.'

'5 points. The name of a god.'

'4 points. A range of mountains in North Africa.'

'3 points. A book of maps.'

If the company still has no idea, then you reveal the remaining letters one at a time. A total of twelve clues before the final letter of ATLAS is exposed.

That presentation is easily achieved by any quiz master. However, if you have a natural flair for anagrams then, for ATLAS, a first clue could be: 'Sat oddly around the French for a large size of drawing paper.'

Easier ones could be:

'Salt a palindrome for a large size of drawing paper.'

'A last anagram describes a large size of drawing paper.'

Many words in the dictionary have more than one

meaning – SET, for example, has the greatest number of meanings of any word in the *OED* – so, merely look for a lengthy dictionary entry and the chances are that you will find a word eminently suitable for this game. It is therefore comparatively easy for anyone to be the quiz master and produce at least ten clues which get progressively easier.

Limit clues to ten. The game can be an individual or team contest according to the number present. Twelve participants being, say, four teams of three people. Alternatively, if you have a large crowd in a hall, teams select their own representatives. You can limit individuals or teams to just one guess so that once a wrong guess is given they are eliminated.

Once you are down to the easy clues you can say such as: 'This next clue is worth 4 points. Who wishes to give an answer?'

You now consider only those people prepared to risk elimination on the unknown. No volunteers, so do not pose that easy question, instead say: 'This clue is even easier than the last one would have been. Are there any volunteers for 3 points?'

If there are still no takers you can, if you wish, bring back into the game any person or team frozen out for a previous wrong guess. Surely someone is going to risk being eliminated on the 2 points question? Admittedly, everyone is baffled as you have been giving them the most peculiar definitions but there has to be a brave soul somewhere. If not, make a final statement: 'This final clue is the easiest of the lot. One point for anyone prepared to have a go and guess it correctly. Minus one point for anyone who is wrong.'

This is necessary otherwise everyone will shout at once as they cannot lose anyway.

16 Who's Who

A game of skill and fun for three or four players, all of whom possess not only a good general knowledge but are experienced games players. Who's Who has a wickedly unique tactical aspect which puts it, in deduction games, in a class by itself.

Players establish a rota which they maintain through the whole session. With four players numbered 1, 2, 3 and 4 this means that if, say, player number 3 takes the first turn to set a challenge for the others, then the order of questioning will be players 4, 1, 2, 4, 1, 2, etc. By adhering to a strict rota and with each player taking his or her turn to set the challenge so all have an equal opportunity of winning the whole, points-based contest.

The person who will set the challenge (hereafter called the tester) has no vested interest in deception but the remaining players (the questioners) are the ones who need to employ subtle tactics. The tester has nothing to gain, the questioners are battling for the point awarded to the one who wins the particular round. A sample game with Granny as the tester has Tom, Dick and Harriet as the questioners.

Granny has chosen a famous person who may be living or dead, male or female, fact or fiction. Tom, Dick and Harriet may ask any questions they wish providing that Granny can give a simple Yes or No answer. She may at times be forced to say such as 'Don't know', or 'Probably', but her fellow competitors are no longer the grandchildren of the days when they played I Spy, and they respect her encyclopaedic knowledge which makes her such a devastating opponent in any game of this type.

Now for the subtle part.

Any player may ask as many questions as he or she wishes in any one particular turn. But, having asked a question, that player may no longer guess at the identity. A player may *either* question at any length or else make a single guess.

In this sample game the rota is Tom first, then Dick, and finally Harriet.

Tom:	Is this person fictional?
Granny:	No.
Tom:	Female?
Granny:	No.
Tom:	British?
Granny:	Yes.
Tom:	Living?
Granny:	No.
Tom:	Alive this century?
Granny:	No.
Tom:	After 1066?
Granny:	Yes.
Tom:	Before 1800?
Granny:	Yes.
Tom:	Sixteenth century?
Granny:	Yes.
Tom:	Royal?
Granny:	Yes.

Tom considers the possibilities. Very likely to be a king, most probably Henry VIII. But could be Henry VII, Edward VI or even James I (who ascended the English throne in the seventeenth century (1603) but was alive in the sixteenth century, apart from being James VI of Scotland during that time). Should he eliminate still further? Or should he pass? He decides to pass.

Dick also thinks that Granny has chosen a king. He decides to test this in a subtle way which, simultaneously, eliminates the boy king, Edward VI.

Dick: Was this person's father a monarch?
Granny: Yes.
Dick: Did this person father a monarch?
Granny: Yes.

Dick dare not eliminate any further as both Harriet and Tom now have the opportunities of guessing before he does. Dick passes.

Harriet, equally versed in the history of the period and equally certain that it is a king, must either make a guess at the three remaining logical choices . . . or is Charles I still possible? In which century was he born? Sixteenth? Seventeenth? Granny would know. Harriet understood Dick's ploy but can she contrive one which will eliminate the most obvious monarch, Henry VIII? Only a fool would ask if he had six wives and Harriet is no fool. But Granny is very well read. Guess or eliminate? Harriet gambles on an eliminator.

Harriet: Did this person marry a lady with three thumbs?

Granny: Yes.

Harriet passes. She knows for certain that it is Henry VIII (the lady being Anne Boleyn) but will Tom or Dick pick up the clue? Whatever happens she knows that Granny will be the major rival in the whole contest as none of them dare select pop stars when Granny is around. Fred Astaire or Ginger Rogers by all means – but a Sex Pistol, never! The days when she allowed them to win in the nursery have long since passed. When Granny plays, she makes the rules. Only the fourth generation, when it competes with Granny, is permitted to tamper with established practice.

17 Kolodny's Game

A very bizarre game. One person decides upon a rule. Everyone now questions him, asking anything they wish. Whatever he is asked, he will answer only with a Yes or a No. Yes, if the question complies with his secret rule. No, if it does not. The task is to discover that secret rule.

The rule can be anything. For example:

(a) If the first word of the question begins with a vowel the answer is 'Yes'.

(b) If the questioner is female the answer is 'Yes'.

(c) Every third question is answered 'Yes'.

(d) Every question containing the word 'you' is answered 'Yes'.

(e) Every question which I answer when rubbing my chin is answered 'Yes'.

There is no need to take strict turns in posing questions – some people kill games by being slow-witted over such a simple task as thinking of a question to ask – but the skill lies in seeing a pattern then posing a question which complies with it. If the answer to that considered question is 'No' then some other rule must apply. As with all games, some people never understand them and much of the fun will arise from a sequence such as this:

Miss Brown: Have you ever been unfaithful to your wife?

Mr Smith: Yes.

Mrs Smith: Henry!

18 Lexiconnery

There is no such word as 'Lexiconnery', but it sounds as though it might be real. In the context of this game it can be defined as the art of creating a word which others can be duped into believing is true.

Do any of the following terms sound genuine?

AMSTERDAMP: A wet odorous smog peculiar to the industrial region of Amsterdam.

BEDSISTER: A mistress or concubine viewed in relationship to a man's lawful wife.

RANGOONERY: Burmese politics.

As it happens, one of them is. But, which one?

Two teams challenge each other, on a points basis, to state which of the above are true and which are false. Unfortunately, it does require research to provide a correct blend of true and false words but teams prepared to undertake this task can lay the foundations for a fun session.

One member of a team scours the dictionary for a word or compound such as GREGORIAN TREE which is a genuine name for a gallows whilst another coins a term such as GRILL SERGEANT for defining as 'the NCO in charge of the cookhouse'.

The format can vary according to circumstances and at, say, a large gathering of merry-making adults, forfeits can be introduced for anyone who was 'lexiconned'. In this company (as opposed to a serious contest between two small teams of sober wordsmiths) the organizer has a prepared list of words and definitions and invites members of the 'audience' to score, say, ten out of ten for a prize or else pay a forfeit on failure. For extra fun a gong is handy, which the assistant strikes as soon as a mistake is made.

The genuine word is BEDSISTER, the others are pure nonsense.

THE
VERBAL TENNIS
SERIES

The Verbal Tennis Series

Three games of which only the third is suitable for children even though it is essentially an adult game.

1 Wimbledon

A subject such as Countries, Cities, Boys' names, Girls' names, Animals, Birds, 2-Letter words valid for Scrabble, or whatever, is chosen and the first player begins by naming any relevant word within that category. The second player has to reply with an equally valid word but one which begins with the last letter of the one just given. A verbal tennis match ensues until a player is unable to respond, makes an error or repeats a word already used. With Animals as the subject a typical exchange could go as follows –

Jack: DOG.
Jill: GIRAFFE.
Jack: ELEPHANT.
Jill: TITMOUSE.
Jack: EARTHWORM.

> *Jill:* MOOSE.
> *Jack:* EYRA.
> *Jill:* ADDAX.

– with Jill winning this particular rally as Jack is unable to think of an animal beginning with the letter X.

This small exchange illustrates three of the skill factors in the game. In each of Jill's replies she has chosen animals which end with an E. This pressurizes her opponent and could easily trap him into repeating himself or make his mind go blank. The choice of GIRAFFE could have led to the simple error of Jack replying with a word beginning with an F, though such an error is more likely at a later stage in a rally. Finally, she played the killer stroke of a word ending with an X.

The X factor is one of the great tactical ploys in this super game. Players, *who must reply within an agreed time limit*, have to beware of saying something like WOLF (FOX is the killer reply) or POTTO (OX) as well as trying to force such errors themselves.

Obviously the first rule is that one cannot begin a rally with a word ending X and the other rules are:

(b) No word may be repeated in a rally.

(c) Each word must be acceptable. In the above example, had Jill disputed EYRA and no dictionary been available to confirm that it is a South American wild cat, Jack would have been forced to give another word in its place. Had Jack replied to Jill's ADDAX with XIPH or XENOPUS then these could be disallowed as the former is an obsolete name for a swordfish and the latter a technical term for a genus of frogs. It is wise to establish ground rules in advance as, for example, with Countries being the subject of a rally many players will say 'Africa' when called upon to name a *country* beginning with an 'A'!

The game is normally played over a number of rallies with the server nominating a different subject each time and players taking turns to serve. With four people it can be a verbal tennis doubles and with three people upwards it can be played on a round robin basis eliminating one person each time.

2 No!

A Wimbledon-type game, only this time a 2-letter word is selected and players have to supply words which begin and end with the same letters as that original word. There are no category limitations but players obviously cannot repeat words, take too long to reply or make errors. Some of the 2-letter words can produce long rallies but a word like NO will quickly end after

Jack: NUNCIO.
Jill: NEO.
Jack: NEGRO.
Jill: NELUMBO.
Jack: NERO.
Jill: NATO.

Jack: NIELLO.

Jill: NOVELLO.

has produced disputes galore. Is NATO a real word? Can you believe that NELUMBO is a genus of water lilies? Isn't NEO merely a prefix not a genuine word? Do we allow surnames such as NOVELLO?

(For a selection of 2-letter words see the Miniglossary, page 449.)

3 Ivan the Terrible

A third form of verbal tennis. Any category is chosen and the name of a famous European monarch is selected as the skeletal framework for play. Suppose that players have to provide the names of cities which begin with, say, each letter of IVAN THE TERRIBLE. The rally ends either with failure during play or by being able to provide the last word. Both the long name and/or the subject can be changed at the commencement of each rally. To end the monarch's name successfully results in a tie but most rallies will break down at some stage, especially if you have a reasonable time limit for replies.

A sample exchange with cities as the subject and IVAN THE TERRIBLE as the basis might proceed as follows:

Jack: ISTANBUL.

Jill: VENICE.

Jack: ANTWERP.

Jill: NICE.

Jack: TURIN.

Jill: HAMBURG.

Jack: EDINBURGH.

Jill: TORONTO.

Jack: EXETER.

Jill: ROME.

Jack: RANGOON.

Jill: ISTANBUL.

Jack: *Challenge!*

Jack wins on the basis of Jill's repetition and so avoids not only a tied game but the prospect of having to think of a third city beginning with the letter E.

(For a selection of European monarchs see page 447.)

THE
LOGOMOTION
SERIES

The Logomotion Series

There are eight games in this series, all of which are based on the principle of logical word association. The children's games are numbers 2 and 3.

Essentially, one will be going on verbal journeys such as from FATHER to SON. A suffix is added to FATHER to make, for instance, FATHERHOOD, FATHERLESS, FATHER FIGURE, FATHERLAND, FATHER THAMES, FATHER BROWN, FATHER TIME, etc. The suffix *must* be a genuine word. The following examples all lead, perfectly logically, from FATHER to SON. Note especially the word OUT. This is one of a number of keywords which are essential ingredients of viability and will be discussed below.

FATHER FIGURE	FATHER TIME
FIGURE OUT	TIME OUT
OUTACT	OUTACT
ACT ONE	ACT ONE
ONE STEP	ONE STEP
STEPSON	STEPSON

FATHERLAND	FATHERLESS
LANDFALL	LESSON
FALLOUT	ONGOING
OUTACT	GOING OUT
ACT ONE	OUTACT
ONE STEP	ACT ONE
STEPSON	ONE STEP
	STEPSON

As many of these games will depend upon the ability to reach a particular destination so the destination needs to be chosen with care.

However, if you can see that this particular destination can be reached from any one of four highly flexible key-words, IN, OFF, OUT or UP, you can almost take it for granted that you can reach that destination from any word you choose.

Thus, knowing that SON can be traced *back* to OUT you can then choose any starting word.

The reverse is not the same. The fact that FATHER leads to OUT does not mean that FATHER can lead to any word you choose. If, say, you wish to go from FATHER to MOTHER you need to be certain that MOTHER can be reached from IN, OFF, OUT or UP.

Therefore, can such as GRANDMOTHER or DEN MOTHER be traced back to one of these keywords? If you cannot see this happening (unless, of course, you tried STEPMOTHER which has the same progression as STEPSON) forget MOTHER as the destination.

The simplest way is to take any of the, say, 'OUT' words, trace it *forwards* for a few words until you reach a word which appeals to your taste. That word is a proven destination. Now add any starting word and you are assured of success. For example:

    OUTBACK – DROP – OFF – SIDE – LINE – UP –
    OUTBACK – OFF – GUARD – DOG – WATCH – OUT –
    OUTBACK – COMB – OUT – LET – OFF – LOAD –
    OUTBACK – FIRE – WORK – OUT – RUN – DOWN –
    OUTBACK – SPACE – OUT – WORK – MAN – FRIDAY –

Now you are certain of reaching any of these words. You can, for the first game discussed below, easily go BACK to BACK, SIDE to SIDE, ROOM to ROOM, MAN to MAN, or, for other games, FRONT to BACK, BOY to MAN, WOMAN to MAN, or any other combination which appeals.

Note that correct spelling, not similarity of sound, is the rule concerning continuation. Also note that O is a genuine word in its own right, and that suffixes such as **-ful** are invalid (it is not a word) whereas **full** is perfectly acceptable. This also means that WIND can take either pronunciation in the same sequence – DOWNWIND WIND DOWN.

1 Back to Back

A two-person game in which you try to repeat the chosen word. Select any word which appeals and is known to be attainable from a keyword. For example, BACK. Make BACK the first element in a compound word or logical two-word phrase such as BACKACHE, BACKBENCHER, BACKBITE, BACK-BONE, BACKBREAKER, BACKCHAT, etc . . . the game is to take turns with your opponent to create equally valid words or phrases from each second element of the word in play. If BACKBONE had been chosen, then the next word or phrase could be such as BONE CHINA, BONE DRY or BONE UP. The winner will be the first person who can get back to BACK in such forms as DRAWBACK, HALF BACK or SETBACK.

Jack: BACK DOOR.
Jill: DOORMAN.
Jack: MANCHESTER.
Jill: CHESTERFIELD.
Jack: FIELD WORK.
Jill: WORKMAN.
Jack: MANDATE.
Jill: DATE PALM.
Jack: PALM SUNDAY.
Jill: SUNDAY SCHOOL.
Jack: SCHOOL WORK.
Jill: WORK OUT.
Jack: OUTBACK!

Jack wins. However, not all games proceed as smoothly. For example:

Jack: BACK DOOR.
Jill: DOORMAN.
Jack: MANIPULATION.
Jill: ???

'Ipulation'? Jill now challenges Jack to produce a word or phrase which begins with this element. If Jack succeeds then he wins the game – providing that he produces a compound word or phrase capable of normal continuation.

Similarly with the sequence:

Jack: BACK DOOR.
Jill: DOORMAN.
Jack: MANCHESTER.
Jill: CHESTERFIELD.
Jack: FIELD???

Jill gives him reasonable thinking time, then states that she has assumed a challenge as he could have said such as FIELD DAY, FIELD EVENT, FIELDMOUSE, etc. and so she wins that particular contest.

But, suppose that the following happened:

Jack: BACK DOOR.
Jill: DOORMAN.
Jack: MANCHESTER.
Jill: CHESTER-DRAWS (chest of drawers).

Jack can either laugh it off and continue with such as DRAWS IN, DRAWS OUT, DRAWS UP, etc. or else insist that Jill produce a reasonable reply within the agreed time limit.

Jill, by giving an answer of sorts, has forfeited the right to challenge his previous word, MANCHESTER. Jack does not have to prove that MANCHESTER is capable of continuation under the circumstances. She must answer sensibly or else he wins.

2 Fore and Aft

A children's quiz. The leader selects words and awards points to the child who can make pairings both fore and/or aft of the given word as:

bank ACCOUNT, ACCOUNT book
sulphuric ACID, ACID test
first ACT, ACT out

3 Fore and After

A children's solo challenge. Any word is chosen and the child has to make the longest possible logical word chain in, say, 60 seconds. The winner is the one who makes the longest chain.

4 Back to Front

An adult's solo challenge. Logical or witty pairings are selected from consideration of a keyword and the contestant has to make the connection within, say, 60 seconds. Some will prove exceptionally simple such as

BACK to FRONT
BACK UP
UP FRONT

LEFT to RIGHT
LEFT OUT
OUTRIGHT

WORK to PLAY
WORKOUT
OUTPLAY

SCHOOL to COLLEGE
SCHOOL TIME
TIME LOST
LOST ART
ART COLLEGE

FULL to EMPTY
FULL MEASURE
MEASURE UP
UPRIGHT
RIGHT HALF
HALF EMPTY

BLACK to WHITE
BLACK OUT
OUTBREAK
BREAK OFF
OFF WHITE

HOT to COLD
HOT SPRING
SPRING OUT
OUTGROW
GROW COLD

PLAIN to COLOUR
PLAIN SPEAKING
SPEAKING OUT
OUTFLOW
FLOW OFF
OFF COLOUR

LAND to SEA
LANDLINE
LINEAGE
AGE-LONG
LONG DEAD
DEAD SEA

Others will take a more complex route such as turning a FROG into a PRINCE but once these have been mastered then the 5 minutes super challenge can be undertaken. For example:

Name a complete pack of cards from ACE to TWO in order:

ACEROSE	CAR**JACK**	SEVENFOLD
ROSE-RED	JACKPOT	FOLD OUT
RED **KING**	POT ROAST	OUTSIZE
KENG HENRY	ROAST DUCK	SIZE **SIX**
HENRY COTTON	DUCK POND	SIXFOLD
COTTON MILL	PONDAGE	FOLD UP
MILL HAND	AGE **TEN**	UPWIND
HANDOUT	TENPIN	WINDAGE
OUTRIGHT	PINPOINT	AGE **FIVE**
RIGHT ROYAL	POINT **NINE**	FIVEPIN
ROYAL BLUE	NINETEEN	PIN-UP
BLUE MOVIE	TEENAGE	UPGRADE
MOVIE **QUEEN**	AGE **EIGHT**	GRADE **FOUR**
QUEEN BEE	EIGHTFOLD	FOUR-PART
BEEHIVE	FOLDER	PART **THREE**
HIVE OFF	ERGOT	THREESCORE
OFF HAND	GOT LUCKY	SCORE **TWO**!
HANDCAR	LUCKY **SEVEN**	

5 Back to Front Snooker

The basic Back to Back game with players making alternative statements, only this time you score points each time one of a particular group of words is mentioned. Suppose that you have 'colours' as the group and score points on the snooker basis of RED 1 point, YELLOW 2 points, GREEN 3 points, BROWN 4 points, BLUE 5 points, PINK 6 points and BLACK 7 points, with WHITE enabling you to have another turn. As with snooker once you mention a colour this allows you to continue the break, thus scoring twice for each colour mentioned. Choose a logical pairing, such as FROG to PRINCE, and see what happens:

> *Jack:* FROGMARCH.
>
> *Jill:* MARCH OFF.
>
> *Jack:* OFF WHITE. (Jack now goes again.)
>
> *Jack:* WHITE FLAG.
>
> *Jill:* FLAGSTONE.
>
> *Jack:* STONEWALL.
>
> *Jill:* WALLPAPER.
>
> *Jack:* PAPER TIGER.
>
> *Jill:* TIGER RAG.
>
> *Jack:* RAG MERCHANT.
>
> *Jill:* MERCHANT NAVY.
>
> *Jack:* NAVY BLUE. (Jack scores 5 points, goes again.)
>
> *Jack:* BLUE-BLACK. (Jack scores 12 points, goes again.)
>
> *Jack:* BLACK PRINCE. (Jack scores 7 points, game over.)

6 Outplay

Choose any logical pair of words as the basis of a verbal journey. At the same time select a particularly popular element of play such as the word OUT. The contest is not to finish the journey but to score a point each time you mention the word OUT. However, once you are ahead on points that is the time to try to end the game as you will then emerge the winner. In order to bring the game to such an advantageous conclusion choose an end to the journey with a word capable of being prefixed by such equally popular elements as IN, OFF or UP. Not that this is necessary but it does make a definite ending more likely in a game where the skills are directed towards forcing play in a different direction.

As with Back to Front Snooker it is essential that a player making a score must continue with the next statement otherwise no advantage can be gained. In the sample contest below, the chosen journey is from SCHOOL to MARKET, the scoring word is OUT and the rules are the same as those given in Back to Back, page 366.

Jack: SCHOOL TIME.
Jill: TIME OUT. (Jill scores 1 point for OUT.)
Jill: OUTCLASS. (Jill scores 1 point for OUT.)
Jack: CLASSWORK.
Jill: WORK OUT. (Jill scores 1 point for OUT.)
Jill: OUTFALL. (Jill scores 1 point for OUT.)
Jack: FALL OUT. (Jack scores 1 point for OUT.)
Jack: OUTCOME. (Jack scores 1 point for OUT.)
Jill: COME OUT. (Jill scores 1 point for OUT.)

Jill: OUTCOME.
Jack: Challenge!

The challenge is on the basis of repetition of the word OUTCOME as it is essential to avoid a stalemate situation of a permanent COME OUT/OUTCOME play. Jill must now give another word and forfeit all of her score. Whilst she loses these points, Jack does not gain them. Play continues:

Jill: OUTLET. (Jill scores 1 point for OUT.)
Jack: LET OUT. (Jack scores 1 point for OUT.)
Jack: OUTSIDE. (Jack scores 1 point for OUT.)
Jill: SIDEBOARD.
Jack: BOARD GAME.
Jill: GAME POINT.
Jack: POINT OUT. (Jack scores 1 point for OUT.)
Jack: OUTWIT. (Jack scores 1 point for OUT.)
Jill: WITTICISM.
Jack: Challenge!

And Jack wins the game by 6 points to 1 as Jill cannot provide a word beginning with TICISM.

Note how many times in the above exchanges the word UP could have featured, so producing the conclusion with the statement UP-MARKET. Jill could have said TIME UP, WORK UP, and COME UP. Jack could have said LET UP, BOARD UP, and POINT UP. Not that this particular ploy is essential but it does demonstrate how easy it is to ensure a definite ending.

7 Dropout

A round-robin Back to Front type game only it has no stated ending element. It is an elimination game played at speed with players dropping out for mentioning certain taboo words such as IN, OFF or OUT. A player must reply instantly and the usual challenge and validity rules apply (see Back to Front, page 369). To set the game in motion deliberately choose a combination such as COUGH DROP to which the unwary will say such as DROP IN, DROP OFF or DROPOUT, but the skilful will say DROPLET or DROPKICK so inveigling the next player into saying LET IN, LET OFF, LET OUT, or KICK IN, KICK OFF or KICK OUT.

Suitable starting combinations of this type include: ACID DROP, SIT BACK, LOW BLOW, LUNCH BREAK, DOWNCAST, BUILDING CONTRACT, WATERFALL, KEEP FIT, STEADY FLOW, EASYGOING, LEFT HAND, UNDERHAND, RANCH HAND, FORE-PLAY, BALLPOINT, FINE PRINT, OVERREACH, TURN RIGHT, LONG RUN, UNDERSELL, HALF SHARE, DEEP SLEEP, ASSORT, TIDY SPREAD, BEDSPREAD, BED SPRING, LONGSTANDING, LONG STAY, DOORSTEP, PRISON STRETCH, ASSET STRIP, OCEAN SWELL, UPSWING, GO THROUGH, UPTHROW, MARK TIME, TIP TOP, WRISTWATCH, MY WAY, MEN'S WEAR, WATERWEED, HOMEWORK.

8 Vowel Play

A Back to Front points-scoring game but without the double and triple goes essential to Outplay and Back to Front Snooker. The skill lies in avoiding the use of a second element beginning with a vowel as your opponent will automatically score with his or her next play. For example:

> *Jack:* DROPOUT.
> *Jill:* OUTCOME. (Jill scores 1 point.)

Choose any logical journey and have a bonus of 10 points for whoever can complete it. Impose a strict time limit so that it forces the opponent to say the first thing that comes into his head as

> *Jack:* (*thinking*) COME IN, COME OFF, COME OUT, COME UP . . .

having to choose between giving away another point or else surrendering the whole game and its 10 points.

THE
ALPHANUMERICAL
SERIES

The Alphanumerical Series

A long-established concept whereby the letters of the alphabet are accorded numerical 'values' according to the position they hold in the regular sequence: so that A = 1, B = 2, C = 3, etc. culminating in Z = 26. Other than the first game, all are appearing in print for the first time.

1 Solitaire

Discover the 'value' of a person by totalling his or her individual letter values. Grumpy, for example, is 7 + 18 + 21 + 13 + 16 + 25 = 100. Does anyone else total a hundred? If so, what conclusions do you wish to draw from that?

2 X Marks the Spot

X = 24. What geographical location also equals 24? That, in a nutshell, is the game. Snow White has thought of a word, say, TREASURE, which has a value of 107. She has set the Seven Dwarfs the task of discovering a geographical location with a matching value of 107. Sneezy is the first to announce success – DISNEYLAND!

Having found one cache of TREASURE, the little men wish to find more TREASURE somewhere else. Bashful wins this time – CHINATOWN.

Played at home you should rule that the *first* to produce a satisfactory answer is the winner. Instead of seeking TREASURE, you may care to set the company the task of discovering the 'ideal' place for a HOLIDAY (74) or a HONEYMOON (124) or whatever takes your fancy.

3 Battle Royal

Rommel is playing Cleopatra at a game of verbal aggression. Erwin Rommel selects the first subject – say, Military weapons. Now, both of them must think of a weapon, write it down and compute its value. They compare results and the one with the higher score is the winner. Next it will be Cleopatra's turn to select a subject and the game will last for however many 'battles' it was decided in advance to play. They play strictly to the Aldhelm Rules having single words only, no substantive phrases.

4 Grand Larceny

Al Capone has thought of a 'big word', CONURBATION, which he transposes as an alphome set, ABCINNOORTU, which, of course, retains its value of 132. His fellow inmates of Alcatraz are challenged to 'plunder' it *without using more than one of its constituent letters*. Thus, words such as CAB, INN, ROOT or RUT which are easily perceived as

380

aspects of the alphome set *cannot* be employed. Obviously, if Robert Stroud can come up with a word equal to 132 using all bar one of the alphome's letters he could take the lot! However, if we presume that he attempts to 'lift' the first four letters of the alphome, ABCI, he now has to produce a word of equal value, such as FED for 15. This leaves NNOORTU available for 'plunder' by the remaining inmates. There are various options now open. The most complicated of these has the company attempting to 'lift' the various letter sets from each other in an attempt to possess the full set, which now has to be rearranged into the original word, CONURBATION. A simpler version is to score points on letter values and the inmate with the highest total is the winner.

The rules are as devious as you care to make them.

5 Thorpe's Progression

Susan Thorpe has suggested the idea of players making increasingly progressive scores and, in consequence, I offer you the following possibility.

A subject is agreed – say, Birds, and a player choosing, say, DRAKE merely announces both its value (39) and its concluding letter (E). The opponent now has to produce a bird commencing with the letter E which scores *more* than 39! EAGLE (30) would be a loser but either EGRET (45) or the green woodpecker EQWAL (48) would keep the game alive until one of the players is forced to drop out.

GAMES OF THE
POSTSCRIPT

Even though new inventions of mine have featured in games previously recorded, each has been tested in play with various of my wordsmith chums who constitute **The Pears Word Games Society**; whereas all of the forthcoming games and series are, as yet, untested in 'combat'. Past experience suggests that, whilst they are practical possibilities, additional rules may be needed to cope with the unexpected. Therefore, feel free to rationalize wherever necessary in order to ensure fun within a framework of 'fair play'.

I will be pleased to hear from any reader who wishes to create his or her own informal grouping similar to my PWGS – calling it (say) 'The Old Hat Association' – I would point out that any such 'Old Hat' rules you devise do *not* constitute a share of my copyright in the Postscript concepts. But, should I incorporate any of your thoughts in any future editions of the **Mammoth** I will give you full credit in print.

I dedicate the Postscript Games to my family of games players – Maxwell Caulfield, Marcus Maclaine, Melanie Barton and Alexandra Lisa Newby – any one of whom normally destroys Daddy in play.

Organizing a Word-based Treasure Hunt

The best treasure hunts have competitors moving from point to point all the while seeking clues to the next destination. This exposition presumes the location to be a typical home and that the residents are willing to have the guests wandering abroad unsupervised. But, a similar hunt can be organized for the office, school, college or whatever.

First and foremost the clues *must* be the work of only one person, as both humour and style vary with individuals so that the contestants will be unfairly confused if, after having mastered the initial techniques, they face clues set by another. If, as is highly possible in the majority of games of this nature, the husband and wife collaborate on the venture then the *finished* product must be the genius of only one of them!

Anagrams are a popular and easily-produced gimmick but then one faces the difficulties of disguising BEDROOM in such as a plethora of 'destinations' as MASTER BEDROOM, SON'S BEDROOM, DAUGHTER'S BEDROOM, GUEST BEDROOM or SPARE BEDROOM that some other device is required. This is easily solved by labelling each of these rooms in some way such as pictures on the doors or even names of (famous) people or places. Thus, clues can direct contestants to these labels and now you can be as cryptic as you wish.

Assemble the company in the main reception room and, working alone or in pairs, they are directed to a choice of envelopes, only one of which contains the clue to their next destination and a second clue. To mitigate against any charges of malpractice add to each clue a 'keyword' which needs to be recorded before any prizes can be claimed. Eventually, after a tour of the house (and outbuildings) the winner will return to the start with a list of 'keywords'.

These envelopes can be marked with such as 'YOU NEED IT', 'IT HAS THE CLUE', 'CAN YOU FIND IT?', 'GO FOR IT' and, finally, 'IT'. Assuming 'IT' to be the correct envelope it will contain your cryptic clue to another room and where to find the next clue, *plus* the 'keyword' either written in a box or in a different colour to distinguish it from the instructions. All of the messages in the other envelopes will tell that the contestant is in error.

All instruction cards *have* to be returned to their envelopes and, at this first stage, clever gamesmen who have opened the *wrong* envelope can bluff of success in order to distract others from picking up the correct envelope. Similarly, those who got the clue can always seek another envelope in order to keep an advantage. Now – a warning to the compiler, do *not* have a series of keywords (such as a proverb) from which competitors can surmise the complete sequence. If you *do* use such as a proverb as a base then either miss out certain words or else change some of them, e.g. **Too many broths spoil the cook.**

If play needs to be confined to a single room then an alternative 'run around' can be provided by displaying around the room various cards upon which are written the individual words of, for example, a palindrome, which can be logically reassembled. Players, armed with pencil and paper, merely record the words and then unscramble them. Here are three of J. A. Lindon's classics from which you could either make a selection or else jumble up all three:

Dennis and Edna sinned.
Red rum, sir, is murder.
Kay, a red nude, peeped under a yak.

And here are two of mine to give you additional ammunition:

Pepsi is pep.
Sam, all ynambu rub many llamas.
(YNAMBU, a large species of tinamou, a bird which resembles a guinea fowl with a pheasant's plumage but is related to the ostrich).

Finally, one the author of which us unknown to me:

Drat Saddam, mad dastard!

The Utility Series

A pair of dice can produce any value from 3 to 12 and one assigns to each of these possible 'throws' a *choice* of letters of similar lexical utility. For example:

3   J, Q, X or Z
4   C or D
5   G or H
6   N, S or T
7   *any* vowel or either of the two semi-vowels W or Y
      (which are aspects of such as CRWTH or CRYPT)
8   L, M or P
9   D or R
10   B or C
11   F, K or V
12   *any* consonant *except* the semi-vowels (see 7 above)

If no dice are available then any variable factors can have similar 'value' attached. If outdoors, then such as passing vehicles, or people coming into focus, or birds in flight, whereas indoors even differing television channels can provide a variety or substitutes for dice. However, avoid differentials (despite their entertainment value) such as distinguishing between beautiful and ugly women as you will only waste time defending your opinion – especially if your other half is in one of his/her 'ratty' moods!

Thus, if an 8 is thrown or (say) a woman in black leading a poodle passes by your table at a bistro in Paris then players have a choice of L, M or P as one of the letters they may utilize in such games as:

1 Creating lists of words in a specified subject.
2 Making a word square of an agreed dimension (say) 3 × 3.
3 The longest possible word without limitation as to subject matter.
4 The first to create such as any 7-letter word.

Winning depends upon challenge: game 1, the greatest number of examples; game 2, the first to finish; games 3/4, the one who succeeds.

To illustrate choice, let us say Hansel and Gretel are playing game 2 with wild birds as the 'dice'. Seeing a pair of rare birds (equating to 11 above) Hansel chose a K, Gretel a V. A common woodland bird (7 above) inspired Hansel to select a U whereas the more intelligent Gretel selected an E. Their game ended thus:

Hansel	*Gretel*
K I T	V A N
E M U	A P E
N	T E D
(W, C and various other letters not considered)	(only various surplus letters unused)

Though only nine letters are needed for a 3 × 3 word square, Hansel and Gretel allowed themselves a total of fifteen letters from which to make a final selection. Note that they utilized different choices in similar positions in their respective squares.

The essential point about this series is that you make all the rules other than departure from sensible word validity attitudes.

Jenny Diver

Jenny Diver was one of the most ingenious criminals ever to be incarcerated in London's Newgate Prison. Hanged for theft, she specialized in picking pockets in churches. Posing as a pregnant woman with false arms folded across her apparently distended belly, she would slip her real hand out of the side of this 'pregnant pouch' and fill it with whatever she could 'dip' from her neighbour.

The game comes in two versions; one is for everyone, the other is purely for wordsmiths. The action in both games is the same: extract an opponent's word by concealing it, Jenny Diver style, inside another word.

First version Players take turns in suggesting 3-letter words which their opponents must try to 'steal' by making that word an aspect of a larger word. Tom, for example, selects the word RAT which Jerry can steal very easily with such as BratS, CratE or even CELEBratE. Wordsmith Jerry can respond with such genuine words as DZO or QAT knowing that his feline opponent will have the greatest difficulty in removing them!

Second version The roadrunner writes down the word TAMENESS stating that it is AMEN within TESS. But, the coyote steals it with PREDICAMENT being AMEN inside another word, PREDICT. British spelling gives such as DOwellING, TOwellED and JEwellER, whilst BElongING, PROlongS and AlongSIDE are available either side of the Atlantic.

Further examples, for which I am indebted to Dr Susan Thorpe, are:

StillING, BAStillE, DIStillABLE; SLouchING, TouchABLE, SouchONG; MISreadS, THreadABLE, PROOFreadS; TOnighT, OVERnighT, BEnighT; FeverISH, LeverED, PERSeverE; REformED, DEformITY, TRIformED; LIMErickS, STrickEN, PrickLY.

Essentially, this is a two-person game but a round robin aspect can be created if others wish to compete, though you might have to make up your own rules as to what happens to the word 'inside' Jenny Diver; can it now be 'stolen' by some one else? Aldhelm Rules apply, though they may be relaxed to accommodate reasonable proper nouns and adjectives.

Murder

Each player writes down the name of an opponent, a weapon and a specific location in the neighbourhood. For example, Snow White wrote down GRUMPY, DAGGER, ORCHARD. She is now attempting to 'kill' Grumpy in the orchard with a dagger. Grumpy, meanwhile, has written down DOC, CHEESE GRATER, GARDEN SHED. (His method of homicide being unique even for an ill-tempered dwarf!)

Using the Bingo Letter-Frequency Table (page 37) which one of the players reads aloud, players now mark off all the relevant letters *one at a time* as they are called out. Once a player has been 'murdered' he is out of the game and play continues until chaos breaks out with arguments arising from the 'dead' preventing the natural conclusion of the last survivor being the winner.

Indian Cinema

Films made in India have an aspect that strikes most Westerners as curious – the cast breaks into song at what seems the most inappropriate of moments.

For the game, one person is invited to tell a joke and as soon as he mentions a word that evokes a song the company leave their seats to sing and dance lustily. Having performed they return to their seats and, like the Indian film actors, return to tranquility. They remain in this state until the raconteur sets them off again!

To gain the maximum fun from this amusement (especially for the slightly inebriated), prime the company in advance of a late-comer's appearance and (ideally) let him arrive to what appears to be a joke telling session.

Alternatively, run it as a semi-serious contest to see if any raconteur can keep a straight face till he reaches his punchline. Forfeits for those who fail; goodies for those who succeed. Delay rewards or punishments until the session has ended.

Idiot Boards

A choice of two games. Supply stiff card and broad-tipped marker pens to various witty folk asking them to write one example only of such as names of people, places or animals. Collect and shuffle these, then hand them to someone who is to enact the role of a prompter.

First version Invite a good raconteur to describe any news-type event, asking him to 'dry up' at any point where he intends to name a person, place or creature. As soon as he has 'dried up' the prompter holds up a random idiot board and the speaker now uses the given word rather than the one he intended. If he corpses (collapses with laughter) he is eliminated and another takes his place.

Second version Random idiot boards are displayed from time to time whilst the raconteur is in midflow. He must now incorporate the word as logically as possible. Corpsing, drying up or otherwise failing to reach a logical conclusion brings immediate elimination. Forfeits or goodies as in Indian Cinema.

Linko

A subject is chosen which involves words with a logical sequence to them, such as the months of the year or even geographical locations which are adjacent. Goldilocks decided upon a 'tour of Europe' commencing with ENGLAND. So, she wrote ENGLAND vertically on the single playing sheet. Daddy Bear now had to extend one of ENGLAND's letters as *any* 4-letter word such that he could utilize its fourth letter as an aspect of his chosen 'neighbour'. He selected the penultimate N, wrote NICE, then used the E as the last letter of FRANCE. Mummy Bear created FORD for her vertically-written DENMARK. Baby bear just chewed the paper and, after Goldilocks had rescued it, our heroine wrote ELSE to link with GERMANY. The sheet looked like this before Baby Bear ate it:

```
E        F o r D      G         P
N        R      E l s E         O
G        A      N      R        L
L        N      M      M        A
A        C      A      A        N
N i c    E      R      N e e    D
D               K      Y
```

Essentially, this is an elimination game whereby those who cannot make a sound move drop out until only the winner remains.

Bandicoot

Apart from being an alternative name for the pig rat, the largest species of rat and native to India, bandicoot is also the name of a small Australian marsupial which practises a unique method of garden theft such that the word is also an Australian verb 'to steal root vegetables whilst leaving the stalks and leaves still standing as though no theft has occurred.'

The company is divided into pairs, a 'gardener' and a 'bandicoot', who will share the same playing sheet, each possessing it at the appropriate stage of the game. Ideally, the bandicoots are dismissed from the room for the first stage but, if this is impractical, they may *not* assist the gardeners during the 'planting' of the crop.

First stage Above a line drawn across the top of their playing sheets, the gardeners write down the name of a root vegetable dictated by the organizer.

The gardeners are then asked a series of general knowledge questions in which each *single-word* answer begins with one of the letters of the word 'above ground' (i.e. above the line). For example:

```
C A R R O T
H M       S A
I S       L R
N T       O Z
A E         A
  R         N
  D
  A
  M
```

Errors in answering or of spelling are not highlighted at this point and it is illegal to write down a miscellany of meaningless letters.

Second stage   The gardeners pass their answers to their partnering bandicoots, who now face the second series of questions posed by the organizer.

This time answers are recorded by *lightly* marking off 'rootstock' letters:

Q. 'Name the chief Greek god'

```
C A R R O T
H M A U̶ S̶ A
I S P B L R
N T H B O Z̶
A E A E   A
  R E̶ R   N
  D L
  A
  M
```

and, in serious competition, also writing down the same answer against a question number:

1   ZEUS
2   STAMPEDE
    etc.

Winning submissions can be audited to ensure that both partners acted honourably and *genuine* errors by the gardener are *not* penalized; but, any by the bandicoot are subject to such actions as a deduction of points (say, one point per letter per erroneous word). Any 'force feeding' by the gardener:

C	A	R	R	O	T
H	B	H	M	R	A
I	C	I	N	S	R
N	D	J	O	T	Z
A	E	K	P	U	A
	F	L	Q	V	N
	*	*	*	*	

results in the submission being declared void.

Note that the organizer has to prepare his or her questions and answers very carefully in order to ensure a good contest.

Tug of War

A lengthy word such as ANTIDISESTABLISHMENTARIANISM is the subject of an anagram dispute between two teams each of whom 'tugs' at different ends of that word. For convenience, we will refer to them as the Latins (those who read from left to right) and the Hebrews (right to left). A spin of the coin decides who goes first and, for convenience, we will assume that it is the Hebrews.

The Hebrews take the concluding letters –ANISM by creating the word MAINS.

The Latins respond with TINA from ANTI–.

The 'rope' now has these letters available:

–DISESTABLISHMENTARI–

So the Hebrews, with an eye on their next-move-but-one merely 'tug' the single-letter word I. By contrast, the Latins gain –DISES with SIDES. The Hebrews have an embarrassment of riches for the letters –ENTAIR– with such as ATRINE, EARNIT, NERITA, RANITE, RATINE, RETAIN, RETINA, RIANTE, TANIER, TIRANE, TRAINE, some of which are so obscure that they would be well advised to choose either of the 'obvious' words, RETAIN or RETINA, to avoid disputes only resolved by consulting one of the better dictionaries.

The Latins settle for an easy BAT from –TAB– even though BALT could have been gained had they noticed it!

The Hebrews now debate among themselves. Only –LISHM– is unclaimed; dare they gamble that such as 'MILSH', 'HILMS' or 'SHILM' can be found in the dictionary if the Latins challenge any of such a choice of potential plays? Failing that, what about 'SHIM', 'MISH' or even 'HIMS'? As it happens, both shim and mish are *real* words defined in the OED and the Hebrews are lucky in their choice of SHIM, a dialect word for a streak of white on the face of a horse. (MISH, incidentally, is a shirt.)

The Latins face a solitary L but now the *real* tug of war begins. They may add to it as many or as few as they like, of the adjacent letters now in the possession of their opponents.

The word LI cannot be used as it is *not* an anagram of a given sequence of letters so they gamble on SHIL (from –LISH–) being confirmed as valid. It is. SHIL is an obsolete spelling of the now dialect adjective SHILL, sonorous.

The Hebrews cannot use the *same* word to regain their lost letters nor can they think of a valid anagram of those same letters; so they discuss the potential of the letters –ESTABLISH– which includes some already held by the Latins.

Can it be done?

The game ends when exhaustion sets in and the winners are the team with the greater number of letters to their credit.

If you require 'big' words for this game consult *The Book of Lists* which has a complete section devoted to them.

Tug of War Niggles The reason why anagrams as opposed to 'discovered words' are the essential basis of this game is to prevent some legalistic Clever Dick from simply claiming the whole word as a single 'tug'. The need for disbarring a previously noted anagram is to mitigate against the banality of the teams constantly repeating the same word over and over again. By making these rules general rather than at the vital pivotal point so it both adds 'bite' to the game and prevents disputes as to where and when the pivotal point arises.

Note that, in the explanatory game above, TINA BALT and I differ from standard Aldhelm Rule valid words in that they are normally written with an initial capital letter but are deemed an acceptable deviation for this particular game.

The Quizzical Series

The organizer poses a series of general knowledge questions all of which have a single-word answer. Players write their answers *clearly* as a continuous line across the top of their papers, thus:

WASHINGTON BEAVER NILE HITLER CHEESE LION CLINTON

using a second line if necessary:

TORONTO KANGAROO SIXTEEN CUSTER EDISON

The correct answers are then revealed and any wrong answers are immediately deleted *but no other words may be added*!

The remaining letters are now available for use in either of the following games:

1 QUIZ A series of questions are posed whereby such answers as LEONARDO can be produced by deleting letters from the original answers. (L from either NILE or HITLER for example).

The game ends at the point where only one possible word is available and the winner (or winners) can state it.

This version requires clever advanced planning.

2 *LIST*   Players are challenged to discover the greatest number of examples of such as fish, birds, girls' names or whatever.

This version requires careful thought only.

The King's Move Series

A Do-It-Yourself Series in which *you* decide all the rules and individual details of action. The author merely provides a basic play concept and sample variations on a theme.

The assembled company are provided with grids of a uniform size such as 7 × 7. True, one *could* ask the players to draw their own grids on blank paper and waste time attempting to ensure uniformity (even wordsmiths can be stupid sometimes!) as well as coping with requests for rulers but either of two previously prepared sets will be more effective. So, either mark off on graph paper a 7 × 7 'playing area' or else draw and photostat sufficient grids for all anticipated contestants.

These resultant 49 squares of a grid will then be filled by virtually random letters, coupled with the odd 'blank' square here and there, and players will subsequently be faced with the task of discovering various significant words by tracing out a 'track' as would be made by a king in a game of chess. Here, for example, the word GAME can be perceived in such an array of available letters:

	w	a	g	t	a
	p	i	E	d	p
	h	A	M	b	o
		G	h	o	

Blank squares can be utilized, if you so desire, as a facility for returning to the same letter to effect a repeated letter – thus in the above example the word GAMMA could have been detected in the track, G, A, M, blank, M, A.

There are various methods of providing the original letters, such as asking players in turn to state unrelated words of any length and which words *all* must insert on their grids in any sequence. Misspellings do *not* matter at this stage. To mitigate against unreasonable 'advance planning' do *not* announce the subject matter until all grids have been completely filled including the desired number of blanks.

Now, you can play any of the following games or, indeed, any game of your own devising which has players attempting to discover one or more words of a specific nature.

1 WHODUNIT Can you discover the name (either forename or surname as you decide) of the 'killer'?

2 TREASURE HUNT Find a specific geographical location or even a generalized situation such as FIELD or ORCHARD or BARN.

3 FUTURE LOVER Either Zodiac names such as SCORPIO or PISCES or Chinese Zodiac names such as RAT or RABBIT.

4 BIG GAME HUNT Who will be the first to 'shoot' a TIGER or even a MAMMOTH?

The winner is either the first to make any such specified discovery or else the results are computed on a basis of one point per letter per word (no score for a blank!) and the player with the higher or highest total wins. You arbitrate on such conundrums as, 'Can I ''shoot'' both a MAMMOTH and a MOTH simultaneously?'

The basic concept was created by Dr A. Ross Eckler as a solitaire exercise in compressing relevant subject matter within as small an area as possible. Calling such items of data chesswords, Dr Eckler has also published similar treatments with Knight's moves. (The idea of discovering significant words within a mass of meaningless letters is the author's and is appearing in print for the first time.)

Child's Play

Many parents have been both amused and bemused by the curious 'language' which one or more of their children have or has displayed at the dawn of their vocalization. My own experience is of listening to the earnest pleading in some mind-blowing tongue of my younger son and, in desperation, turning to my elder boy, Maxwell, for a translation. 'Marcus wants some bread and jam, Daddy,' was the most usual explanation.

The *game* is imparting intelligence to another player by speaking utter nonsensical 'word sounds'. Begin by writing down an instruction (say) 'Give me a glass of Bourbon' and award points – or that drink – to the person who correctly interprets the nonsense.

Conviction

The company divides into two teams and takes turns acting
out two distinct roles. One team, (in this instance, Jack's)
provides the 'judge', the 'defence attorney' and all of the
'defendants'. The judge will possess all available reference
works such as a dictionary, an atlas and a name-the-baby
book. The other team (Jill's) will provide the 'prosecuting
attorney' and all of the 'witnesses'.

Jill, as the 'prosecutor', will ask each 'witness' in turn a
general knowledge question and it is up to her team to
provide the word GUILTY one letter at a time, in a progressive sequence, in their *one word* replies. Jack, as 'defence
attorney', may challenge these replies for the opinion of the
strictly impartial judge. Each member of Jack's team will
be prosecuted in turn but will remain silent other than to
prompt Jack, if need be, to raise an objection.

A typical play sequence will follow a pattern along these
lines:

Jill: Name a country.
Witness 1: Greenland. (Judge writes down a G)
Jill: Name a type of bee.
Witness 2: bUmble. (Judge writes down a U)
Jill: Name an English city.

Witness 3: edInburgh.

Jack: Challenge. Edinburgh is a Scottish city!

Judge: Objection sustained.

Jill: May I re-examine the witness?

Judge: Only if you ask the *same* question.

Jill: Name an English city on the river Avon.

Jack: Objection. The advocate is leading the witness. I move for an acquittal.

Judge: Objection sustained. The prisoner will be released.

The next 'criminal' is now called and it is up to Jill to think of *different* questions to pose otherwise Jack can object on grounds of collusion!

It follows that the two 'lawyers' need to be quick witted and that the judge commands natural respect. It is up to you to create your own 'case law' in the course of playing sessions of this game. The winning team being the one with the greatest number of 'innocent' players.

In the above cross-examination, Jill was attempting to elicit the answer brIstol from the third witness and may well have continued to produce such answers as fouL, beauTiful, derbY to complete a GUILTY verdict.

Is Nothing Sacred?

With the *Oxford University Press* simultaneously publishing in both the USA and UK a 'politically correct' Bible which has God of indeterminate sex and, by denying the existence of such as the blind and the lame, making it extremely difficult for Christ to perform miracles so this challenge is for the normal, well-adjusted, folk who constitute the majority. Tell a dirty joke in 'politically correct' language!

Your Money or Your Life

The company divides into two teams, which separate to plan their strategies. They have to come up with as many examples of words in an agreed subject as they have decided to play rounds. Ideally, 'difficult' words are the best. Then, they must apportion the letters of those words among themselves on a word-by-word basis. The teams will take turns at answering questions which give them a choice of subjects. In the sample round which follows, those posing the questions are the team led by Mattie Ross. Lucky Ned Pepper's gang must use their general knowledge to reply, each answer they give utilizing as its initial letter the letter that player has been allocated. With small numbers participating then some or all of the team may have more than one letter at his or her disposal and may use *either* letter as the idea is to baffle the opposition by answering anagramatically.

'Your money or your life?' demands Mattie of Ned Pepper (who has both the Q and the H of his team's opening round word).

'QUETZAL', replies Ned who, though he has named both a life form (a South American bird) and a currency (the Guatemalan dollar) is spared J. Noble Daggert's pedantic objections by Rooster's rising to his full height and giving the little lawyer his best one-eyed glare.

'Boy or girl?', drawls Rooster at the player seated next to Ned.
'ULYSSES', replies Mexican Bob.

'Fish or fowl?' asks J. Noble Daggert.
'OWL', says Quincey.

'Your money or your life?', demands the aggressive Mattie.
'CENTIME', replies Moon.

With H, B, E and R completing the letters elicited from the Pepper gang, Mattie and her team have just (say) 60 seconds in which to unscramble those letters and name the 'geographical location' of the agreed subject. Ned gains the points for his team when he eventually reveals the answer as one of the smallest of the Channel Islands, BRECQHOU!

Whilst most party-goers will want to take turns at being the questioners and the answerers it is entirely up to you how you organize the game, but ensure that reference works are to hand in the event of any dispute and decide what penalties to impose in the event of a player giving a ludicrous reply. For example, had Mexican Bob replied 'EUNICE' to Rooster's question does the Pepper gang forfeit all that particular round's points to Mattie's team? If a player is unable to answer, do you apply the same penalty? Finally, do you award a fixed points total (say)

10 per word or a point-per-letter-per-word? Have team captains agree the ground rules in advance of play.

British Gas

In 1995, the privatized gas supply system in the UK claimed that it was 'mere coincidence' that, whilst cutting wages for their minor employees, their chief executive took an astonishingly high increase in his personal income. The British Government, who broke the previous state monopoly for a private one 'in the interests of competition', disclaimed any responsibility saying that it was 'up to the shareholders to object'!

The *game* consists of players writing down short, flexible names such as TED, PAT or ENA who are now 'chief executives'. The players, one at a time, will now quote other, longer, names as 'minor employees', the idea being the removal of any letter from these 'employees' to increase the size of one's original word as an andagram.

In the sample game following, Robin Hood has chosen DON; Maid Marion, ANN; and the Sheriff of Nottingham, KEN. As he will be the last to make a selection from his word, the Sheriff begins by saying, 'RICHARD'.

Robin: I'll take the I for ODIN.
Marion: A for ANNA.
Sheriff: C for NECK.

It is now Marion's turn to state a name and she says, 'ELIZABETH'.

Robin: R for RODIN.
Sheriff: Arrest that man! I can't stand this game!
Marion: Neither can I. Let's play Postman's Knock.

But, after Robin has killed all the Sheriff's men and apologized for continuing to use RICHARD when ELIZABETH was the name in play, they compete again with new 'chief executives' and Marion wins with the sequence:

TED, TIED, DIETS, DIGEST, GOISTED (obsolete form of GHOSTED), DOGGIEST.

Robin gave up at the third 'employee', whilst the Sheriff matched Marion word-for-word till she was left to nominate any 'employee' she wished in order to complete her winning sequence.

Postman's Knock

I have happy memories of kindergarten sessions of the old game, in which I and all the other boys were anxiously awaiting the decision of the prettiest girl in the class. She, on the other side of the door, would announce that she 'had a letter for . . .' and whichever boy she named would be rewarded with a kiss when he went forward to claim his 'letter'. Sadly, many of my own 'letters' came from girls other than Wendy who, perversely, fancied Captain Hook.

As a *word* game, the company divides into a male versus female contest and who am I to deny Wendy the chance to relive happy memories of chaste sexual encounters with Hook?

Alternating vowels with consonants, the 'letters' offered by one sex for the other have to be assembled into logical words. Naturally, Wendy will supply Js, Os, Xs and Zs with her kisses and Hook's crew will be equally awkward.

Work out your own rules and have fun!

The Siberian Baby Mammoth

A concept for word lovers stuck in some such place as an airport lounge with only a well-read newspaper and a pen. Decide upon a subject such as '*regular* Christian names' which, of course, eliminates examples such as NEWT (Newt, Gingrich, the Republican politician) and CHELSEA (Chelsea Clinton, the First Daughter), plus a motivation such as 'Soviet moles'. These names then need to be discerned, *concealed* in the paper's reports.

There are two types of discernment; either the traditional 'hidden word' beloved of puzzle setters or else in a variety of transposed forms. For example, STEPHEN:

(a) Traditional puzzle . . . wa**ste phen**ol . . .
(b) Adjacent transposition . . . pet hens . . .
(c) Letter-by-letter . . . waS . . . THE . . . PartNEr . . .

Note that both (a) and (b) are likely to be rare and that (c) may well have purists insisting upon the relevant letters occurring in the correct sequence. Agree format and all rules in advance.

To play, each has a page and a pen, and a strict time limit is imposed unless Granny wishes her darlings to have a 'fair chance' against the grown ups. In my experience,

Granny Rules supersede those of Saint Aldhelm or any other lexical jurist! Incidentally, Granny Rules would disbar NEWT and CHELSEA for grown ups but validate them for little darlings. Similarly, with 'animals' as the subject in a 'big game hunt', Granny Rules would permit LEPPARD (as in DEF LEPPARD) for her darlings but deny it to Mummy and Daddy.

This series honours the baby mammoth found preserved intact in the Siberian wastes and, of course, was especially created for this book.

Opposites

Whilst George Armstrong Custer has the reputation of being an heroic cavalry leader who enjoyed an incredible promotion to field rank, his exploits were more than eclipsed by the brilliant Confederate cavalryman, Nathan Bedford Forrest, who rose from private to Lieutenant General during the course of the Civil War. They are matched in a contest to see who can repeat any of his words first. Custer has 'girls' names' and Forrest 'boys' names' with the Southerner to go first.

Forrest writes the word MICHAEL somewhere in the middle of the single playing sheet. Custer now has to cross MICHAEL with the name of a girl. His response of SHEILA is, to put it mildly, stupid as the L or the I or the A have the

```
              S
M I C H A E L
              E
              I
              L
              A
```

potential for a repeat of MICHAEL and victory for Dixie. However, Forrest is a gentleman and has pity for the

Yankee officer who graduated bottom of his class at West Point. He merely writes CHARLES, which his Union opponent immediately crosses with JEAN – completely overlooking the fact that that same E could have been utilized for a winning SHEILA.

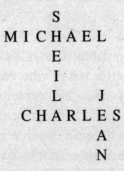

```
            S
   M I C H A E L
            E
            I
            L        J
   C H A R L E S
                     A
                     N
```

With the N the only available letter to continue the sequence of crossing the previously written word without coincidentally creating such as a 2-letter word which needs to be validated:

```
                J A S P E R
   C H A R L E S
                     A
                     N
```

Forrest considers such as KENNETH, ANSELM and ANTHONY but rejects them as each holds potential for a Northern victory and he has already been sufficiently generous to his tenderfoot opponent. Instead, he opts for CONRAD. Always one for the spectacular, Custer pencils in a cleverly contrived LEONORA oblivious of the fact that both its R and A have potential for CHARLES whilst the A gives Forrest a chance to repeat his first word for a maximum points victory.

```
              J
    C H A R L E S
              E A
    C O N R A D
              N
              O
              R
              A
```

Score points on a basis of one point per written 'own category' word; hence, 5 points for MICHAEL contrasted with 3 points for a possible CHARLES.

Any categories which have natural opposites can be chosen and ultimate victory decided by total score over an agreed series of battles. If a player cannot produce a response within a reasonable period of time (say, that of an eggtimer), then victory goes to his opponent, scored at one point per word of either player's category.

Love and War

'All's fair in love and war' is only partly true in this game – one *must* abide by the Aldhelm Rules in any perceived action utilizing the basic concept of two players each attempting to be the first to reach the other side of a grid by linking words to their own previously written words, but not exceeding a limit of writing four new letters per move. An initial lengthy word of a maximum of 10 letters is chosen, either relating to one's perception (such as KENTUCKY for a horse race) or by some random method such as sticking a pin in any available prose and choosing the nearest long word.

In the sample game which follows, Doc Holliday will have a 'little word' word power equating to that outlined in the restrictive 3 from 2 Table appearing on page 435 whilst Big-nose Kate, the lady who provided what was then termed his 'horizontal refreshment' will be more knowledgeable. They have visualized a 'gold rush' from their current residence, Tombstone, to the California state line (the bottom of the grid). Consequently, TOMBSTONE is written vertically-descending on their grid. Kate, going first, writes the word ZEAL, linking it to the ONE of TOMBSTONE to create (cross-word style) the words, ZO, EN and AE, whilst leaving the L suspended one line nearer to the 'finish'.

Doc, who is attempting to descend in a similar fashion, is faced with difficulties posed by her clever opening move. He too must begin by linking to any of the letters of TOMBSTONE (*not* Kate's ZEAL) and, glancing at the 3 from 2 Table, it will be seen that for him to utilize any of the concluding letters of TOMBSTONE is impossible, as AE has no given suffixes (note that such as AEA, a type of cord made from candletree bark, is mentioned in the introduction to the table but Doc is presumed to be ignorant of it). Doc's only option is to 'sidetrack' and, for this, he begins to create an alternative descending track by writing IRE against the first three letters of the starting word simultaneously creating TI, OR and ME. Note that such as TOAD linked to form ST, TO, ZOA, END would have been a more dramatic and possibly better move but we are presuming him to be inferior to his paramour.

```
        T I
        O R
        M E
        B
        S
        T
        Z O
        E N
        A E
        L
```

Kate now extends ZEAL as ZEALOUS and Doc responds by linking TIME to create MET. Knowing that Doc could, in two moves, extend this to TIMELESSNESS, Kate decides upon neutralizing such a ploy by writing a blocking word across the page. Hence, her terminal S provides the initial letter of SHARP. Sure enough, Doc now extends TIME as TIMELESS.

```
          T  I
          O  R
          M  E  T
          B     I
          S     M
          T     E
          Z  O  L
          E  N  E
          A  E  S
          L     S
          O
          U
          S  H  A  R  P
                   E
                   A
                   R
```

Kate uses her R of SHARP to continue a descent with REAR (with thoughts of such as REARING for her next move). However, Doc is not deterred, he merely goes *through* her SHARP with a clever ESSAY which also creates the valid 2-letter words ES and YE. Defensively, Kate continues her bedevilment by writing the four letters EAVY beneath the H of SHARP for HEAVY/EYE.

```
        T   I
        O   R
        M E T
        B   I
        S   M
        T   E
        Z O L
        E N E
        A E S
        L   E S
        O   S S
        U   S S
        S H A R P
        E Y E
        A   A
        V   R
        Y
```

Kate is now in a very strong position, she alone has access to the most extreme letters, the terminals R of REAR and Y of HEAVY. Doc's ultimate letter, the Y of ESSAY, is neatly blocked.

But a clever play is still available to him. He could still approach the 'California state line' with ESS/SLOPS/EYES for (say) a 'sidetrack' of EYESIGHT on his next move and a plethora of choices of descent.

To continue their game would be mere self-indulgence on my part except to give Kate's VERSION as yet another tactical move which she could then convert to AVERSION in such as an ABLE descent.

```
T       I
O       R
M E T
B       I
S       M
T       E
Z O     L
E N     E
A E     S
L   E S S
O   S   L
U   S   O
S H A R P
  E Y E S
  A     A
A V E R S I O N
B Y
L
E
```

What size grid and can one go *through* the terminal line?
The grid need not be square but must have a reasonable width for 'sidetracking'. It can, therefore, be such as 10 × 20 or any other dimension you can create. If the 'length' is short then the initial word has to be in harmony. The 'winning word' *must* end at the finishing line. Note that 'part words' cannot be written, e.g., such that Kate's ABLE becomes ABLEBODIED by moves along the lines of 'ABLEBOD' followed by adding IED. By contrast, Doc's TIME, TIMELESS, TIMELESSNESS is perfectly legal.

Have typewriter correction fluid handy to cope with

errors and illegal moves. A player who makes a move resulting in the use of typewriter correction fluid forfeits that turn. Finally, whilst grids or graph paper are not essential if both players write neatly, they do assist in ensuring that spaces are clearly defined. Clear definition shows that Kate could not convert able into ENABLED as that would produce an illegal 'EEYES' even though NA is perfectly acceptable on the line below.

The Words Word Table

In order to establish the 'shape' of an unknown word the quickest way is to find its vowels. True, there are some peculiar words such as OOMPH which prove exceptions to the normal rule but a table such as this will lead you directly to at least one vowel within seconds. Even OOMPH will have its second letter revealed in just nine guesses at the most.

SEEER	EXINE	ARABA	BANAL	VIVID	BOOBY	IGLOO	OUUEN	XYLYL
sever	exile	Arabs	canal	livid	booty		outen	
lever	axile	crabs	cabal	lived	booth		outer	
lover	anile	cribs	cabel	lives	broth		cuter	
loves	anils	crits	caber	gives				

You begin by saying SEEER. If the response is nil move directly to EXINE. Thus all five possible positions for an E, the most commonly used letter of the alphabet, have now been covered. A similar, but imperfect, treatment is accorded to the other vowels. A direct horizontal run of SEEER, EXINE, ARABA, BANAL, VIVID and BOOBY has covered, from the standpoint of normal vowel usage, over 90 per cent of the 5-letter words in the English language. This means that, nine times out of ten, you are going to get a positive response in just six guesses at the unknown word.

If the answer for SEEER is one or more then you progress *down* the SEEER list until you receive the answer 'Nil'. When you receive this answer of nil then you know that the letter you are seeking is the one you have just changed in the word *directly above*. Thus, if you are told 'One' for SEEER but 'Nil' for SEVER then the letter you have discovered is the middle E. If it is 'One' for SEEER, 'One' for SEVER but 'Nil' for LEVER then you have *accidentally* discovered a consonant, the S. This is a bonus and you should still continue the hunt for vowels. If you are told 'Two' for SEEER, 'Two' for SEVER, 'One' for LEVER (this is the S, of course), 'One' for LOVER and 'Nil' for LOVES the word you are seeking begins with an s and ends with an R. As you have eliminated all possibility of an E being part of that word so it *has* to be something like SOLAR or SONAR (you will not be facing 'clever' words like SKIRR at the beginner level of play) and so you are still really hunting for vowels to establish the 'shape'.

If you receive a reply of 'Nil' to SEEER move directly to EXINE for your second guess – to explore the SEEER list under these circumstances is a sheer waste of time and effort. Therefore, you travel along the top line until you obtain a positive response and, as previously stated, by the time you have guessed with SEEER, EXINE, ARABA, BANAL, VIVID and BOOBY you are virtually certain to gain a positive response.

But a negative response is still possible (and by negative this means no vowels – consonants are a bonus) and you *know* that the word is going to be a 'funny' one. It could be such as IGLOO, so try it. A nil response now eliminates three of the few remaining vowels. A positive response is a problem. How can you change IGLOO letter-by-letter in order to identify the relevant letter? You may be able to but you would need to know some very peculiar words to achieve this. The better policy is to try the most likely (such as the O in the fourth position) and guess with such as STROP which can be changed to STRAP for confirmation.

If nothing happens with IGLOO try the short OUUEN list. It will not turn out to be a QU- word as QU- is *always* followed by one of the vowels which you have already eliminated. It will, if the answer is positive, be a word like THUMB.

If it is *still* nil then it is going to be one of the following non-vowel words – and xylyl followed by crypt is as good a pair to start with as any.

crwth crypt cysts dryly fyrds ghyll gymps gyppy gypsy hwyls hymns lymph lynch myrrh mysts nymph pygmy pytch rynds rythm shyly shynd skynd skynk slyly styth sylph synch syncs synds thymy tryst tymps tynts wryly wynds wynns wytch xylyl xysts

(Note that these words have been culled from a variety of dictionaries so restrict your selection to those in your own dictionary.)

Finally, if you are wondering why the I and the U for the fifth positions have not been covered try constructing a word like COYPU or RADII for which you have not already had a previous 'positive' response. The same is equally true for the U in the fourth position as even a 'clever' word such as GYRUS has had its Y revealed by XYLYL. True, your opponent might know a word such as THRUM but if you play at a level which has words of this type then you are already an expert and will know how to cope with it anyway.Thus you would also know words such as UMPTY or YCLAD to complete a personal Words Word Table which has all of the vowels and the Y in every possible position.

3 from 2 – A Table of Basic Linking Words

Taken from my own *Pears Advanced Word-Puzzlers Dictionary* (Pelham Books 1987) this table was compiled to illustrate the creation of 3-letter words from a base of 2-letter words and was strictly limited to those available for serious Scrabble play in any country which utilized *Chambers 20th Century Dictionary* as its arbitration work. Despite that, my book also noted such 2-letter words as QI (in Chinese philosophy, the life-force) which subsequently appeared in Chambers so becoming 'valid' for official Scrabble. The *PAW-PD* also had 3-letter words such as QAT (an Ethiopian bush which yields a narcotic) which has also 'made it' for British and Commonwealth Scrabble, though for Doc Holliday in Love and War (page 424) any of the following have proved useful: AEA (a type of cord made from candletree bark) and the obsolete AEI, AEL, AEN, AER together with AES (Irish fairies) and AET (OAT in the Shetland Island dialect).

The central column consists, therefore, of just *some* of the 2-letter words available for word play. The outer letters when added, as shown, fore or aft of their related 2-letter words produce just *some* of the 3-letter words found in both British and American dictionaries. Hence, for AT, the fore letters give a choice from such as BAT, CAT, EAT whilst the solitary aft letter provides ATE. Incidentally, the *PAW-PD* also provides ATT, an alternative spelling of AT, in its sense as a Siamese pewter coin. AT is also a small Laotian coin hence ATS as a plural for either of these meanings.

Readers who wish to compile a similar table (be it restricted to either or both Scrabble reference works or even 'general' word play) should appreciate that it frequently entails 'double entry' as both EA and AT, for example, share the word EAT with differing letters fore and aft. Your own table will then provide you with both a 'training list' for easy reference in early stages of learning useful words for any of the crossword-style games and, subsequently, an arbitration tool. Space follows the table to enable you to add whatever 'small words' you wish.

```
      b c d f g h l m p r s w  AD  d o s
              g h k m n s t v w  AE
                  b d f h l p y  AH  a s
                          s t  AI  a d l m n r s t
      b c d g h j l m n p r t y  AM  p
      b c d f g m n p r t v w  AN  a d e n t y
          d e f g h k l m p r t v w  AS  h k p s
  b c e f g h k l m o p r s t v w  AT  e
      c d f h j k l m p r s t w y  AW  e l n s
                  l p r s t w z  AX  e
  b c d f g h j k l m n p r s w  AY  e s u


                              BE  d e g l n t y
                              BO  a b d g h o p r s t w x y
                          a  BY  e s
```

	DA	b d g h k l m n p s w y
a u	DO	c d e g h n o p r s t w

k l p s t y z	EA	r s t u
b c d f g j l n p r s t v w	EE	l n
r	EH	s
b c e g m s t z	EL	d f k l m s t
g h r w	EM	s u
b d e f g h k m p r s t w y	EN	d e s
h p	ER	a e g k r s
h l m o r t y	ES	s
h k s v y	EX	

FA	b d g h n r s t w y
FY	s

	GI	b e f g n o p s t
a e	GO	b d e o s t v y
	GU	b e m n p r s t y

a c	HA	d e g h j m p s t w y
s t	HE	m n p r s t w x y
c g	HI	c d e m n p s t
m o p w z	HO	a b d e g p s t w y

a b d f g h k l m n r t	ID	e s
g k	IF	s
a b d f g h k l p r s t w y	IN	k n s
b g	IO	n
a b h l m n s t w	IS	h m
a b c d f g h k l n p r s t w	IT	a s

JO b e g t w y

s KA e s t w y
s KY e

a LA b c d g h m p r s t w x y
LI b d e g n p s t
LO b g o p r s t w x y

MA c d e g k m n p r s t w y
ME l n s t u w
MI d l m r s x
MO a b d e g o p r u w
MY s

am NA b e g m n p y
NO b d g h r t w y
b c f g h j k l m n r s y OB i s
b c d g h m n p r s t OD d e s
d f g h j m r t v w OE s
o OF f t
b d f n o p s OH m o s
p OI k l s
c d e i o s t w y ON e s
b c d g l m t w z OO f h n p r s
b c d f h l m o p s t w OP e s t
b c d f l m n o t OR b c e s t
f m s y OU k p r s t
b c d h j k l m n p r s t v w y OW e l n s
b c f l p s v OX
b c f g h j l n s t OY e s

s	PA	d h l m n p r s t w x y
	PI	a c e g n p t x
	PO	a d h l m p s t w x z

| a e i o u | RE | d e f h m n p s t v |

a i	SH	e y
	SI	b c m n p r s t x
d	SO	b c d g h l n p s t u v w x y
	ST	s y

e i	TA	b e g i j k m n p r s t u w x
a	TE	a d e f g l n s w
	TI	c d e g l n p s t
	TO	d e g m n o p r t w y

b d f h j l m p r t v y	UG	h s
b c f g h l m r s t	UM	s
b d f g m n p r s t	UN	i
c g h o p s t y	UP	s
b c f g l n o p	UR	d e n s
b g o p s y	US	e
b c g h j n o p r t	UT	s

| a e o | WE | h s |
| t | WO | e g k n o p s t w |

a b d e k l n o p r s t w	YE	a n p s t w x
	YO	b n s u w
a	YU	g k p s

| d | ZO | a o s |

439

Useful Proverbs and Maxims

Adversity makes strange bedfellows
All things come to he who waits
Ask no questions and hear no lies
Attack is the best form of defence
A bad excuse is better than none
A barking dog never bites
A bellowing cow soon forgets her calf
The best men are but men at best
The best things come in small packages
Better be an old man's darling, than a young man's slave
Better be envied than pitied
Better one house spoiled than two
It is better to be born lucky than rich
It is better to travel hopefully than to arrive
Better to wear out than rust out
A bleating sheep loses a bite
You cannot get blood from a stone
Blue are the hills that are far away
You can't tell a book by its cover
None but the brave deserve the fair
Brevity is the soul of wit
You cannot make bricks without straw
Every bullet has its billet

A burnt child dreads the fire

A cat in gloves catches no mice

A chain is no stronger than its weakest link

Don't change horses in mid-stream

It is as cheap sitting as standing

The child is the father of the man

Children and fools tell the truth

Never choose your women or your linen by candlelight

Let the cobbler stick to his last

Coming events cast their shadows before

A man is known by the company he keeps

Conscience makes cowards of us all

Councils of war never fight

Happy is the country with no history

A creaking door hangs longest

What can't be cured must be endured

Curses like chickens come home to roost

Don't cut off your nose to spite your face

Cut your coat according to your cloth

The darkest hour is just before dawn

Desperate diseases must have desperate remedies

The difficult is done at once the impossible takes a little
    longer

Throw dirt enough and some will stick

Dirty water will quench fire

Discretion is the better part of valour

Distances lends enchantment to the view

Do right and fear no man

Give a dog a bad name and hang him

Every dog is allowed one bite

What's done cannot be undone

A drowning man will clutch at straws
We must eat a peck of dirt before we die
He that would eat the fruit must climb the tree
Every man for himself and the devil take the hindmost
The exception proves the rule
Experience is the best teacher
Faint heart never won fair lady
The female of the species is deadlier than the male
He who fights and runs away lives to fight another day
Fine feathers make fine birds
Fine words butter no parsnips
Fingers were made before forks
First impressions are the most lasting
A fool and his money are soon parted
There's no fool like and old fool
Fortune favours the brave
There's no such thing as a free lunch
Never look a gift horse in the mouth
All that glisters is not gold
Go abroad and you'll hear news of home
God made the country and man made the town
God sends meat but the devil sends cooks
Whom the gods love die young
A golden key can open any door
The greater the sinner the greater the saint
All is grist that comes to the mill
A guilty conscience needs no accuser
The hand that rocks the cradle rules the world
Handsome is as handsome does
Hard words break no bones
You cannot have your cake and eat it

There is honour among thieves
Hope for the best and prepare for the worst
The husband is always the last to know
It's an ill wind that blows nobody any good
Imitation is the sincerest form of flattery
Jack is as good as his master
Why keep a dog and bark yourself
What you don't know can't hurt you
He who laughs last laughs longest
One law for the rich and another for the poor
A liar ought to have a good memory
Life isn't all beer and skittles
Listeners never hear any good of themselves
Little pitchers have large ears
Lookers-on see most of the game
The age of miracles is past
Where there's muck there's brass
The nearer the bone the sweeter the meat
Necessity is the mother of invention
You can't put new wine in old bottles
Old sins cast long shadows
Opportunity makes a thief
Out of debt out of danger
Things past cannot be recalled
He who pays the piper calls the tune
If you want peace you must prepare for war
One picture is worth ten thousand words
Politics make strange bedfellows
Praise the child and you make love to the mother
Procrastination is the thief of time
It is easier to pull down than to build up

There is always room at the top
The rotten apple injures its neighbours
Save us from our friends
Second thoughts are best
Self-preservation is the first law of nature
The sharper the storm the sooner it's over
Shrouds have no pockets
Silence is a woman's best garment
A soft answer turneth away wrath
Speech is silver but silence is golden
The squeaking wheel gets the grease
A still tongue makes a wise head
Never give a sucker an even break
From the sublime to the ridiculous is only a step
A tale never loses in the telling
Talk of the devil and he is bound to appear
If a thing's worth doing it's worth doing well
Think first and speak afterwards
Three may keep a secret if two of them are dead
He that will thrive must first ask his wife
He travels fastest who travels alone
The tree is known by its fruit
Two of a trade never agree
The unexpected always happens
Virtue is its own reward
One volunteer is worth two pressed men
When the wine is in the wit is out
It is easy to be wise after the event
All work and no play make Jack a dull boy

Some European Monarchs

This list is limited to those monarchs with picturesque names – you can easily supplement it with lists of monarchs with their numerals spelt out, of US Presidents, of various European Presidents, and of any other famous figures useful for the game of Ivan the Terrible (see page 358).

THE HOLY ROMAN EMPIRE
Louis the Pious
Charles the Bald
Charles the Fat
Louis the Child
Henry the Fowler
Henry the Saint
Conrad the Salic
Henry the Black
Rudolf of Hapsburg
Adolf of Nassau
Albert of Hapsburg
Henry of Luxemburg
Wenzel of Luxemburg
Rupert of the Palatinate
Sigismund of Luxemburg

NORWAY
Halfdan the Black
Harald Fairhair
Erik Bloodaxe
Haakon the Good
Harald Greyskin
Haakon of Lade
Olaf Tryggvason
Svein Knutsson
Magnus the Good
Harald the Stern
Olaf the Quiet
Magnus Barelegs
Sigurd the Pilgrim
Haakon the
    Broadshouldered

SCOTLAND
William the Lion
The Maid of Norway
Robert the Bruce

PORTUGAL
Alfonso the Fat
Pedro the Severe
Maria the Mad

ENGLAND
Ethelred the Unready
Edward the Confessor
Richard the Lionheart

RUSSIA
Ivan the Terrible

THE EASTERN ROMAN EMPIRE
Julian the Apostate
Leon the Isaurian
Leo the Chazar
Michael the Amorian
Michael the Drunkard
Leo the Wise

Michael the Caulker
Matthew Cantacuzene

SWEDEN
Eric the Victorious
Olaf Scatt-King
Inge the Good

DENMARK
Gorm the Old
Harald Bluetooth
Svein Forkbeard
Eric the Evergood
Olaf Hunger
Valdemar the Victorious
Eric Ploughpenny
Valdemar Atterdag

FRANCE
Louis the Saint

POLAND
Boleslaw the Wry-Mouthed
Boleslaw the Modest
Wladislaw the Dwarf

Miniglossary

Few popular family dictionaries carry a high percentage of the words which comprise this listing so, to comply with the Aldhelm Rules, you cannot play to this compilation unless you have previously agreed that it may be considered a supplement to your own dictionary. *Pears Advanced Word-Puzzler's Dictionary* is the main source for most of the words; it was compiled from many sources including the *OED* and all three editions of *Webster's International*, none of which is likely to be a typical family arbitration work. The Miniglossary follows the pattern established by 'crossword solving books', listing words according to the number of letters in each word.

Single-letter Words

Apart from the letter Q which is the name of the half-farthing, a long-obsolete British coin, these consist of the five vowels and the semi-vowel Y. A, I and the poetic exclamation O are the three obvious words recognized by the American Cryptogram Association for codebreaking puzzles set in the English language. Two of the remainder are included in this edited quote from the *Oxford Guide to*

Word Games ' . . . and even U (as in U and non-U) is acceptable . . . and as for Y, [Dmitri Borgmann] has discovered a town called Y in Michigan'. To which can be added the curious name of a Scottish river, E. (The *Oxford Guide* in fact credited A. Ross Eckler with this 'discovery' but Ross wishes *true* 'credit' to be given.)

Two-letter Words

Although some of the words listed below have more than one meaning, only one meaning has been given for the purposes of a mnemonic. Preference is for a meaning which justifies lower case.

aa   *n* a cooled cindery substance consisting of sand, earth, stones and melted lava

ab   (*British dialect*) *vb* to hinder, pain, disadvantage

ac   (*Middle English and obsolete except as a syllable in English place-names*) *n* oak

ad   (*Middle English*) *n* a funeral pyre

ae   (*Middle English*) *n* law of nature

af   (*British dialect*) *prep* of

ah   *interjection* of surprise

ai   *n* the three-toed sloth

ak   *n* mudar, either of two Indian shrubs

al   (*Middle English spelling form*) *n* awl

am

an

ao   *n* the personification of light in Maori legend

ar   *n* the letter R

as

at

au (*Middle English form*) *n*/*vb* awe

aw *n* a type of waterwheel floatboard

ax

ay *interj* oh!, alas

ba *n* the second letter of the Arabic alphabet

be

bi (*slang*) *n* a bisexual person

bo *n* a Japanese Buddhist monk (in this sense the plural is **bo** but, to justify **bos** consult your own dictionary and *if listed* use the plural it gives)

bu *n* a Japanese coin (*see* bo *above for plural*)

by

ca (*Scottish*) *n* a pass or defile between hills (*plural* caas)

ce *n* the bebization equivalent of the musical syllable 're'

CH despite its acceptance as a word by the British Scrabble movement and appearance in *Official Scrabble Words*, it is not a word and never has been! It is an aphetic form of the pronoun **ich** (I) and occurs only as part of a compounded phrase in such British dialects as that of Shropshire. These dialects use such compounds as **chad** (I had); **cham** (I am); **chud** (I would); **chill** (I will).

ci (*Early English*) *n* a dog (*plural* cwn)

co (*obs*) *n* a jackdaw

cu (*obs*) *n* a cow (*plural* ky *or* kine)

cy *same as* ky

da *n* ambary, an East Indian fibre plant

de

di *n* a musical tone between doh and re (Further to my

fulminations under **CH** I mention in passing that, whilst **di** is given in the British *Official Scrabble Words,* it is *not* given in *Chamber's Dictionary*, the word source for that suspect work!)

do

du   (*Scottish form*) *vb* do

dw   (*obs Scottish form*) *vb* du

dy   (*obs form*) *n* die, one of a set of gaming dice (*plural:* **dice, dies, dyce, dys**)

ea   (*formerly standard English now confined to some British dialects*) *n* a river, running water

eb   (*obs form; now confined to a British dialect*) *adj* ebb, shallow

ec   (*Middle English form of archaic*) *adj* eke, also, too, moreover

ed   (*obs except as a syllable in both Christian names and English place names*) *adj* fortunate

ee   (*Scottish*) *n* eye (*plural* een)

ef   *n* the letter F

eg   (*obs except as a syllable in English place names*) *n* water

eh   *interj* expressing (mild) surprise

ei   (*Middle English but still extant as a syllable in English place names*) *n* water

ek   *same as* ec

el   *n* anything in the shape of the letter L (*plural* els *but a plural* ellen *applies a Dutch measure of cloth*)

em   *n* the letter M; a printer's basic unit of typeface measure

en   *n* half an em as a printer's measure

eo   (*Middle English form*) *pron* you

ep (*Middle English, still extant as place-name syllable*) *n* an aspen tree

er *interj* expressing hesitation

es *n* the letter S or anything of that shape (*plural* **esses**)

et (*British dialect*) *interj* a command to a horse to advance

eu (*obs form*) *n* yew

ex (*colloq*) *n* one no longer enjoying a particular personal relationship (*plural* **ex's** *or* **exes**)

ey (*now confined to British dialect except as a syllable in English place names*) *n* water

fa *n* the twentieth letter of the Arabic alphabet

fe (*obs*) *n* livestock

fi *n* a musical tone between fa and so

fo (*British dialect*) *n* a measure of eight square yards

fu *n* an administrative district in China or Japan (*plural* **fu**)

fy *interj* of disgust

ga *n* the bobization equivalent of the sol-fa musical tone **fa**

ge *n* the bobization equivalent of **ti**

gi *n* a judo or karate costume

go

gu *n* a primitive two-stringed kind of Shetland violin

gy (*obs*) *vb* to control or direct

ha *n* though written differently, the sixth and twenty-sixth letters of the Arabic alphabet

he

hi *interj* to attract attention

hm *interj* expressing doubt, perplexity, etc.

ho *interj* of exultation, surprise

hv (*Middle English form*) *adv* how

hw (*Middle English form*) *adv* how

hy (*British dialect*) *interj* to attract attention

ia (*obs Scottish form*) *n* jay

ic *another ancient variation on the theme of* **ich**, *see* **CH** *though this is or was a genuine word!*

id *n* a term in psychoanalysis for a concealed part of the psyche motivated by instinct independent of a sense of reality, logic and morality

ie *n* any of various screw pines, climbing plants having a screwlike arrangement of the leaves

if

ig *same as* **ic**

ih *same as* **ic**

ik *same as* **ic**

il (*Middle English*) *n* a hedgehog

im (*Middle English form*) *pron* him

in

io *n* a large Hawaiian hawk and the only one native to those islands

ir (*obs form*) *n* ire

is

it

Iu (*Middle English form*) *n* Jew

iv (*British dialect form*) *adv/n/prep/vb* in

iw (*Middle English form*) *n* yew

ix (*British dialect form*) *n* axe

ja (*British dialect*) *n* jaw

je (*obs form of archaic*) *adv* yea

jo (*Scottish*) *n* a beloved one (*plural* **joes**; *the plural in the sense of a Japanese measure of distance is the same as the singular*, **jo**)

Ju (*obs form*) *n* Jew

ka *n* in the ancient Egyptian religion, the spiritual self

ke (*obs form of the Scottish and also English dialect*) *n* kae, the cry of a jackdaw

ki *n* a Chinese liliacious plant

ko *n* a Chinese liquid measure (*plural* **ko**)

ku (*English dialect*) *n* an eye ulceration

ky (*formerly standard English now literary Scottish and English dialect*) *n pl* cows

la *interj* lo! see!

le *variant form n* li

li *n* a Chinese measure of distance, approximately a third of a mile (*plural* **li**)

lo

lu (*Orkney*) *vb* to listen

ly *n* an Ammanese measure of length

ma

me

mi *n* the third note of the tonic sol-fa system of musical notation

mo *n* a Japanese unit of weight (10 mo = 1 fun)

mu *n* the twelfth letter of the Greek alphabet

my

na (*Scottish*) *adv* no, not

ne (*Middle English*) *n* a nephew

ni *n* the bobization equivalent of **ti** or **te** in the tonic sol-fa

no

nv (*Middle English form*) *adv/conj* now

ny (*obs form*) *n of assemblage* nye (of pheasants)

oa (*Scottish dialect form*) *pron* I

ob   *n* a familiar attendant upon a Hebrew witch

oc   *same as* **ac**

od   *n* a supposed magnetic force which creates the effect of hypnotism

oe   *n* a small island

of

oh   *interj* of such as pain, terror, shame

oi   *interj* to attract attention

ok   *same as* **ac**

ol   *n* a hydoxal group which has the oxygen atom bonded to two metal atoms

om   *n* a type of mantra or passage taken from a Hindu religious work and uttered as an incantation

on

oo   (*Scottish*) *n* wool

op   *n* optical art

or

os   *n* a geographical ridge (*plural* **osar** or **osars**; *plurals in other senses are* **oca**, orifices; **ossa**, bones)

ot   (*British dialect*) *n* an urchin

ou   (*Scottish*) *interj* of concession

ow   *interj* of pain

oy   (*Scottish*) *n* a grandchild

Oz   (*colloquial*) *adj/n* (of) Australia

pa   *n* a Maori fortified village

pe   *n* the seventeenth letter of the Hebrew alphabet

pi   *n* the sixteenth letter of the Greek alphabet

po   (*Middle English*) *n* a peacock

pu   *n* a Chinese measure of distance (*plural* **pu**)

py   (*obs form of*) *n* pie, in such senses as a magpie

qi   *n* in Chinese philosophy, the physical life-force

qu   *n* the half-farthing, a British coin no longer in circulation (*also spelt* **q**)

ra   *n* the tenth letter of the Arabic alphabet

re   *n* the second note of the tonic sol-fa

ri   *n* a Japanese measure of distance and of depth (*plural* **ri**)

ro   (*obs*) *n* rest, repose

ru   (*Middle English form*) *vb* rue, to repent

ry   (*obs form*) *n* rye, the plant

sa   *n* the fourth letter of the Arabic alphabet

se   *n* a Japanese measure of area

sh   *interj* a command to silence

si   *n* the original seventh musical syllable of the tonic sol-fa

st   *interj* to attract attention

so

su   (*British dialect*) *pron* she

sy   (*British dialect form*) *n* scythe

ta   *n* though written differently, the third and sixteenth letters of the Arabic alphabet

te   *n* same as **ti** only in the given sense

ti   *n* the seventh note of the tonic sol-fa

to

tu   *n* a Chinese measure of distance equal to 250 li

ty   (*obs form*) *n* tie

ua   (*Middle English form*) *adj/adv/n/conj* woe

ug   (*formerly standard English now only British dialect*) *vb* to dread

uh   *interj* expressing an inarticulate sound

um   *interj* expressing hesitation in speech

un   (*British dialect form*) *pronouns* one, him

uo (*Middle English form*) foe

up

ur *interj* expressing hesitation in speech

us

ut *n* the original first syllable of the tonic sol-fa

uu (*Middle English form*) *n* yew

uv *same as* **uu**

uz (*British dialect form*) *pron* us

va (*Middle English form*) *n/adj* woe

ve (*obs Scottish form*) *pron* we

vg (*obs standard English form now dialect*) *vb* **ug**

vi (*variant form of Middle English*) *n* vie, a short biography of a saint

vo (*nonce*) *n* a size of a book

vp (*obs form*) *adv* up

vs (*obs form*) *pron* us

vy (*obs form*) *vb* vie

wa *n* a Siamese measure of length

we

wg (*obs Scottish form, now dialect*) *vb* **ug**

wi (*Middle English*) *n* battle, conflict

wo *interj* calling a hawk to stop or to return

wp (*obs Scottish form*) *adv* up

wr (*Middle English form*) *pron* our

ws (*obs Scottish form*) *pron* us

wu (*Middle English form*) *adv* how

wy (*variant form of literary Scottish and English dialect*) *n* quey, a heifer

xa (*obs form*) *n* shah

xi *n* the fourteenth letter of the Greek alphabet

xu *n* a monetary unit of Vietnam (*plural* **xu**)

ya *n* the twenty-eighth and final letter of the Arabic alphabet

yd (*obs*) *n* corn land

ye

yf (*obs form*) *conj* if

yi (*British dialect form of archaic*) *adv* yea

yk (*obs form*) *pron* I

yl (*obs*) *n* an isle

yn (*obs form*) *n* inn

yo *interj* of effort

yr (*obs form*) *n* ire

ys (*obs*) *pron* his (in the sense of theirs)

yt (*obs form*) *pron* it

yu *n* a Chinese wine vessel

yw (*Middle English form*) *pron* you

za *n* though written differently, the eleventh and seventeenth letters of the Arabic alphabet

ze (*obs form*) *demonstrative adj* the

zi (*Middle English*) *same as* **ze**

zo *n* a yak/Ladaki cow hybrid beast of burden (*plural* **zos**)

zy *same as* **zi**

Useful Addresses

Quite often only one member of a family has a fascination with words that has him – more usually, her – desperate to find an opponent of equal worth so if you fall into that particular category the following names and addresses might prove useful.

SCRABBLE   Many countries have a network of clubs for devotees of this magnificent game and as it is manufactured by three different companies so each holder of the game's copyright is the best organization to approach according to where you reside. These are:

USA and Canada: Selchow and Righter Corp., New York
Australia and New Zealand: Scrabble Australia Pty Ltd.
UK and most other countries: J. W. Spear & Sons PLC, Enfield EN3 7TB, Great Britain

But, if you merely wish to gain useful information for domestic play or even wish to participate in Postal Scrabble then you may care to subscribe to one of the best privately produced magazines available – the only one which caters for the postal enthusiast – *Onwords*. My only criticism of it is that it defends, though not blindly, that dreadful production, *Official Scrabble Words*. Write in the first instance to the editor/publisher:

Allan Simmons
Onwords
Shilling House
1 Woolmer Hill
Haslemere
Surrey GU27 1LT
Great Britain

CODEBREAKING This highly entertaining activity is conducted via a members' magazine, *The Cryptogram*, the journal of:

The American Cryptogram Association
PO Box 6454
Silver Spring
MD 20906
USA

WORDSMITHERY I strongly recommend the *Journal of Recreational Linguistics* despite its leanings towards two of my pet hates, 'logology' and computerized word play; nevertheless, if only for the wit of David Morice, the poetic ingenuity of Kay Haugaard, and the remembrance of the past genius of Dmitri Borgmann and Leigh Mercer you should enjoy subscribing to:

Word Ways
A. Ross Eckler
Spring Valley Road
Morristown
New Jersey 07960
USA

The above three journals all have overseas readers.

WORD-BASED PUZZLES The American National Puzzlers League is the oldest continually active puzzle organization in the world and though I have no personal knowledge of it I understand that it produces a magazine, *The Enigma*, and holds game-playing conventions annually in the USA. I am informed that the editor of *Games Magazine*, Will Shortz, 55 Great Oak Lane, Pleasantville, NY 10570, USA, is the 'man-in-the-know'.

COMPUTERIZED WORD PLAY Ted Clarke, Menanhyl, Trenance, Newquay, Cornwall, TR8 4DA is the editor/publisher of *Wordsworth* described as 'a magazine for the PC Program User' and although he describes me in *Word Ways* as a 'Luddite' I have to acknowledge that he writes very entertainingly and so I suggest that if computers are your thing then it would do you little harm to become one of his subscribers.

I presume that the above journals, *Enigma*, *Games* and *Wordsworth* also cater for an overseas readership.

Other word game activities are promoted in, for example, the UK by the international organization of eggheads, *MENSA*, and also by a private individual in hotel chains for weekend social fun. He contacts the top UK wordsmiths and invites them to such as the London Hilton where, amongst other activities, they play Chesterfield.